Once upon an Evil Time

11-3-04
To David
with best wishes
Dieter Steiner

Dieter Steiner • Diane Marcou

QUIXOTE PUBLICATIONS

Quixote Publications
490 Merrimak Drive
Berea, OH 44017

This book was previously published by Quixote Publications as
War Child 0-9633083-4-3 © 1995 by Dieter Steiner and Diane
Marcou.

Library of Congress Cataloging-in-Publication Data

Steiner, Dieter, 1931-
　[War child]
　　Once upon an evil time / Dieter Steiner, Diane Marcou.--[2nd ed.]
　　p. cm.
　"This book was originally published in 1995 under the title War child"--Pref.
　　ISBN 0-9677583-2-7 (alk. paper)
　　1. Steiner, Dieter, 1931- 2. World War, 1939-1945--Germany. 3. World War,
　1939-1945--Personal narratives, German. 4. World War,
　1939-1945--Children--Germany--Biography. I.Marcou, Diane, 1932-II.Title.

D810.C4S755 2000
940.53'161--dc21   2002068151

*This story relates actual events in the life of Dieter Steiner. How-
ever, names and descriptive details of some characters, other than the
immediate family, have been altered to respect their privacy.*

*To aid the reader, a glossary of German words and phrases ap-
pears at the end of the book.*

*Cover: A summer day at a beach, forever fixed in a long-ago time.
Dieter Steiner (r) and his brother Wolfgang stare at a camera,
unaware they are naive participants in an ominous scene.*

*Dedicated in loving memory
to my wife Susan Steiner
(1950-2000)*

Preface to the Second Edition

This book was originally published in 1995 under the title *War Child.* Its publication coincided with the fiftieth anniversary of the ending of World War II, the war after which the world said—if anyone remembers—"never again."

But in July of that anniversary year, the world watched the Bosnian town of Srebrenica in its bloody lurch toward being designated Europe's worst massacre since World War II. It was just one, albeit the largest, of many slaughters of innocents—on both sides—during the twentieth century. Two years ago a new millenium began, carnage continued, and then it hit here in America.

Sadly, there never has been a *never* again, only an *again and again.*

Some readers will recognize in this memoir of growing up in the shadow of the Third Reich opinions they may have harbored since childhood: racial, ethnic and religious prejudices and the conceits of entitlement and self-righteousness. But they feel no shame or need to apologize. After all, they never actually *did* anything, and some of their best friends are (fill in the blank). Does anyone really believe that attitudes are benign if not acted upon?

This story tells of one person's journey from prejudice and bigotry to tolerance and empathy, learned the hard way. We can learn from his experience. A solution to hate is there for us to grasp. Our journey, if there is to be one, needs that first step.

If history is any prophet, the fires of intolerance-induced genocide, ethnic cleansing, and slavery, perpetrated in the names of Supreme Beings or Supreme Commanders, will continue to ignite. Feeding those flames will be our silence and inaction. For the inferno to cease, a generation must have the courage to say "NEVER AGAIN!" and mean it. Its members must take action and repudiate long-held, harmful beliefs. It must be a generation that will cleanse its soul and refuse to pass on to its descendants the hatreds the world has lived with so long.

For what generation are we waiting?

D. S. and D. M.
May 30, 2002

Author's Note

When I started this project with Dieter, I found myself awash in memories of World War II from my own vantage point—that of a loyal, patriotic, victory-gardening, tin-can-collecting, war-song-singing American schoolgirl. Having fewer pairs of shoes, less butter, and not as many cakes and pies didn't bother me much at all. And courage came easily in the darkened theater when I imagined myself saying goodbye to a handsome soldier on the screen, or when I stood at attention before the Servicemen's Honor Roll or in my Girl Scout uniform at the memorial service for Dean Mount, and again, for Rich Wells, where I struggled to remain dry-eyed.

But my sacrifices were small and my courage slight compared to others of my generation, for when I was a child in New York, cheering the progress of Russian troops as they surrounded Berlin, my grandchildren's other grandmother, Raisa, was a child in Siberia, mourning a father killed in action, and my friend Jill was a child in the English countryside, living with strangers to escape the bombing of London. Dieter was just a child, too. In his hiding place in a cellar in Berlin he listened to the guns and grenades as battles raged above him, and waited to be killed by the Russian troops I cheered on.

Diane Marcou

January 30, 1995
In memory of David Bowman 1951-1995
St. Petersburg, Florida

A Note About My Family

I was born in Germany on August 25, 1931, in the small town of Grimma, about fifty kilometers east of Leipzig and 100 kilometers west of Dresden.

I know almost nothing of my biological father, Wilhelm Steiner, except that he was a pharmacist. My mother, Elisabeth, was born September 26, 1906. She spoke little about her life except on rare occasions, when she mentioned that she worked in a bank during the Depression years, counting laundry baskets full of paper money. Following the collapse of the bank, she worked from daybreak until darkness picking beets. "At least my family had beets to eat," she said. "And we didn't starve like so many did." But for the remainder of her life, when she saw beets, she turned her head.

My parents divorced around the time I was two, and I only remember a few visits with my father during the late thirties. He died in 1944.

Sometime around 1935 my mother married Karl Drescher in Leipzig, and the three of us moved to Berlin.

Karl Drescher was a few years older than Mutti and a graduate of the University of Heidelberg. He was born in Würzburg, a medium-sized city in the southwestern region of Germany about 110 kilometers east of Frankfurt. His close-knit family consisted of his father, Heinrich, whom we called Opa, a long-time employee of the German postal system. His mother, Emma, known as Oma, was a housewife. His younger brother, Willie, joined the Arbeits-Dienst, the Federal Work Force, before the outbreak of war in 1939 and later became a member of the Wehrmacht, where he was a corporal.

Karl Drescher quickly won my love and support, and although I didn't take his surname, he was, in all respects, my father. He had a large library in his study and read often, a trait he passed on to all of us. He loved to canoe and kayak and spend time outdoors. He felt that a healthy mind required a healthy body. Vati and Mutti took us often to the lakes around Berlin, and holidays were always joyous times for the family.

Vati traveled in his position with what I believe was a natural gas company in Berlin. He was fluent in English and had several business friends and associates from America.

On August 14, 1937, my brother Wolfgang was born, followed by Peter on August 5, 1940. Soon after Wolfgang's birth, Vati hired Ruth Schuber, a young woman from Moabit, to help Mutti. She quickly became a loving, and well-loved, member of our family. She left at the end of the war in 1945.

For fifty years I have carried these memories. I share them now so that you will know how my family, just one of millions, survived almost six years of World War II during the darkest chapter in the history of mankind. I have tried to understand how millions of people, like me, could have allowed themselves to be led down a path of total physical, moral, and spiritual destruction in such a short time. Many of those millions have passed on and found their peace, but I am still here, a leftover of that evil time. Years ago, I promised myself to do something to make our world a better place. When my time is up, I hope I will find that I accomplished my goal in some small way.

Dieter Steiner

Wilhelm Steiner, Mutti, and Dieter, 1932

Vati and Mutti, 1936

Summer of 1936

"Dieter, come and see Herr Wise. He's in the living room with Mutti." My father stood in the doorway to my playroom, a big smile on his face. "Herr Wise has a present for you, and he wants to tell you something before he leaves."

"But he talks funny, Vati."

He laughed. "I know. Don't worry, I'll tell you what he says."

He led me down the hallway, past Herr Wise's big suitcase covered with all those colored stickers. Herr Wise put something behind his back when I walked in.

He bent over and shook my hand. "Guten Morgen, Dieter."

"Guten Morgen, Herr Wise." I tried to peek around him to see my present.

He laughed, and then with a big sweep of his arm, handed me a flag. It was the prettiest flag I had ever seen — red and white, and a blue box with lots of little white stars.

"Danke!" I held it up and waved it above my head. "Danke!"

"That's the flag of Herr Wise's country," Vati said. "America. Can you say that? A-mer-i-ca."

"A-mer-i-ca," I repeated, waving my gift, "A-mer-i-ca."

Herr Wise smiled and said something to my father I didn't understand. I looked at Vati.

"Herr Wise thanks you for letting him stay here during the Olympics. He says a kind, smart boy you are, and that when you are older, you can come to America to visit him."

"Ja! When I go to school? Then I will be old enough?"

Vati and Mutti laughed and Vati told Herr Wise what I said, and he laughed, so then I laughed, too, but I didn't know why. Mutti took my hand. "Herr Wise must leave now. Say goodbye."

"Auf Wiedersehn."

Herr Wise covered my hand with his.

"Auf Wiedersehn, Dieter." He picked up his suitcase, and Vati and he went outside.

My mother and I walked onto the veranda and watched as Herr Wise shook my father's hand and climbed into a taxicab. Mutti waved goodbye, and I waved my wonderful new flag.

1

I'm told that the Berlin of 1938 was the true embodiment of a capital city, a shiny metropolis in the heart of Europe reaching for its pinnacle. Its mood then was euphoric. Its zest was contagious. The reason, of course, was Adolph Hitler's frenzied nationalism.

When members of the Sturmtruppen, or SA, paraded through the Brandenburg Gate, their flaming torches illuminating its ancient arches, jubilant Berliners lined the streets with their right arms raised high.

I would have been among them, I'm sure, had I been old enough, for at age seven, grandiosity appealed to me.

We lived in a spacious, high-ceilinged apartment on Beeren Strasse in the suburb of Zehlendorf-West, about halfway between the center of Berlin and the city of Potsdam. It was a mere five-minute walk to the S-Bahn station, part of Berlin's vast elevated and underground electric train system. Surrounding the station were the only stores within a few kilometers, one or two groceries, a hardware store, a bakery, a tiny cafe for cake and ice cream, and a small but fancy hotel with an equally fancy restaurant. Swastika flags flew from many of them, or hung down in front of their windows, and members of the SA mingled with shoppers on all the streets. Aside from the presence of the flags and troopers, Zehlendorf-West was a quiet suburb. Since it was some twelve kilometers to the west of the center of Berlin, for the most part the noisy hoopla of the city's celebrations and parades seldom reached there. So far my life had been gentle and good, yet I remember vividly the day it veered in a different direction.

We'd walked to Herr Müller's grocery, and my mother held the door for me to enter. We were barely inside when a grimacing clerk stepped abruptly in front of us and blocked our way.

Mutti looked at him. "Ja?"

"You didn't salute, Frau," he said loudly. Some of the customers standing nearby looked startled and turned away. I stood closer to Mutti.

"What do you mean?" she asked.

"Heil Hitler," he answered, holding his arm in salute. "You do not enter here without saluting, or you will not be served."

He saluted again. "Heil Hitler!"

Mutti stared back at him.

He put his face right up to hers. "Heil Hitler!" he yelled.

"Heil Hitler," she muttered and grabbed my hand. We walked out past the trooper, who smiled at the clerk and slapped his shoulder.

"They're crazy," my mother said when we reached the corner. "Salute! Who do they think they are?" We crossed the street faster than usual. "Won't serve me? Customers we've been since we came to Berlin, and they won't serve me?" She looked over her shoulder and then stopped in front of a store across from Herr Müller's shop.

"Why didn't we get our groceries, Mutti? What did he mean we wouldn't be served?"

"Later I will tell you." She looked in the window and adjusted her hat and just stood there, looking in the window.

14

"Why didn't you salute, Mutti? It's fun. Look." I stuck my arm out. "Heil Hitler. Heil Hitler." People on the sidewalk looked at me and then at my mother. "Heil Hitler," I crowed.

"Sh-h-h, Dieter. Enough." Her look begged me to stop. I put my arm down. "When I grow up, I'll be a soldier."

"Not today, Dieter. Don't tell me that today."

Everywhere I went there were storm troopers now. The brown-shirted men drove trucks through the neighborhood, past our house, several times a day. Always they were singing, shouting, and saluting. Sometimes people on the sidewalk returned the salute, and the troopers clapped and yelled. When we saw them, my friends and I saluted and shouted, "Heil Hitler!" One day a group stopped in front of us and shouted back.

"Good soldiers," one said. "Show us how you march."

We formed a line and marched back and forth on the sidewalk. "Heil Hitler!" we yelled.

"Heil Hitler," they called back. "For the Vaterland!"

"For the Vaterland!" we yelled back, and all of us, men and boys, cheered.

As soon as they were gone, Ruth came out and grabbed me by my collar and pulled me back into the house. She told Mutti, and my mother looked upset. After dinner, Mutti and Vati sat me down in front of them.

"Dieter," my father said, "Mutti tells me you saluted the SA today."

I smiled. "Ja. I always do. When I grow up, I want to be one."

"Nein, nein, nein," my mother said, pulling me to her. She smoothed my hair. "Too young you are for such thoughts."

"Your mother's right. And it's not safe for you to be around them." Vati shook his finger at me. "Trouble they

15

cause. They stir things up, hurt people. Remember the way Herr Müller's clerk treated Mutti?"

"But he wasn't an SA. He didn't wear a uniform."

"You think a uniform matters? They all act the same." Vati leaned toward me. "You want to do such things?"

"I won't say mean things like he did. I'll just march, and ride around in trucks, and wear my uniform."

Vati shook his head. "You don't understand. Those men arrest people, Dieter, and beat them with clubs. Young boys should not be near them."

"When I'm big, can I be near them?

Vati sighed. "He doesn't understand, Lis. How can we make him understand?" He shrugged. "What's happening isn't good." He looked at the floor a moment, then at Mutti, then back at me. "Listen to me. You and your friends—play something other than soldier. Play Trappers und Indianers, or Indianers und Gendarmes, like you used to. Too young you are to imitate the storm troopers. Verstanden?"

I nodded, but I still thought I'd look good in a uniform.

"Look!" my friend said. "Something's going on." Ahead of us the street was crowded with people, and the SA were everywhere. We ran to see. I pushed my way through all the grownups, and then I saw the shops. Some had their windows out, the counters splintered, and furniture and boxes and bottles—everything—was thrown on the sidewalk. Glass crunched under my feet as I tried to get through the crowd to see better. With the windows broken, everything was open and I saw right inside the stores. Yellow stars, with the word *Jude*, were painted on the walls.

In the bakery, the shelves had been toppled and the glass cases smashed. Cakes and pastries were piled in heaps and flour spilled from ripped-open sacks. Just inside the door of the grocery were broken milk bottles, the milk mixed with whatever had been in the barrels and cabinets now lying on their sides. Everything was torn up.

What happened? Who did it?

"Just the Jew stores," someone said. "They only did the Jew stores."

"Look, over here, Dieter," my friend called. "Look at what I found."

He stood outside Herr Weinberg's Hardware holding a box of pocketknives. "They're brand new." He held several in his hand. "Which one do you want?"

"But this is Herr Weinberg's store. He's my father's friend."

"He's a Jew. That means we can take anything we want."

"We can?" *Such pretty knives they are.* "The green one. Give me the green one."

He gave it to me and then held out the box. "Want another?"

"Isn't there anything else?"

"Not any good things. Everything else is smashed."

Disappointed, I put the green knife in my pocket and poked with my foot among the broken kegs of nails and screws lying in the doorway. My toe hit something hard. I pushed the keg away.

"Putzi?" I knelt beside Herr Weinberg's big yellow cat. "Kitty, kitty?" I touched him. He was cold and hard, like a board. *I've never touched a dead cat before.* I touched him again. *He's not soft like when he was alive.* I backed away.

"I'm sorry, Putzi."

An old man bent down and patted my cheek. "Don't let them see you cry," he whispered. "Go away from here. Go on to school, go!"

I ran all the way.

Everyone in the classroom was talking about the shops. We showed each other the things we found on the sidewalk.

17

"These are Jew things," Kloster said. "If they break up other places we can get more."

"Are they going to?" Before anyone answered me, Herr Beiderman arrived, and we dropped into our seats. The SA trooper with him clapped his hands for attention.

"As Deutsche you should be proud," he said. "Last night we punished the Jews. The only shops destroyed were Jew shops where they stole money from the people. In the future all stores will be owned by Deutsche loyal to our Führer, Deutsche your parents will be proud to buy from." He folded his arms. "Jüdische Schweine who steal will pay. Get on with your lessons now. You are the future of the Vaterland!"

Herr Beiderman nodded in agreement. The soldier looked like a statue, tall and straight, his arms folded over his chest. I remembered what Vati said. *But he looks so important! Even Herr Beiderman thinks so.*

I didn't want to do schoolwork. I wanted to get home and tell Mutti that Herr Weinberg was a Jew, and his store was gone, and I had a new knife. And that I'd touched a dead cat.

But Mutti wasn't happy with my news. She took my knife. "That's a terrible thing you did, Dieter. It didn't belong to you. I'm showing it to your father."

"But Herr Weinberg's store is gone and the knife was on the sidewalk, so he can't sell it, can he? What if I just keep it until he gets his store fixed up, then give it back?"

"Nein, Dieter. You shouldn't have taken it."

No one could tell me why the Jew shops were ruined. "It's not for a young boy to question," Mutti said, and later, when Vati came home, he told me he'd explain some other time, when he had an answer.

"Do you think Herr Weinberg will get another cat?"

Vati didn't look up from his paper. "Probably not, Dieter."

"Can't we find one for him? If I find one, can we give it to him?"

18

"Ja, Dieter, that will be nice."

"Vati, was Herr Weinberg's cat a Jew cat?"

He put his paper down and looked at me, but he didn't answer.

"Vati, was he? Was he a Jew cat?"

"Does it matter to you, Dieter?"

"Well, I wanted to get him another cat, and I don't know where to find a Jew cat."

Vati pulled me onto his lap and hugged me close. "I don't know either, mein Junge," he whispered. "I just don't know."

Mutti kept the knife. I couldn't find a cat for Herr Weinberg, although I looked. It was just as well; Vati came home one day and said Herr Weinberg had moved. Kristallnacht became a memory after awhile. Mutti said I should spend more time with my schoolwork, but I was still swept up with dreams of wearing a uniform and parading down the streets of the city. When I finished my homework, I was back outside strutting to the martial music no one heard but me.

In the spring we moved to Babelsberg-Ufastadt, a pleasant suburb even farther from the center of the city. This apartment was as large as the last, and it had the added advantage of a big fenced yard that guaranteed the safety of young Wolfgang, now one-and-one-half years old. Next to us lived the Ludwigs, who owned a large, two-story villa, a grand mansion of a house, in my eyes. Herr Ludwig, a South American businessman, was, as my father was, often away from home. Frau Ludwig and my mother talked over coffee. Their daughter, Helga, two years older than I, became my good friend. Her brother went to school in Switzerland. I felt quite important living beside such wealth. I was glad we'd moved to Babelsberg, and I was happy in my new home and school.

*(Above) April 20, 1939. We occupied the lower floor
of this building from 1939-1945. The exterior shows little
change in the picture below, taken in the fall of
1994, fifty-six years later.*

A few blocks away lived my new friend Manfred
Klugbauer, who was as eager as I to play war. His father,
unlike mine, was an active Party member. Horst Pagel was
another new friend. Together, we all fought the enemies of
the Vaterland and bragged of our futures in the SA.

In school, the current of war energized us all. Blitzkrieg
was the new word after German armies smashed their way
through Poland, and when we sang "Deutschland Über

20

Alles," pride surged through me. I wished I was older. Every morning, when I passed clusters of people reading newspapers and talking about the latest maneuvers, I imagined myself on the battlefield, shooting my way through enemy lines. Sometimes I pretended to be hit and clutched my wounded side with one hand while I fired my imaginary rifle with the other. Though I might be wounded, Dieter Steiner couldn't be stopped!

Herr Schmaulder kept our attention riveted in school. He showed us pictures in the newspapers of dead German soldiers, killed by the terrible, bloodthirsty Poles, and he read us stories of brave and courageous soldiers who, even in the face of death, took the enemy by surprise. "We are superior," he said, "in every way." I had no trouble believing him.

A large Army truck, its sides plastered with pictures of our Führer, chugged around the corner. Horst and I, walking home with my mother, saluted as it went by. Another truck followed, and I tried to hold Horst's arm, so I could salute first. We wrestled, and he smacked the back of my head.

"Genug!" Mutti said as she pulled us apart. "Two good friends fighting over whose arm sticks out first? You should be playing, not hurting each other. You, Dieter, was ist los?"

"It's important. The one who salutes first the most times can be Deutsch. The loser has to be a Pole."

"Ach Du Lieber!" Mutti shook her head. "Such foolishness. Why can't you just be boys?"

After a summer and fall made exciting by talk of war, winter arrived overnight. The branches of the pines in our back yard, bent under the snow's weight, hung almost to the ground. Mutti had dressed Wolfgang in warm clothes and brought him to me.

21

"From the basement get your sled and take him for a ride, Dieter. The fresh air will do him good."

"But it's Saturday. I'm supposed to play at Manfred's."

"Games come after. First, your brother. He needs the fresh air." She pulled her apron on over her head and tied the strings behind her. "You won't be hurt to play with him for an hour."

"An hour? Do I have to?"

"Jawohl, Herr Steiner. One hour. Ruth and I are baking bread this morning. We don't need you underfoot."

Outside I plunked him on the sled and pulled him toward Klugbauer's yard. Manfred was waiting for me. He had on his grandfather's old Army helmet even though it almost covered his eyes and he always had to hold on to it when he ran. "Ach Scheisse, Dieter. Why'd you bring him?"

"My mother says the Zwerg needs his fresh air. I can't come over until I take him for a ride. Wait for me."

Once in the park, I pulled the sled in big, wide, circles, and Wolfgang held on tightly and laughed. I pulled him faster and faster, in smaller and smaller circles, until the sled turned on its side and he fell off. I grabbed his belt, stood him up, and turned him around. His face was covered with snow and he looked scared. "You're a fat snowman," I said, laughing at him. He stared at me, then squeezed shut his eyes, opened his mouth, and screamed.

"Stop that, Wolfgang. People are looking at us. Besides, you're not hurt. All you did was fall off." He screamed louder. A woman hurried over and bent down, wiping Wolfgang's red face with a lacy, white handkerchief. "Was ist los mit dem Kleinen?"

"He fell off the sled."

"I saw what happened." She dabbed at Wolfgang's face, even though he tried to push her away. "You pulled him too fast."

"Nein, nein, Frau. It's not my fault. I didn't make him fall off—stop crying, Wolfgang—you're not hurt—he did it by himself." I tried to put him back on the sled, but he kept his legs straight and screamed.

"Sit down, Zwerg," I hollered, plopping him on the sled.

"Don't pull that sled so fast, Junge!" the woman called as I ran toward home.

"Back so soon?" Mutti called from the kitchen. At the sound of her voice, Wolfgang cried louder. She rushed down the hall and scooped him up.

"What happened? What makes my baby cry like this?" She rocked him back and forth. "There, there, Wolfgang, it's all right." She turned to me. "Explain this please?"

"He wouldn't stop, Mutti. I pulled him in circles and I thought he liked it, but he fell off somehow and started bawling. And he won't stop. I thought you'd want me to bring him back."

"You did the right thing, Dieter. You're a good boy, and such a help to me." She patted my head.

I peeked up at Wolfgang's wet face as Mutti hugged him. The snow from his clothes made Mutti's apron all wet down the front.

"Your brother loves you, Wolfgang," Mutti said, kissing his eyes and nose. "Not all boys would be so good to their little brothers." She hugged us close to her and kissed the top of my head. "So good my boys are."

"Then can I have a sheet, Mutti? And maybe a pillow case, before I go to Manfred's?"

"A sheet and pillow case? You're changing your bed? Without taking off your coat?"

"There's snow. I need them for camouflage, so I can sneak up on the Poles and shoot them dead."

"Genug, Dieter! You know how I feel about those war games. And now good sheets you want to ruin?"

23

"Then I'll use something else."

She followed me into the kitchen and watched as I took a white paper bag from beside the ice box, cut two holes in it for my eyes, and pulled it on over my head.

"These ideas, Ruth, where does he get them?"

Ruth put down the rolling pin and wiped the flour off her hands. "The world, it's crazy now, Frau Drescher. Nothing is the same any more."

Ruth started to take dishes to the kitchen. I pushed my chair back and stood up, but Vati motioned for me to stay.

"Sit down, Dieter. I want to ask you something." He folded his napkin into a stack and leaned back in his chair. "Tell me. Have you seen Sollie Weigel?"

"Nein, he hasn't been in school."

"Absent he's been? For how long?"

"A long time. A week, maybe. He must be sick."

Mutti stopped sewing and looked up. "A week, Karl. I told you something—"

"Ja, I hear." Vati turned to me. "If he's not in school tomorrow, stop at his apartment on your way home to see if—"

"Karl, you think that's safe?"

Vati held his hand up. "It will be safe for Dieter. He's only asking about his schoolmate. No one will think anything of it."

"Think what of it?" I asked.

"Your mother likes you coming straight home, but she doesn't mind this time, do you, Lis?"

"Ja, that's all, Dieter. I'm sometimes cautious." Mutti smiled. "So, do as your father asks. Check on Sollie."

"You could call Frau Weigel," I offered.

"Ja, but the phone—it rings. No one answers. We're afraid—"

"Ja, Dieter," my father interrupted. "We're afraid there may be illness there. Stop by tomorrow and see."

24

Sollie was still absent the next day, so on the way home, I turned down Linden Strasse.

I climbed the stairs to the second floor and rang the bell at his apartment. I waited, but no one opened the door. I rang the bell again and put my ear against the door. "Sollie," I called. "It's Dieter. Let me in." But I didn't hear anyone inside, not even his baby brother. *You can always hear Josef crying, even out here in the hall.* I started to leave but stopped. *What if he's sick and in bed? Maybe he can't hear me.* I knocked hard on the door. "Sollie," I yelled. "It's Dieter. Do you want to know about your homework?"

"Stop that noise! They're gone." I jumped and turned around. The neighbor's door was open just a crack and she looked out at me.

"I came to see Sollie. You know him?"

"Who are you?" she whispered.

"Dieter Steiner. I'm his friend."

She opened the door a little bit more, just barely poked her head out to look, and waved me closer.

"They took them last week," she said in my ear. "During the night."

"They moved?"

"They took them," she repeated.

"His parents took them? Where? Where'd they go?"

"Quick. On with you. Go away and do not come back!"

"But where—"

Without a sound, the door closed. *His parents took Sollie and his brother? They ran away in the night?* The hall was quiet. I looked around to see if someone was watching. I wanted to get home. I hurried downstairs, two steps at a time.

25

2

"I'm in the kitchen, Dieter," Mutti called. "Did you stop at the Weigels? Were they home?"

I pushed open the kitchen door. My mother was at the sink, and she turned around, a potato in one hand, a paring knife in the other. "They moved." I told her. "The neighbor said they left. Can I have a raw potato?"

Mutti handed me a potato slice. "Here's the salt. Now, what is this? They moved?"

"That's what she said. She wasn't very nice. She told me to go away, so I did. She probably made them leave, too." I bit off a piece of potato. "Isn't that funny, Mutti? That they moved away so quick?"

Mutti looked at the clock. "Your father will be home soon. Why don't you wait by the gate? When you see him turn the corner, you can run down and meet him."

I swung on the gate until I saw Vati down the block. I jumped off and ran toward him.

"Guten Abend," he said, smiling and patting my shoulder when I reached him. "How's my oldest son this evening?"

"Sollie moved away," I said, catching my breath. "He moved away from here, Vati. He didn't tell me he was moving."

"You are sure? You know this for a fact?"

"They took him and his little brother and they moved. In the middle of the night. Isn't it funny to move in the middle of the night?"

"That's good if they moved. Who told you, Dieter?"

"The neighbor. She acted funny, too. First she hollered and then she whispered. She whispered it to me right in my ear. 'They took them in the night.' That's the way she said it. Like it was a secret, or something."

"Ach Du Lieber." Vati grabbed my arm, and we stopped in the middle of the sidewalk. "Wait. Wait, now." He looked up and down the street, then pulled me over to the curb. He lowered his voice. "Talk slow."

Again, I told him.

"Now let me understand this, Dieter. She said *'They'* took them during the night?"

Why's he asking me this again? "Ja, Vati. That's what she said." We'd reached the bench of the bus stop.

"Let's sit here for a minute. Did you tell your mother about this?"

"Ja, I told her as soon as I got home. Do you think Frau Weigel will write her and tell us where they've gone? If she does, can I go visit?"

"The Weigels are Jews. Did you know that?"

"Like Herr Weinberg and his cat?"

Vati sort of smiled, but then he looked serious. He put his arm around me and rested his chin on my head. His voice was real low. "The Weigels are good friends, and I am afraid that—" Vati suddenly hugged me with both arms and pulled me onto his lap. He rocked me back and forth, like he does Wolfgang. I looked around, hoping no one saw us. After a few minutes he stood me up in front of him. His hands were warm as he held my face up to his. "These are terrible times, Dieter. It is enough that adults must live with their mistakes, but innocent children . . . " He stared at me for a long time.

27

"You *must* understand this. We have to be careful. You cannot talk about Sollie—"

"But Vati, he's my—"

He put his fingers against my lips. "Not any more. Don't tell anyone what that woman told you. Don't mention it in school. Don't tell anyone the Weigels came to visit. And if someone in school asks you where Sollie is, say 'I do not know; I have no idea.' I know my boy can do that, can't you?"

"But Vati, where did—"

My father put his finger to his own lips this time. "Sh-h-h. No more, Dieter." He took my hand. "Come, your mother is holding supper for us." He didn't talk the rest of the way home. When we got there, he spoke to my mother and Ruth, and they all went into the study and shut the door.

A few days later, when I came home from school, a woman I didn't know sat in the living room with Mutti. Her hair was in a knot at the back of her head, and she reminded me of Frau Klinger, the mean lady at the library.

"Dieter, say Guten Tag to Frau Witte here. She is our new neighbor upstairs, with her husband, Hans." I shook hands with Frau Witte, who kept my hand in hers.

"He looks like you, Frau Drescher," she said. "Thin, and such good posture." She tugged at my hand. "Sideways please turn, so I can see your back." She nodded. "Ja, very good posture. Deutsche boys have reason to stand straight with their heads up. You know why, Dieter?"

I straightened my back and stood as tall as I could. "Because we are the superior race, and we will conquer the world!"

"Ja?" Frau Witte clapped. "And why is God so good to us?"

"Wir danken unserem Führer." I stuck my chin out as I

28

stood at attention. "And when I'm a soldier, I will fight all enemies of the Vaterland."

Mutti leaned forward. "Dieter, don't you have—"

"Frau Drescher, he learns well in school. You must be very proud."

Mutti sat back and drummed her finger on the arm of the couch. "Ja," she said, nodding. "Very proud."

Frau Witte smiled and grabbed my hand again. "You're old enough for the Hitler Jugend, aren't you?"

I pulled my hand from her grasp and stood at attention. "I would like the HJ, but I want to join the Sturmtruppen." I snapped my arm out. "Heil Hitler."

Frau Witte's arm shot up in response. "Heil Hitler," she said with a big smile. She turned to Mutti. "Wunderbar! Frau Drescher, wunderbar. What a loyal young man you have here. And he stands so straight."

"Ja, doesn't he?" Mutti looked mad. "Excuse yourself, Dieter, and go to your room. I'm sure you have lessons."

Frau Witte nodded at me and smiled wide. "I'd like a son like you."

I looked in the mirror. I did stand straight, though not as straight as I had in front of Frau Witte—then I had to hold my breath to keep my shoulders back that far. I walked back and forth, watching my reflection, but soon my back hurt. *How do the storm troopers do it? They must practice all the time.* My shoulders began to slump.

I've got it!

I took a ruler from my desk and in the bathroom found adhesive tape and scissors. Back in my room, I fastened long strips of tape to the ruler, then laid it on the floor. I took off my shirt and undershirt and lay down, pressing my back against the ruler so it fit across my shoulder blades. I reached up and pulled the adhesive over my shoulders and the long strips on the sides of the ruler around my chest.

29

Now I can stand at attention all the time. I stood up and looked in the mirror. My shoulders were very straight.

When Ruth called me to supper, I marched in and sat at the table. I pressed my back against the chair and sat with my head up, looking straight ahead.

"Are you all right, Dieter?"

"Jawohl, meine Mutter."

"Well, danke, junger Mann." She smiled at my father. "Such politeness."

Vati nodded. "A welcome change, after so much arguing. Perhaps he's turning over a new leaf." He reached over and patted my head. "You should always be so polite to your elders. Let's hope it lasts."

"Jawohl, mein Vater."

"Well, I'm glad I'm included in this new behavior." He winked at my mother and picked up his knife. "Pass the butter, please, Dieter."

I reached for the butter dish, but the tape on my shoulder pulled and hurt. I stood up, leaned over the table and, keeping my elbows at my sides, picked up the dish with both hands. Bowing, I placed it in front of Vati.

"What is this, Dieter? Now you are a butler?" He shook his head and smiled at Mutti, who picked up her napkin and held it over her mouth.

"Your arms, Dieter. Do they hurt?"

"Nein, meine Mutter. I am practicing being a good soldier."

I sat back down and started to eat. I had to keep my elbow at my side, and bend over to eat from my fork. I was the last to finish. Ruth brought out a compote of sweet cherries over cake, my favorite dessert.

"Nein, Dieter. No dessert without first drinking your milk."

"But Mutti . . . "

" 'Mutti,' it is when you want something?" She laughed. "Still it is, milk before dessert."

I reached for my glass and stopped. The adhesive pulled. *Everyone's watching.* I stood up, bent over the table, and picked up the glass with both hands. I drank the milk without stopping and set the glass back on the table, still using both hands. I sat back down.

Vati shrugged. My mother nodded. "Now he can have dessert, Ruth."

Ruth placed the dish in front of me.

"Danke, Fräulein Schuber."

Ruth put her hands on her hips. "Fräulein Schuber? What's this Fräulein Schuber business?"

"Good Deutsche are respectful. I'm going to call you that from now on."

"Unser Kleiner talks like a grownup now? Nein, Dieter. Just call me Ruth. You'll still be a good Deutscher." She laughed. "Are good Deutsche allowed to lick the cherry bowl in the kitchen?"

"Oh, ja." I quickly finished the compote. "May I be excused, Vati?"

"Vati, is it? What happened to mein Vater?" He laughed hard.

"Danke, Vater," I said, nodding. "Danke, Mutter." I nodded again. "Danke, Fräulein Schu—Ruth." I nodded once more, then stood up and clicked my heels together.

"Und wir danken unserem Führer," I said proudly, and saluted. "Heil Hitler." I turned around to go to the kitchen.

"A minute please, Klaus Dieter Steiner." Vati grabbed my arm. "Sit down." He pushed me onto my chair.

"What is this thanking of the Führer? You think he put the food on this table? Nein, Herr Steiner; I did that. You think he was in the kitchen and cooked our supper? Your mother and Ruth prepared this meal. The Führer had nothing to do with this supper. We don't thank him for what he doesn't do. I want no more of this in our house, verstanden?"

"But we say that in school. And today, when I said it to Frau Witte, she liked it."

"This is not school. Frau Witte is not family."

"But I want—"

"Genug!" Vati was really mad. "You do not thank the Führer in this house, ever, and—"

"Karl, lower your voice."

"—you do not argue with me." He turned his back, and I was happy to leave.

I went into the kitchen and licked the cherry bowl. *Vati's mean sometimes. I won't be like that when I'm a father. Frau Witte thinks I'll be a good soldier. Maybe I can go to her apartment and thank the Führer.*

I filled the tub with just a little water, just enough to cover my legs. Then I washed very carefully around the adhesive. Even so, the ends of the tape came loose and when I got out of the tub and dried off, I added more tape around my chest and over my shoulders. I pulled on my pajamas and went out to the living room.

"Gute Nacht, mein Vater," I said and kissed him.

"Sleep well, Dieter."

"Gute Nacht, liebe Mutter."

Mutti laughed. "What a wonderful junge Mann we have here, Karl." She kissed my forehead, then grabbed me and swung me onto her lap to hug. "Mein Gott! What is this thing?" She poked my back, then stood me up in front of her. "What do you have in here?" She unbuttoned my pajama top, pulled it down around my shoulders and turned me around. "Oh, Dieter . . . no." She shook her head and laughed, then turned me around again, so Vati could see my back. "Look, Karl. Look at this."

My father leaned forward in his chair. "Dieter, explain, please?"

"I can't stand straight without it. Frau Witte said I looked good when I was standing straight, but I could only do it a little while." I smoothed the tape that had loosened when Mutti pulled down my pajama top. "I only want to be a good soldier."

Vati smiled. "Son, you are not a soldier." He pulled me over in front of him. "Look at me. A young boy you are. A fine Deutscher boy. More important things there are for you to practice than looking like a telephone pole. If ever you are a soldier, Gott verboten, time will seem to stand still when you have to stand straight. For now, a boy who does his lessons and does what we tell him to, that's all we ask of you. Verstanden?"

I nodded, and tried to keep the tears from spilling down my face.

Mutti reached for my hand. "Let's get this ridiculous stuff off of you." We went to the bathroom and she sat me on the commode, facing backwards. "First I am taking off this measuring stick. It will hurt, but I know a good Deutscher soldier like you won't mind a little pain." She cut some of the tape, then yanked.

"It hurts! Don't let it hurt!"

"Don't you remember, Dieter? You're a soldier. Soldiers don't cry." She peeled the tape away from my back and tried to reach under my arm to my chest.

"I'm not a soldier yet. Vati said I wasn't." I pushed her hand away. "Ich bin kein Soldat!"

"But you want to be one, and that's why you did this stupid thing. Now, Herr Soldat Steiner, you will see what happens to soldiers."

3

"I have another card, Vati." I handed the postcard to my father as he sat down in his chair opposite Mutti and me. "Read for me, please."

"From New York City this time, Dieter," he said, looking at the card. "Your wall will soon be covered."

My mother laughed. "Already his wall is covered. Just ask Ruth what dusting them is like." She stopped knitting and looked up. "Maybe you should tell Herr Wise not to send him any more cards. When Herr Oscher delivered the mail today, he said to Ruth, 'Why does the junge Mann get this mail from America?' She said it was for his postcard collection, and he said 'Tell Herr Steiner his collection is large enough.' I think you—"

"Tell him it is large enough?" Vati interrupted. "Now it's our mail! Even postcards to a child?"

"Just tell him, Karl, no more cards. Now read it to us, please."

He looked at Mutti a moment, then looked back at the card. "He says, 'Dear Dieter—I am here in New York City which has more people than any other city in the United States. This building is so high I saw you playing in your back yard when I was at the top. Hope all is well with your family. Regards, Herr Wise.' Vati laughed as he gave it back to me. "See how tall the building is? It's the Empire State Building. He thinks he saw you from there."

"Americans think they can do everything, even see across the ocean. I don't believe him."

"Herr Wise is only making fun. Can you no longer take a joke?"

"Herr Schmitt said Americans brag that they are the greatest people on earth and can do anything. They're not. Deutsche people are."

"Why do you act this way about my friend? I thought you liked him."

"I do—I guess. But he's not Deutsch. Herr Schmitt said we should never mix with foreigners."

Vati shut his eyes and sighed. "Then maybe the flag he gave you, you should throw away. That's foreign, you know."

"Throw away my flag?"

He nodded. "Throw it away. Keep your Herr Schmitt happy." He sat back in his chair and looked at Mutti. "I don't understand it, Lis. Is there no—"

"Not now, Karl," my mother interrupted.

"Isn't it enough with war talk and soldiers and parades? Other things there are to learn in school. It is no place for propaganda."

"Not now, Karl," Mutti said, shaking her head. "This isn't the time." She turned toward me. "How many postcards does this one make?"

"Twenty, or maybe twenty-one." I stared at the picture. "Herr Schmitt says New York City is a Jew city, and Deutschland would be a better place if all the Jüdische Schweine moved there."

Vati sat up on the edge of his chair. "Everyone you should not hate!"

"Karl. He doesn't—"

"For what reason do you talk like this? Your mother

and I—we never tell you these things. Ruth doesn't speak of Juden this way." He leaned forward. "But this Herr Schmitt—you believe him. Why not your mother? Me? Ruth?"

"He's eight years old, Karl. He doesn't understand." Mutti laid her knitting needles in her lap and reached into her basket, bringing out a large ball of yarn. "Sit here with me, Dieter," she said, patting the seat beside her. "Help me wind this yarn."

I moved closer to Mutti.

"You ignore this, mein Schatz? You, the sweetest, kindest, person I know. He speaks this way and you can ignore?" Vati stood up and walked to the window and stared outside. I kept my eyes on the yarn as Mutti wound it around and around on my hands.

"I have to tolerate this, Lis?" he said, still standing at the window. "Hate is filling him up, against people he doesn't know, and I have to keep still?"

Mutti stopped the winding and held onto the ball of yarn. "You think we have a choice, Karl?" she said quietly, not looking at him. She smoothed out the unfinished sweater in her lap and took the yarn from my hands. "We try. We do the best we can." She looked around at him, still standing by the window. "We are good, honest people, Karl, but we can't change things so, please. Until a better way we have . . . Later, we'll discuss." She patted my cheek. "Go. Put your new postcard with the others and count them for me. Your father and I, we'll talk."

As I always did when Herr Wise sent a new card, I took down those already on the wall and counted them, one by one, into a pile. " . . . nineteen, twenty." I added the new one on top. "Twenty-one! I was right!" I held the ruler at the side of the stack. Almost three centimeters.

From the desk drawer I took out my notebook and wrote under the heading *Post Karten,* "12 Oktober 1939-No. 21- New York City—2 1/2 cm. high." I spread the cards on the

36

floor, rearranged them, and then tacked them back on the wall, my American flag in the center.

I went back to the living room. Mutti was alone. "I have twenty-one cards now," I announced.

"Wunderbar, Dieter. That's a nice collection, even if you get no other cards."

"You know, I was thinking. When Herr Wise gave me my flag, he was here—in Deutschland—so that means he bought the flag here. Ja?"

"Maybe so. Maybe he bought your flag here."

"So the flag was made in Deutschland, right?"

"Ja. I suppose it could have been."

"Good then, it's not a foreign flag, so I can keep it."

"You figure well, Dieter." she said. "Perhaps you will grow up to be a bureaucrat." She covered her mouth with her hands, then laughed. "Ach Du Lieber! Don't tell your father of my prediction. He would be upset."

"Who would be upset?" Vati said, coming into the room. "Do you talk about me?" He smiled at Mutti. "Tell me, who is upsetting me now?"

She reached up and took his hand. "Dieter has decided his flag is not foreign since Herr Wise gave it to him in Deutschland."

"That's right, Vati. So if it's not foreign, it can't be verboten."

"Your Herr Schmitt, you think he will understand your reasoning?" He winked at my mother and sat down, settling back in his chair.

"Shush, Karl. Genug." Mutti turned and smiled at me. "Ja, Dieter, I think that's a good way to solve your problem. But don't mention your flag to Herr Schmitt. Or anyone else, in school or out, in particular, not to Frau Witte."

Vati shook open his newspaper. "Oh, definitely do not mention your flag to that woman, that Nazi."

"Karl! Remember what we said."

"Frau Witte said she'd give me Swastika flags. I told her we didn't have any and she said 'No Swastika flags?' She can't imagine that."

"You see, Lis? His only concern."

"I told her you said you were too busy to get them, and she said 'No one should be too busy to show support for the Führer,' so she's going to give us some. Did you know they have pictures of the Führer on almost every wall? With little Swastika flags over them." I looked at the walls of our living room. *Eins . . . zwei . . . drei paintings—and a mirror.* That's all. "We should have his picture and flags."

"Parades and buildings, that's where flags belong," Vati said. "Not on the wall of the living room like it was the Party's office."

"Herr Schmitt asked yesterday how many of us had the Führer's picture at home. And Swastika flags outside."

Vati put his paper down. "And did he say anything when you didn't raise your hand?"

"Nein, Vati."

"Good. So it should be. All is not crazy, perhaps." He picked up the paper again, turned a page, and settled back into the chair.

I looked at him out of the corner of my eye. *I didn't exactly lie to you, Vati, but I did to Herr Schmitt.*

He continued to read and Mutti to knit, while I planned where I'd put the Swastika flags Frau Witte promised to bring me.

4

"Dieter, wake up. Frau Kundert has something for you."
Mutti's voice startled me awake. "Get dressed; she's sitting
on the veranda."

"I'm coming." I crawled out of bed and stood up, rubbing
the sleep from my eyes. I dressed quickly, walked down the
hall, and opened the door. I squinted in the bright sunlight.
Frau Kundert sat in a chair holding a small box.

"Guten Morgen, Dieter."

What's in the box? "Mutti said you have something for
me."

"Ja, I do." She opened the box and held up a little orange
kitten. "Would you like to take care of this?"

Instantly, I was wide awake. "Ja, Frau Kundert." I moved
closer.

"Here, you hold her, Dieter. See if she likes you."

"Ja, she'll like me. I know she will." I reached for the
kitten, and it squeaked a *meow-w-w-w.* It pushed its little
head against my hand and meowed again and again. "See?
She likes me."

Frau Kundert smiled. "Ja, she does. Do you want her?"

"Jawohl! But I don't have any money."

She laughed. "I don't want money, lieber Junge. But you have to promise to take good care of her. So much sadness and sorrow there is. So much hate. The animals don't hate, no matter who we are. But no one cares about them anymore. You will love her?"

"Ja, ja, ja, I promise!" I opened the front door. "Dicker," I called. "Come here, quick! Look what Frau Kundert gave us."

Wolfgang saw the kitten and smiled.

I held the kitten down so he could pet her. "She's ours, Dicker. I promised Frau Kundert I'll take good care of her."

He jumped up and down. "Me hold, me hold."

I handed him the kitten. "Be careful. She's just a baby."

He held her tight to his neck. She squirmed and burrowed into his hair. Wolfgang laughed and hunched his shoulders.

Frau Kundert reached over and petted the kitten. "That means she likes you, Wolfgang. I knew she'd like you boys."

Mutti came out on the veranda. "What do you tell Frau Kundert?" she said.

"Ja, Wolfgang. What do you tell Frau Kundert?" I poked him in the side.

"Danke." Wolfgang said.

"Dieter?" Mutti stared at me.

"Danke, Frau Kundert," I said. "Has she got a name?"

"If you give her one. She's yours now." Frau Kundert patted my arm. "From the animals we should learn, Dieter. They don't hate. Boys and girls shouldn't hate, either. Auf Wiedersehn."

Mutti bent down and rubbed the kitten's ear. "I thought you'd like her. Now what will you name her?"

"She looks like Putzi, Herr Weinberg's cat. He was a good cat. Let's name her after him."

"Herr Weinberg?" Mutti smiled. "You remember . . ."

She paused. "Ja, Putzi. That would be fitting. A nice

name. Take her to Ruth, Wolfgang." Mutti opened the door. "She'll fix some food for her."

Wolfgang walked carefully back inside, laughing as the kitten squirmed around his neck.

"Ruth," I called. "Come see Putzi."

I put a towel in a cardboard box, and Putzi's bed was made. Wolfgang sat down on the floor and pulled the box between his legs.

"She likes her bed, Dicker. She's purring. Hear her?"

I held her to his ear, and he smiled. "That's purring, Dicker. She sounds like a motorboat."

5

I brought the newspaper in from the living room. "Listen."
I read the headline out loud: **"JUNGVOLK TO JOIN HJ."** I
read a few lines of the article. "Dufte! I have to join."

I handed the paper to my mother. "Look, Mutti, this
means I can wear a uniform. I'll be like a real soldier."

Vati frowned. "We don't read the newspaper at supper.
Put it away."

I folded it up and put it on the counter. "But I have to be
a member now. Can I go tomorrow and join?" I went back
to the table and sat down. "I'll be a good Hitler Junge."

"You wait. You don't join. You wait for them to come
to us."

"But Karl, if he has to . . . " Mutti's voice trailed off.
She cut up the green beans on Wolfgang's plate and handed
him a spoon.

"Dieter can wait, Lis." He passed me the bowl of potatoes. "Eat your supper."

"But Vati . . . "

"Don't whine, Dieter. The war, it might be over, and
you won't have—"

"But I want to be a member. I want a uniform and I
want to march." I stood up, straight and soldier-like. "Heil
Hitler!"

"No more, Dieter." Vati grabbed my sleeve and pushed me down into the chair. "You heard what I said. Finish your supper." He tore off a piece of Brötchen and swirled it around and around in the soup. He sat there, staring into the bowl. He banged his fist.

"I won't stand for it!" he shouted. He threw the dripping bread across the room and slammed both fists on the table. "He will not become a puppet of that id—"

"For God's sake, Karl, stop it." Mutti jumped up and pointed to the ceiling. "Such chances you take."

I looked at the ceiling and back at them. I didn't understand. Mutti never liked me playing soldier, but now, she sounded like she was on my side.

"We have no choice, Karl. They will force him . . . " Mutti put her fingers to her lips and looked toward the window.

"Then we wait for them to force him." Vati took a deep breath and sighed. "I am sorry I was upset, Dieter. I did not mean to lose my temper. We'll discuss this no more." He reached for another piece of bread.

"But when will they force me? When can I join, Vati?"

"That is it, Dieter. We'll let them come to us."

"They will not only come to us, Karl, they'll come *for* us." Mutti picked up her plate and put it in the sink where Ruth was washing the pots. "Hungry I'm not." She walked from the kitchen and my father left his supper and followed her.

Ruth hurried over and sat down in Mutti's chair, next to Wolfgang. She picked up the paper and read the article. "This means you, Dieter. Are you excited?" She took a napkin and wiped Wolfgang's face. "You have always wanted a uniform."

I reached for the paper and read the article again. Even if Vati made me wait for them to come, I knew they'd come soon. They had to. I watched Wolfgang in his highchair, making a mess of his food. *He's such a baby.*

I finished my supper and walked into the hall. As I passed the study I put my ear against the door.

"You know what can happen, Karl."

"I don't care; someone has to do—" I couldn't hear all Vati said; *he must be walking around.* I pressed my ear closer. " . . . future, the life . . . when Herr Steucher escaped . . . "

" . . . can't take these chances, not with the boys—" Mutti's voice was easier to hear.

"Stop that, Herr Steiner!" Ruth grabbed my arm and pulled me back. "When that door is closed Herr Drescher expects privacy." She pushed me ahead of her. "What would he say if I told him you were listening? Do you want me to tell him, Herr Steiner?" By now we were at the end of the hall, far away from the study. "Here you should stay—" Ruth pushed me into the playcorner, "—where you won't get into any trouble."

I sat down on the floor in the middle of our toys. *I can't play with these any more. I'm going to be in the HJ.* I got up and goose-stepped around the room. *Maybe I'll have a torch.*

What will it be like? I wondered. *Will I carry a gun? When will they come for me?*

The next morning, before I went to school, I ran upstairs.

"The HJ, Frau Witte. I'm over eight, so I have to join. It was in the newspaper. They'll be coming for me to join."

"Coming for you? You need an invitation? On your own you should sign, like a good child of the Vaterland."

"I can't. My father says I have to wait for them to order me."

"Wait for an order? Herr Drescher says you should wait for an order?"

"Ja. He said I might not have to go if the war is over. They'll come before the war is over, won't they?"

Frau Witte patted my head and smiled. "Of course, Dieter, new-member-to-be of the HJ. They will come for

44

Dieter, new-member-to-be of the HJ. They will come for you shortly. Of that I am certain."

I was sitting on the overturned bucket in Wolfgang's sandbox and drawing lines in the sand, when Ruth came out of the house. She sat down next to me and watched awhile.

"You are writing, or drawing pictures?" she finally asked.

"I don't know. I'm bored. There's nothing to do. No one to play with but Wolfgang."

"What is this? You always have to be playing? Can't you just enjoy a moment of peace and quiet? Look at that sunset." She waved in its direction. "All orange and red. See how pleasant everything looks."

"Ja." I answered, without looking. "It's pretty."

Ruth put her arm around my shoulders. "This is not the way you act. What bothers you so much you don't talk?" She put her hand on my chin, but I turned my head. She reached over and grabbed my chin again and made me look at her. "Tell me, Dieter. Was ist los?"

I pulled away and jumped up. "Why isn't Vati a soldier?"

"That is it? You want your father in the Wehrmacht?"

"Manfred's father is a soldier. He fights for the Reich. So is Konrad's."

"Sh-h-h," Ruth said. She grabbed my hands and pulled me toward her.

"Don't be so loud."

"Vati just goes to work," I cried. "He's not even in the Par—"

Ruth clamped her hand over my mouth and dragged me into her lap. "What kind of boy are you? Stop talking like this." She looked around at the house, then turned back to me. "The Wehrmacht is not where your father should be. He should be here, in the back yard, with you over his knee." She took her hand from my mouth.

45

"Do you understand what I am saying?"

I turned away, but she grabbed my arm.

"Look at me," she said. "Your father doesn't have to wear a uniform for you to be proud. Herr Drescher is a fine man, and he takes care of his family. It is only the young men without family who will be soldiers first. You understand that, don't you?"

"But if he had a uniform—"

"Genug, Dieter!" Ruth pulled me right in front of her, her face up close to mine. "Soon you'll wear the uniform of the Hitler Youth. Do you understand? It is enough for one family."

She stood up and pushed me down on the edge of the sandbox. "Stay here until you change your thoughts, Herr Steiner." She turned her back on me and started toward the house.

I jumped up. "What's wrong with two uniforms?"

She wheeled around and started back. "Dieter Steiner, I told you—"

"I'm sorry, I'm sorry," I cried and sat back down. She bent over me, her hands on her hips.

"What did you say, Herr Steiner?"

"I'm sorry."

"Be sure that you are. And stay here until I call you for supper."

I didn't like Ruth very much at all. And she was not my mother. But I stayed there until she called from the back door for me to come in.

While I ate, I looked at Vati. *He always wears a suit. It's always a dark brown suit. He'd look good in a uniform, especially if he had medals on his chest, like Manfred says his father has. And I could stand up in class when—*

"On my face there is something, Dieter?"

"Nein, nothing." I looked away, then back at him. "I was just thinking . . . about school. That's all. Just thinking."

46

"Dreaming appears to be more like it." He winked at my mother. "It appears we have a dreamer in the family, Lis. Our oldest son makes dreams from staring at me."

"It's good it's not nightmares," Mutti said, and laughed. *They think they know everything. We're at war and they sit here and laugh. And make jokes.*

"Manfred's father is a soldier." Vati didn't say anything. "I *said*, Manfred's father is a soldier. So is Konrad's."

"Ja, so you've told me. Finish your supper and carry your plate to the kitchen." He reached behind him for the newspaper. "See here, Lis," he said. "They talk of the possibility of women in the factories." *He's not even listening to me. He'll be sorry someday when I'm a soldier. They'll both be sorry.*

47

6

"Manfred knows war secrets."

"Ja?" Ruth folded the napkins on the ironing board. "You think he knows war secrets? He is important?"

"He says his father and mother are always talking about Hitler and he says he listens, even when they tell him not to. He's heard all kinds of things, some things he wasn't supposed to hear."

"Put these in the drawer, bitte." She handed me a pile of napkins. "How would his parents know war secrets? His father is an important man?"

"He must be. Manfred says he knows where the troops are going and everything."

Ruth laughed. "Ja, I'm sure the High Command is telling Manfred's father where the troops are going." She smiled as she sprinkled another batch of napkins and rolled them up. "Better it is that they tell Manfred's father his son tells tales. Enough talk of war, Dieter." She nodded toward the door. "Why don't you rake the leaves? The lawn is covered."

Everybody talks about the war except in our house.

Herr Ludwig was working in his yard when I came up from the basement with the rake. And Helga was with him.

"Hello, Dieter." She smiled at me through the fence. I waved and turned away. *I hate it when I blush. I can't let her see my red face.* I sneaked a look at her. *She's so pretty, her hair shines like gold.* I stood where I could glance in her direction every now and then. After I got used to her being there, I didn't feel the blush anymore. I dug the rake into the leaves, picked up a large clump, and swung it with all my might. I glanced over my shoulder. *She's looking at me.* I raked fast, back and forth, until I got all sweaty. I stopped to take off my sweater. When I pulled it over my head, I stretched the yarn so I could peek at Helga again. *She's still looking.* I wiped the sweat off my face with my sleeve and picked up the rake again. I got all the leaves from the far corner of the yard and soon the pile was almost as tall as me. I looked over to see if Helga noticed. *She's still watching!*

Finally, I finished. I leaned the rake against the tree.

Helga moved up against the fence. "That's the biggest pile of leaves I've ever seen," she said. "Can I jump in them?" She smiled as I walked toward her.

"What is this mountain you've made?" Vati came around the corner of the house. "Lis," he called, "you and Ruth come out when you get a chance and see the biggest pile of leaves we've ever had." *Everybody's going to be here.* "And tell Wolfgang, too," he added. "Looks very good, Dieter. What do you think, Herr Ludwig? Does not my son make the biggest leafpile you've ever seen?"

Herr Ludwig walked over to the fence. "Ja, Herr Drescher. I have been watching him. Like a grown man he's been working." He winked at my father. "Helga's been watching him, too."

Vati laughed. "Aha! I see. Well, sometimes a little motivation is all that's needed to get the job done. Now, I think they are dry enough. Let's burn them."

"But Vati, Helga and I were going to jump in them."

49

"No, we'll burn them before they blow away. You don't need to jump and spread them around the lawn. You've done too good a job to mess them up now."

Helga turned back toward her house.

"I want to do it anyway," I said loudly, but Helga kept walking away. Just then Wolfgang came running from the house, wearing his toy helmet and holding another one in his hand.

"You wear," he said.

I pushed his hand back. "That's a toy, for babies." I looked to see if Helga could hear me. "I want to wear the real helmet," I said in a loud voice, "like soldiers do."

Vati laughed. "It will be a long time before you're old enough to wear a helmet. You should play along with Wolfgang."

He treats me like I'm a baby, too. "I'm almost nine, and old enough to be a Hitler Youth." I jumped up and saluted. "Heil Hitler!"

Vati and Herr Ludwig looked surprised. "Heil Hitler," I said again. They looked at each other and then, together, said "Heil Hitler, Dieter." I glanced sideways and saw that Helga had turned around and was watching. *Now she knows I'm going to be a good soldier.*

The new year of 1940 began with gray, cold, windy weather. Lots of snow meant lots of sledding, and cold weather guaranteed ice skating on the lake, but my friends and I didn't spend all our time with such childish events. We listened proudly to the news on the radio about the smashing successes of our soldiers. In school, members of the Hitler Youth enjoyed privileges that were the envy of the rest of us. Some of them wore their uniforms to school and walked the halls with military precision, intimidating the rest of us, who were, unfortunately, too young or handicapped to be members. I was, of course, eligible to join, but my father

50

still insisted I wait until they come for me, so I languished with growing impatience for their arrival.

I coveted their black uniforms and their power. When they saluted, the rest of us were required to return the salute, step aside, and allow them to pass. On the S-Bahn many HJ members, with great gallantry, opened doors and offered their seats to women. Although I offered my seat to women, I was a poor imitation of those in uniform. I ached to join ranks with these examples of the Master Race.

Frau Witte showed me her nephew's picture. "See how big and strong he looks."

"Ja, he does. Someday I'll have a uniform like that."

Frau Witte looked surprised. "Die HJ has not come for you? I do not understand. I gave them . . . You have heard nothing?"

"Not yet. I wish they would."

"The Führer needs you!"

"I know, Frau Witte." I shrugged. "I want to join, but my father says I have to wait."

"It's been long enough, Dieter. I'll see what I can do." She smiled and put her finger to her lips. "Sh-h-h," she said. "We don't tell anyone our secret."

"Nein, I won't tell." I went in the house bursting with the knowledge I'd soon have a uniform of my own to wear.

Just before dark a few days later I sat at my window, staring outside when a Hitler Youth and another man rode up on bicycles. They stopped in front of the house and leaned their bikes against our fence.

I ran to the kitchen. "Mutti, they're here! Die HJ ist hier!"

She wiped her hands on her apron and quickly went to Vati's study. "Karl, go to the door. They're here."

Vati let them in and took them to his study. He looked at

51

me as they walked past him into the room. His mouth was clenched and he looked like he did when he was very mad.

Mutti made us all sit in the kitchen while she stood in the doorway and watched down the hall. "I told him, I told him," she kept saying, her hands in fists over her chest. "I knew this would happen."

How can she say these things? What if they hear her?

Finally the door opened and Vati came out.

"Komm' hier, Dieter. You are invited to join the HJ."

"Jawohl!" I clicked my heels together and raised my right arm in salute and walked past him into the study. The men returned my salute, but they didn't smile. The civilian looked at me.

"How old are you?"

"Eight-and-a-half." I clicked my heels again and stood as straight as I could.

He walked up close to Vati. "He should have been registered. He does not look sick to me."

"He was sick."

I wasn't sick, Vati. What are you do—

The man handed me a small piece of paper. "Your group number is five-eighty-two. This is the address. Meetings are Wednesdays at four o'clock sharp. You will be there. In uniform."

He looked back at Vati. "You are responsible for his being there, Herr Drescher. If he does not show up, you will be arrested. The whole family. Like gypsies!"

"But if the boy is sick, he—"

"Scheisse!" the man shouted and poked his finger into Vati's chest. "He will be there next Wednesday. Verstanden?"

"Jawohl."

They raised their arms. "Heil Hitler."

"Heil Hitler," Vati said. He walked to the front door and opened it and they marched out.

"Bist Du froh, Herr Steiner?" he said when he closed it.

52

7

"My son needs a uniform," Mutti told the clerk. "He will be a Pimpf."

"Ja, Frau; a Pimpf?" He looked at me. "And you are proud to be a Pimpf?"

I smiled and nodded. "It is an honor to serve my Führer."

"He already knows what to say! My son is a Pimpf. A month ago he joined. Could barely wait for his uniform."

"Dieter, too. Could we see—"

"A proud moment it was. After his first meeting we had a party." He looked at me again. "You will have a party?"

A party! I like that. "Ja, Mutti? I can have a party?"

"I'll talk to your father." She moved closer and put her purse on the counter. "Could we please see a uniform?"

"But, of course, Frau. He will need the winter one; one moment please." He came back with a black jacket and pants. "And here's the belt—look at this buckle, all the boys like this." He gave Mutti the uniform and showed us a dressing room. "In here," he said, pulling aside a curtain. "I will get the rest of the uniform while you change."

Mutti stood outside while I pulled on the black pants, tucked my shirt in, and put on the black jacket. I looked good, just like a Hitler Youth. I wrapped the belt around me and pulled it tight. "There's not enough holes in the belt, Mutti. It doesn't fit." Mutti pulled back the curtain and looked at me. "Oh, Dieter, you're so thin. It's too long." I walked with Mutti back to the counter. "He needs a smaller belt," she said.

He went into a room behind the counter, and when he came back, he handed me another belt. "This should be about right," he said. "Hold your arms up." He ran it through the belt loops and pulled it tight. "This fits."

Mutti stuck her finger between me and the belt. "Ja, this is good. We can't get it too tight; he's a growing boy."

The clerk nodded. "Aren't they all? Now here's the shoulder strap and cap. Try these on." Mutti put the strap over my shoulder and connected it to the belt while I held the cap. She finished and stood back. "That looks good, Dieter. Now try on your cap."

I held it by the visor and put it on my head. Then I looked in the mirror. *What a wonderful hat.* "Am I taller, Mutti?"

"Not yet. But the uniform, it makes you look taller."

"And he'll be taller when he puts on these shoes." The clerk motioned to a chair. "Come, sit down, and we will try these."

When he finished tying my shoes, I stood up. I remembered when I taped the ruler on my back. *I don't need that now; it's easy to stand straight.* I looked in the mirror. "Heil Hitler," I said.

"Not yet. You need to put this on your cap to be complete." He handed me a little diamond-shaped pin, a small Swastika in its center. "Here," he said, pointing to a spot just above the visor. "It belongs here."

I pinned the emblem to my new cap and put it on.

"I wish the HJ had been around when I was young," the clerk said. "Such training." He stepped away from the counter. "Your name again?"

"Dieter Steiner."

"Come with me, Dieter." I walked with him to the middle of the store. He clapped his hands. "Look, another new Hitler Youth—Pimpf Dieter Steiner." He turned to me and stepped back. "Now you can salute, Dieter."

"Heil Hitler," I called. "Heil Hitler."

The clerk and two men returned my salute. Some of the other people walking through the store stopped and looked. An old woman with a cane walked over and stood by the counter. "Ja, such a good-looking young soldier here," she said. "My grandson just joined, too. The Vaterland is proud of these boys." She looked at Mutti "You, too, are proud, ja?"

"Ja," Mutti answered. "How could a mother not be?" But she didn't smile. I looked in the mirror again, and then at Mutti. She didn't say anything.

"Don't you like my uniform?"

"It's nice." She was quiet for a moment. "You look all grown up." She paid the clerk and he thanked her. As we walked out, I looked in the mirror one more time. *I am all grown up. I'm a Pimpf!*

On the way home I looked at myself in all the shop windows. "Everyone's looking at me, Mutti."

"Ja. I can see."

A brownshirt leaned against the doorway of the tobacco shop, and I started marching as we passed by. "That's good, young one," he said. He saluted Mutti. "Er ist ein guter Deutscher, Frau." Mutti nodded but didn't answer him. I looked at the little kids who weren't old enough to be members of the HJ. They all looked like babies. When we got home I ran up the steps and waited for Mutti to unlock the door.

"You can take that off now," she said. "Only to the meetings do you wear it. Is that understood?"

"But can't I wear it around the house?"

"We don't need a soldier in the house."

"But I want to wear it. At least let me show Ruth."

Mutti called toward the kitchen. "Ruth, we have a soldier out here. Please come look at him so he can take off his uniform."

Ruth came into the living room. Wolfgang ran behind her. "Oh, Dieter," she said. "How grown up you look!"

"I am a real soldier. I'm a Pimpf. Heil Hitler."

Wolfgang's arm shot up. "Heil Hitler." He goose-stepped in front of me.

"You're a *baby*. The war's going to be over before you'll be old enough to join the HJ."

"Gott Sei Dank," Mutti muttered. "Enough, Dieter. Do not tease Wolfgang. Now Ruth has seen you. Change your clothes." Mutti handed me the paper sack with my old shoes and trousers. "You can put these on again."

"But what about Vati? Can't I keep it on until Vati comes home, please? I promise I'll change as soon as he sees it."

Mutti smiled. "All right, but it is in the clothespress before supper."

When my father arrived, I strutted around the living room, my chin up, my mouth a grim line. He failed to return my many salutes, saying the day's work had been hard and he was too tired to expend much effort on saluting. I realize now that what I had taken for a lack of pride was no doubt resignation that he no longer had control of my conscience.

"It's Wednesday," I said as I sat down at the kitchen table.

Vati poured me a glass of milk. "So it is, Dieter. Just like it was last week and just like it will be next week." He winked at Ruth as she put my cereal bowl down. "Do you think there's anything unusual or special about today being Wednesday?"

"Nein, Herr Drescher. It is always Wednesday in the middle of the week."

"Tonight's my first meeting. I get to wear my uniform."

56

Dieter Steiner, 1942

"Meeting? What meeting? A church meeting? A school mee—"

"Hitler Youth!" I reached over and shook his arm. "You're making jokes, Vati."

My father looked at me. "Ja, Dieter. I know it's your first meeting. I wish it was a church meeting . . . " He folded his napkin and stood up. He looked like he had something else to say, but he just stood there.

Mutti came in. "Karl? The breakfast you don't like? I'll fix something else."

He waved her away. "Nein. I'm not hungry." He kissed her on the cheek. "I'll go in early." He patted my head. "I'll take you tonight, son. Be ready when I get here."

"The Hitler Youth owns this building, Vati. Helmut told me."

"He seems to know everything, this Helmut."

"He does. His father is a soldier. His father says the HJ owns the whole building."

"That's good for the HJ."

We walked through the double doors and turned to the right and went downstairs. It was just one big room with benches on one side. A lot of boys were already there.

"Look at all the flags," I whispered. "And the pictures. There's Hitler and the Kaiser."

Vati pointed to another picture. "You know him?"

"Ja, Frederick the Great. We studied him in school. But I don't know the rest of them."

"I'll tell you sometime. Now we get you registered."

"It's just like a museum, isn't it?" I whispered again. "Look at the maps. There's the world, and Europe, and—"

"Willkommen," the officer broke in. "Ich bin euer Gruppenführer."

Vati handed him a paper, and I tried to stand very straight and tall.

"A new member, ja?" The leader looked at the paper. "Klaus Dieter Steiner?"

I nodded. The boys on the benches stopped talking and turned around and stared. I felt my face flush. One of the boys laughed, and some of the others whispered.

"Achtung!" the officer yelled, and snapped his heels together.

The boys jumped to attention. "Heil Hitler!" they said, arms flying straight ahead.

"Come with me." I followed the officer to the front and stood at attention next to the podium. No one smiled. I remembered Helmut said soldiers shouldn't smile. I kept my face serious but my heart was beating in my ears.

"A new member we have," the Gruppenführer said. "Welcome to Pimpf Klaus Dieter Steiner!"

All arms went up again. "Heil Hitler!" they shouted.

"Hei—Heil Hitler." I stammered. I looked for Vati but saw only his back as he went up the stairs.

He was outside waiting for me when the meeting was over.

"Why didn't you stay and watch, Vati? It was fun."

"I'll watch another time. We need to get home."

"I met Siegfried. He lives just two blocks from us. We're going to go to meetings together. And I'm going to learn to box. And they showed us every place on the maps where the Army is. And Siegfried says his mother lets him wear his uniform at home. Can I wear mine at home?"

"Nein."

"But Siegfried does. I think they all do. Why can't I?"

"Let's just get home, Dieter. My head is aching. I am not good company tonight."

I looked forward to wearing my uniform on Wednesday nights and marching down the street to the meetings. I never tired of saluting people on the sidewalk. Most smiled and saluted back. One night at supper I told my father I could threaten someone if they didn't salute me. He stopped eating and pointed his fork at me. "If you ever threaten anyone, I'll burn your uniform and you will attend your meetings in your pajamas," he warned. "Verstanden, Pimpf Steiner?"

In the beginning the meetings were much like school, except that I wore a uniform and learned to drill. I learned military history and the superiority of the Aryan race. Later I advanced to military exercises where I learned survival techniques. I was introduced to small-caliber handguns and learned to handle them, disassemble, clean, and put them back together. I learned how to position myself when firing a weapon and to judge the effective distances of bullets.

After that came the war games. We eagerly awaited these, for then we were like real soldiers. In the woods surrounding our meeting place, we crept around and behind trees and bushes, in dugouts and on our bellies. We who wore green arm bands fought the enemy—those in arm bands of red. Sometimes our war went on into the night.

Mutti grabbed my arm when I came home. "What is this face?"

"We were in the woods. We—"

"The woods? This time of night?"

"It is our meeting. Tonight it was—"

"This black face is a meeting? A meeting to do what?"

"Attack and kill the enemy, defen—"

"Genug!" She snapped the dish towel around my legs. "You are children, and they teach you to kill?" She pulled me to her and wrapped her arms around me. The black on my face rubbed off on her apron. "This is insane! You are my baby!"

I pushed away. "I'm *not* a baby. Wolfgang's a baby. Not me!"

She grabbed my shoulders. "You will always be my baby, Klaus Dieter Steiner. I will always worry about you. And I worry about your future. What about your schooling? Your lessons? Your homework? The HJ does not care about your education?"

I jumped to attention, my arms at my side, my head up. The HJ and the Vaterland come first," I announced. "The Gruppenführer said the teachers know this. They're proud of us, he said. 'There is no worry if you are a loyal member of the HJ!' he told us."

"In a few years the Vaterland will worry because it will be a country of *uneducated* loyal members of the HJ. Idioten!" she yelled. "Men who will know how to shoot and kill but be unable to design a building or perform an operation . . . or run a bank! The only thing you'll learn is to be a Soldat or a Polizist. Someone with a gun. This is a future for my son?" She pushed me out of the way and rushed to the bedroom. She went in and slammed the door shut.

"What's wrong with Mutti?" I asked my father. "She's not happy I'm in the Hitler Youth?"

"Later, Dieter," he said. "Your mother's tired. Clean your face and do your lessons."

"I'm too tired from my meeting. I'm too tired to do my homework."

"You will do it in the morning, then, before breakfast. Now clean that face. Ask Ruth to help." He went into the bedroom and shut the door behind him.

Ruth sat in the kitchen reading. I walked over beside her. "You want to hear what we did tonight at the meeting?"

Ruth looked up. "Ach Du Lieber! Such dirt. Where have you been?" She grabbed my hand and led me to the sink. "Wait right here. I'll fetch the cold cream." In a moment she was back. "Use this," she said, handing me a jar and a roll of tissue. "Rub it in well and then wipe it off." She placed a folded washrag on the edge of the sink. "When you're finished, wash it with soap. I can't believe they have you children do these things."

No one wants to listen to what I did. I bet Helmut's family listens. I wiped the cold cream all over my face and wiped it off with the tissue.

I walked over to Ruth. "Is it all off?"

"Not completely. Wash it with the soap."

I went back and washed and left the dingy washrag wadded up in the sink. I was too tired to do anything more. I went to my bedroom, put on my pajamas, and crawled into bed. I waited for a long time, but Mutti didn't come to kiss me goodnight. *I don't care. She still thinks I'm a baby.*

8

"What time is it, Ruth?"

She stopped pulling the sled and pushed the sleeve of her jacket up far enough to see her watch. "Almost five, Dieter. Don't worry, we'll be back in time. Supper won't be served without you. Come along now."

"I'm cold," Wolfgang whined and rocked the sled. "My feet cold!"

"Ja, ja, Dicker. We're going. You should walk, and you'll be warm in a hurry. See? I am." I unbuttoned my jacket and fanned myself with the sides.

"Don't have him walk, Dieter. We'll take forever to get home." Ruth walked a little faster through the snow piled on both sides of the sidewalk.

I ran up the snowbanks and jumped down in front of her. "What do you think Mutti's secret is, Ruth?"

She smiled. "You'll see. Let's wait until she tells us."

"You know it, don't you?"

She laughed.

"That's not fair! Can't you tell me what it is?"

"Nein, nein, nein. No longer would I take care of you if Frau Drescher couldn't trust me. Besides, if I tell you, it isn't a secret anymore, ja?"

Vati talked more than usual during supper, asking Ruth about the weather, and the snow, and her friends, and me about school, and my friends. He asked about Putzi. He asked about Helga. Mutti laughed whenever he said anything and then they all looked at me and smiled. Mutti's cheeks were red, like they were painted.

"Mutti, you promised you would tell—"

"First supper is finished," she interrupted. "You can wait."

I finished my supper and looked at Vati. He leaned back in his chair. "Well, Lis? Go ahead."

Mutti smiled. But she didn't say anything.

"Ja, Mutti?" I said. "You promised."

She laughed. "Mein lieber Dieter, how would you like to have a baby brother or sister sometime later this year?"

"A baby? You're going to get a baby?"

Vati laughed and reached for my mother's hand in the middle of the table. "Ja. We are going to 'get' a baby. In August."

"A baby. For the Führer!" I stood up, went around the table, and saluted Mutti. "For the Vaterland, meine Mutter! You'll get a medal."

Vati grabbed my arm. "Your mother does not have a baby for the Führer!" He spun me around. "Come with me," he said and marched me to the living room.

I walked back to the table and over to Mutti. "I'm glad you're having a baby, Mutti."

"Karl? What did—"

"Dieter didn't understand, Lis. He does now, don't you, Dieter?"

I nodded.

"So, then, you may be excused. Your mother and I have things to discuss."

I went back to the living room and pretended to read a book. I tried to listen to what they were saying, but they talked too low and I couldn't hear. After a while they came in and sat down together on the sofa. They acted like I wasn't even there. I looked over the top of my book at Mutti. *Why is she going to get a baby? There are already two of us. Unless it's for the Reich, why does she want another one?*

(Left to right) Peter, Mutti, Wolfgang, Opa, Dieter.
Vati is standing in back. August, 1940.)

August 20, 1940

"Don't ask me again," Ruth said. "Soon they will be home. You will have your new brother for a long time."

It was almost noon when the taxicab pulled up and I heard Mutti's laugh. "Ruth, they are here," I yelled and out-ran Wolfgang to the front gate just as they reached it.

"I want to see him," I said, trying to reach the bundle in Mutti's arms.

She laughed and raised the bundle a little higher. "Wait, just wait until we get inside, will you?" Mutti gave the baby to Vati, and Ruth helped her up the stairs to the veranda. Mutti sat down in the big wicker chair and held out her arms. Vati carefully put the baby on her lap and kissed Mutti.

"Here, you hold him. He is so small he scares me." Vati smiled. "Let the boys see him now."

Mutti opened the blanket, and I looked at my new, squirming brother. Wolfgang climbed onto the side of the chair.

"Nein, Wolfgang." Mutti moved his hand. "You cannot poke him."

Ruth went to pick up Wolfgang, but he wrapped his arms around Mutti's arm. "Nein! Stay with Mutti." He put his head down. "Nein, Ruth."

"Wolfgang!" Ruth tried to undo him from Mutti's arm but he held tight.

Mutti laughed. "I love you, too, Wolfgang. This is your little brother. He is just a baby."

"Me Mutti baby." He started to cry. "Me baby." Mutti kissed his head.

"Later, Wolfgang. Mutti loves you very much. You are my big baby, see, and Peter is my little baby." She kissed him again. "We have two babies now, all right?"

"Me big baby?"

"Ja, you are Mutti's big baby. And a big baby like you has to be careful with a little baby. Ja?"

"Ja."

"Here then, you can hold his hand."

Wolfgang held Peter's hand and smiled. He looked up at Mutti. "Little baby."

"Ja, little baby Peter."

I bent over them and touched the baby's face. "Willkommen, Peter. Ich bin Bruder Dieter."

9

"I'm nine years old, Mutti! I'm nine." I slid into a chair at the breakfast table. "I'm almost ten."

"Ja, that you are. Is ten the magic number?" Mutti passed a bowl of cereal to me.

"I'll be in another class next year. With bigger boys. When you're ten, you get to do more things."

Vati walked in and patted the top of my head. "Why don't you enjoy being eight for a while?"

"Eight?" I stood up. "I am nine years old today, Vati."

He smiled. "You are? I thought you were still eight. Lis, can our boy be nine today?"

"Ja, I think so."

"Ruth, what do you say? You think he is nine?"

Ruth put her finger to her cheek and thought a moment. "Ja, Herr Drescher. I just remembered. Nine he is. Nine years old today."

"See, Vati. I am."

"You can't be so old so quick. How could I not see you getting older?" He shook his head. "You just passed right by me." He smiled and pulled something out of his pocket. "For you, my nine-year-old son. Happy Birthday."

I went around the table and pried open his closed hand. "Nine Marks!"

"Mein Gott! Karl. Nine Marks? You think this is good?"

"He is old enough now. He needs to learn to handle money." Vati put his hand on my shoulder. "One Mark is for your spending. The rest you save. Soon you will have more."

"Danke, Vati. Danke." I kissed him. "You didn't forget, did you?"

"Nein, Dieter. I was just teasing you. Remember. Only one Mark you spend."

"Ja, Vati. Only one."

Later that day we had my favorite cake covered with fresh fruit. And at dinner Mutti gave me a watch. That night I was in bed, unable to sleep. I tossed and turned, trying to decide how to spend one Mark.

Suddenly, the door to the bedroom flew open "The sirens! They're coming," Mutti said. "Quickly. Get Wolfgang up. Get to the cellar. The bombers, they are coming!" I jumped out of bed and put on my clothes. "Dicker, get up. Quick." He stirred but didn't wake up. I shook him. "Dicker! Wake up!" I left him in his pajamas and put his shoes on him. "Stand up. We have to go to the cellar."

"I sleepy," he said, rubbing his eyes. "I want my bed." He tried to climb back in.

"Nein, Wolfgang." I pulled him away from the bed. "Downstairs now. Komm' schnell." I pulled on his hand, and he stumbled beside me.

Mutti held Peter in her arms. "You dawdle, Dieter. Move! This is serious. Ruth, bring a blanket in case it is damp down there. Karl!" She looked around. "Karl, where are you?"

"Right here, Schatzi." He was at the kitchen closet. "The flashlight I'm looking for. We will be all right. The sirens do not mean they are here yet, remember?" He closed the closet door and came over to Mutti. "I'll carry the baby," he said, taking Peter and motioning her down the stairs. "You, too,

Dieter. You hurry along Wolfgang." He looked behind me. "Where's Ruth? . . . Ruth! You, too. Come along."

Ruth came out of her bedroom, her arms around a blanket. Vati nodded toward the cellar, and Ruth rushed down the stairs. The back door opened and Frau and Herr Witte came in. They waited as I pushed Wolfgang ahead of me. "Schnell, Dicker. You'll be hit by a bomb if you're too slow."

"Bomb." He held onto the railing, stopping on each step as he went down. "Bomb." He peeked through the railing and saw Mutti. "Bomb, Mutti."

"Nein, Wolfgang," Mutti said. "Nein bomb. Dieter, stop scaring him." She and Ruth and the Wittes were sitting on the straight-backed chairs I'd helped Vati put around the walls of the cellar; long shadows fell behind them from the one bulb that hung down from the middle of the ceiling. Wolfgang ran to Mutti and held up his arms. Mutti picked him up and sat him in her lap.

"We won't get hit, Dicker," I said. "The British won't get over Berlin. Göring promised. Our planes knock them down first."

"Knock down?"

"With guns. Right out of the sky." I held onto an imaginary gun. "Bang, bang, bang!"

Wolfgang slid off Mutti's lap and held his arm out. "Bang, bang, bang. Bang, bang, bang." He laughed and turned toward Mutti. "I shoot."

"Oh, such nonsense. But Danke, Dieter. At least you do not scare him."

I put my arms out and ran around the little space in front of the chairs. *"Rr-r-rm-m-m-m-m-m-m-m,"* I said. "I'm the British trying to drop bombs on Berlin. *Rr-r-rm-m-m-m-m-m-m.* What are you going to do, Dicker?"

He ran after me. "Bang! Bang! I shoot. Bang!"

"Cra-a-a-ack! Swoo-oosh! Dicker got me. Watch me crash!" I spun around and dropped on the floor. *"Baroo-*

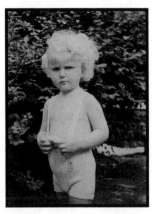

Wolfgang, before haircut,
1940

Ruth, with Wolfgang, 1940
after haircut

oom! I've exploded." I rolled over on my back, my arms stretched out. "Dicker's a Deutscher ace."

"Ace, Mutti. Me ace."

"Ja, if it keeps you happy down here, then you be a Deutscher ace."

Suddenly there was a swooshing sound and an explosion somewhere nearby. Frau Witte put down her book.

"That was close," said Vati. "Not close enough to hurt us. But it hit something near here."

"Das Schwein!" Frau Witte shook her fist at the ceiling. "I hope our planes shoot down that pig!"

Vati looked at her. "Tell me, whatever happened to Göring's promise?"

"He did not count on the English getting here. He'll take care of them. One bomb does not make a war."

"How many do, Frau Witte? Just how many bombs make a war?"

The all-clear signal sounded and Frau Witte stuck her book under her arm and motioned to Herr Witte to leave. He stood up and followed her past Vati.

"Let me know, Frau Witte," Vati called. "I'm anxious to understand this war."

"You take such chances, Karl," Mutti said after they were gone. "She can report you."

"For my saying I'm anxious to understand this war? For that the authorities would be upset?"

"Ja, they would. And they would—"

"I can teach you about the war, Vati. I know as much as Frau Witte now." I walked over and took his hand. "You want to know what I know?"

"Gott Sei Dank. How lucky I am to have you to tell me all about the war. A child can tell me. A child shall lead them . . . " He shook his head. "This is the new Deutschland, Lis. Children will lead." He turned back to me. "Ja, Dieter. I want you to tell me what you know. For one thing I am proud. You share your intelligence."

We went upstairs, and Vati and I went into the living room. I sat beside him on the sofa and told him everything I'd learned about the war. I got my map of the world and pointed out all the places we had conquered. I told him why we were at war. And how the war would end—with Deutschland over everything. He listened.

"You know well, Dieter. But do you care about people?"

"Ja, Vati. I care about people."

"Do you care about Jews?"

"Nein."

"Did you like Sollie?"

"Ja."

"And Herr Weinberg?"

"Ja."

"And Julius Hirschberg?"

"Ja, but—"

"Ja, you say. And ja, they are all Jews, so you say, 'ja, but.' You want to tell me they were different. Am I right? Is this the way you think?"

"Ja, they are Jews, but they *are* different."

"Dieter, there is no difference. It is only that you know

72

them, so you think they are different from other Jews. There are good Jews and bad Jews. And good Catholics and bad Catholics. Good gypsies there are and bad gypsies. But no one is so bad we should mistreat them. All people have a right to live peacefully, Dieter. Even in Deutschland. Verstehst Du?"

"Even if they take our money? And cheat?"

"There are always some people who steal and cheat." He smiled. "But we take care of the bad ones, Dieter. Not all people, just the ones who are guilty."

"Now I don't know who to hate. The Gruppenführer says everything that is not Nazi is bad." I looked at him. "Do you really like Jews, Vati?"

"Jawohl, I do. All kinds of people I like. Some I do not. They are only people. Some are nice, some are not. Don't be afraid to like people, Dieter. If too filled with hate, your heart will have no room for love. You're nine now. When you are older, your heart will crack if it has no love. Remember that. Your heart will crack."

"What is this? Still up and talking?" Mutti reached down and pulled me off the sofa. "Nine years old does not stay up any longer than eight years old. Give me a kiss goodnight and go to bed."

I kissed her and kissed my father. "Gute Nacht," I said. "Danke for the watch and the money. This has been a good birthday. The British even bombed on my holiday. I'll always remember that."

The next morning I joined the crowds heading toward the S-Bahn tracks. When I got there, I saw a small group standing around a hole in the ground near the tracks, staring and pointing. Some of them laughed. I pushed through them and saw the small hole, maybe two meters across and not more than half a meter deep. The air smelled like burned gunpowder, and trees around it looked like they'd been ripped by a thick-bladed saw.

"Those marks in the trees. What happened?"

"Shrapnel," a man said. "Pieces of metal. Sharp as razors. It can cut your head off."

"My head?"

"Ja. Your head. You get underground when the sirens sound. Unless you're tired of your head."

I stared at the little hole before getting back on my bike. *This is what they'll drop? It won't hurt our house. Our walls are too thick. When the Stukas bombed Poland, our bombs made big holes. They can't hurt us.*

"Such a little bomb," I said going out on the veranda.

Vati looked up from his paper. "A little bomb?"

"Ja. We don't have to worry. England can't hurt us with little bombs." I walked over and looked at Peter in Mutti's arms. "You don't have to be afraid, Mutti. They can't hurt us."

"Gut! We will no longer worry about war." She winked at Vati.

"Ja," he said. "You are sure they will only send little bombs? Maybe you should look at the hospital in Babelsberg. A bomb hit there, too."

"The hospital? They bomb sick people?"

"Ja. That is war. Everyone is shelled. Everyone is bombed." He looked at Mutti. "Is that not how you remember war, Lis? Everyone is hurt?"

"Ja, Dieter. You should listen to your father. Countries do not care about hospitals. In war everyone is hurt."

"Can I go and see?"

Mutti put the paper down. "If you come right back. The radio says thousands are going there to look." She shrugged. "Who wants to look at damage? Crazy people."

"They probably believed Göring," Vati said, without

looking up. "They can't imagine British planes made it here. Ja, crazy they are."

There were so many people in the street around the hospital that the police were there. The crowds looked up at the hole in the tiled roof, right next to the huge red cross painted on a white circle. "Ach Du Lieber! So many sick. And they bombed anyway." "Mein Gott! Beasts they are." "Who could do this to sick people?" I walked toward the front of the building. Lots of windows were broken, and pieces of the roof tiles were scattered all over the street. *How could they do this?* I pedaled back home and ran into the kitchen.

"Vati! How could they bomb a hospital?" I asked, panting for breath. "People in there are sick, they're not soldiers. The red cross should tell them that."

"A bomber can't see in the dark, Dieter. Besides, that's what I said. They do not care. That is what war is, to not care about anything but winning. Let's hope their bombs don't get any bigger. But just in case, I think I better do something with my wine cellar, ja? Just in case."

The next weekend I helped Vati move everything out of his wine cellar. I carried potatoes and apples in separate boxes to the front room. "Keep them away from the window," Mutti warned. "They'll spoil if you don't."

Vati moved his wine bottles from the small rack along the back wall. He was extra careful carrying his favorite, Boxbeutel, in those small, short, stubby green bottles. He stacked the boxes on top of each other and lined them up against the wall, where they took up less room than before.

By afternoon we were finished and we moved the old chairs back in the room and set them in front of the boxes.

"Now let's hope we don't have to use this room very

often," Vati said, standing in the center of the room and looking around. "How do you like it, Dieter?"

"I don't. I don't like having no windows. And there's only one door."

"Ja, but it is safe. The walls are thirty or forty centimeters."

Doesn't matter. I don't like it. I feel trapped.

10

The civilian saluted the Gruppenführer and turned to us. "Hitler Jugend, I am here to issue new orders, orders that come from the Führer himself." We gasped. *The Führer told him to come here.* "Deutschland is at war. We cannot aid the enemy." He looked up and down each row. "Anyone could be the enemy." He slapped his hand on the podium so suddenly some of us jumped. He leaned over. "Even one of you."

He caught my eye and seemed to stop for a minute. I blinked and looked down at my lap. *I don't look like an enemy!* I tried not to breathe, but it seemed I only breathed harder. "The Führer himself told me to come here," he said again, "and ask you boys to help him find those who are enemies of the Vaterland."

We shuffled in our seats and sat up straighter.

"Your orders are to keep your eyes and ears open. To everyone you should listen: parents, friends, teachers, shopkeepers. Even your friends at school. Anyone who talks bad about our Führer"—*Vati does!*—"or his officers, or complains about the war effort"—*that, too*—"or listens to foreign radio stations"—*Mutti and Ruth!*—"are enemies of the Reich. You are under orders to report them to your

Gruppenführer so they can be dealt with." He walked around in front of the podium and bent over slightly.

"You think you cannot turn in your parents or your friends, ja?" He smiled, and stepped back. The room was quiet. "Remember, if they do these things, they hurt Deutschland." He raised his eyebrows and gave us a questioning look. "Do you want to destroy the Vaterland?"

"Nein!"

"Of course not." He wagged his finger from side to side. "Do not be afraid to turn them in. They will not be hurt." He smiled again. "They will only be taught that they are wrong, and be shown the right way to serve the Führer." He shook his head. "You see, you need have no fear for them. A favor you will do them, ja? And you will perform an act of courage for Deutschland. Versteht Ihr?"

"Ja," we said, nodding.

"As members of the HJ, you are permitted to hide under open windows and listen. You are permitted to walk into yards without knowledge of the owners. At home you can pretend to be asleep but should listen at the doors of your parents' bedrooms or any other places where they assume they are alone. Write down what you hear. Dates, too. Records are important. You boys know how to keep records?"

We nodded again.

"You will be rewarded every time you report an enemy. You will like that, ja?"

"Ja!"

"Remember, the Führer does not request this. The Führer orders it. This is your duty." He clicked his heels. "Heil Hitler."

We jumped up at attention. "Heil Hitler!" we yelled.

I built a hideout by the rabbit cages in the backyard, a place where I could be by myself—away from Wolfgang in particular—and think. There were so many things I had to consider, and Vati kept after me all the time. He hated the Führer, and I couldn't understand why. I loved marching and meetings. I liked the respect some people showed me, particularly teachers at school. I liked feeling I belonged. Vati didn't seem to care if he belonged or not, and Mutti just didn't like the arguing we did, though she seemed to get angry with him as often as she did me. The hideout offered me a place to be alone and read. Or think. Or, when I was lucky, play house with Helga. We had to sneak out there or else Wolfgang would want to follow, and I didn't like playing with both of them. I wanted to be alone with Helga. One time, after I complained to Ruth that Wolfgang was always following us out there, she fixed a lunch and said she'd play with Wolfgang and not let him know where we'd gone. She even gave me a tablecloth and napkins, like we were on a picnic.

Helga ate around the insides of the bread and put the crust down on the cloth.

"You don't eat the crusts? My mother says you have to eat them if you want to be strong. I always eat mine."

"You want them?"

"Ja, bitte." I stuffed the crusts in my mouth all at once.

Helga pointed at me and laughed. "You look like a squirrel."

I bared my teeth and chomped like a squirrel would, and she laughed louder. *She's pretty when she laughs. I think she likes me.*

"This is like camping, isn't it, Dieter? Have you camped?"

"Ja, my father likes to. And canoe. He took us to Würzburg and we stayed in a tent by a river. Did you ever stay in a tent?"

She shook her head. "When my brother went to school, Vater took us to Switzerland and we stayed in the mountains. In a log cabin. With a fireplace. Mutter said it was just like camping because we didn't have a toilet inside." She hid her face in her hands and giggled. "I had to squat on the ground to pee."

"To pee? You can't stand up and pee?"

"I can't stand up and do it. I don't have a *thing,* silly."

"You don't? What happened to it?"

"Dieter! Girls don't have *things.* Don't you know that?"

"Nein. I heard they have Brusts when they grow up."

"You mean you never saw your mother, or Ruth, in the bathroom?"

"The door is shut. How could I see?"

"I have a brother. And he showed me his thing one time." She giggled. "It's funny looking." She looked at me. "If you want to, we can look at each other without any clothes on."

"Ja, I want to do that!"

"We have to be very careful because our mothers will be mad if they know. Tomorrow, if we're sure no one is around, we'll do it."

The next day I went right over after breakfast. Helga told her mother we were going to her bedroom to play. She closed the door to her room and smiled.

"Are you really going to show me, Helga?" I whispered.

"Ja, of course I am." She took me by the arm and led me across the room. "Now, you stand right here. And don't move." She walked to the opposite side. "Now I'll stay over here." She unbuttoned her blouse and I saw her undershirt. She stopped and looked up. "What about you? You have to, too."

"I will." I didn't want to stop looking at her, so I fumbled with the buttons on my shirt.

"No, Dieter. Not your shirt. Take down your pants!" She already had her skirt off and was pulling down her panties.

At first my zipper stuck, but I tugged it loose. My pants fell around my ankles. I pulled down my drawers.

"Where is it, Helga?"

"This is it." She pointed to the space between her legs. "I don't have a thing like you do."

"Don't girls have more than that?" I shuffled toward her, my pants around my ankles.

Her arms flew up. "Dieter! You stay over there!"

"Sh-h-h, your mother will hear."

"Then don't come any closer. Promise?"

"All right. I just wanted to see it up close." I stretched toward her, trying to get a better look. "That's nothing, Helga," I said. "There's nothing to do anything with."

"Well, it's better than something hanging between your legs. I don't see how you can walk."

We stared across the room. "Can't I come closer, Helga? Just a little?"

"Nein! Don't you dare, Dieter Steiner. I'm getting dressed." She put her panties on and her undershirt.

I still stared.

"You need to get your clothes on, Dieter."

"I want to look some more."

"Helga? You and Dieter are still up there?"

At the sound of her mother's voice I scrambled into my clothes. We went quickly downstairs.

"Maybe you should go home, Dieter. I need to talk to Helga."

She knows! I hurried as fast as I could out into the yard. Mutti was at the back door when I opened it.

"Ja? What is this?" She put her hand on my forehead. "You look feverish. And how did I let you out of the house with your shirt buttoned so funny? Are you all right?"

"I'm a little bit tired. I think I need to lie down for a while."

"Ja, you should. You may have something."

I hurried to my bedroom, jumped on my bed, and landed on my back. I was so excited I couldn't keep my eyes closed

81

so I stared at the ceiling, where Helga's *thing* danced before me eyes.

I began to think of Helga as my girlfriend though I didn't tell anyone, including her. Yet, when I was alone at night, and looking out my window over to her bedroom, I wanted to see her again with no clothes. Manfred's brother, Fritz, showed us a picture of natives on an island. Manfred pointed to it. "See her Brusts? See how big they are. That's why women wear brassieres. Did you ever see Brusts, Dieter?"

"Nein," I lied. I couldn't tell him about Helga and me.

"We can go talk to Frau Baumgart," Manfred said, a big smile on his face. "You ever talk to her?"

"I say hello."

"Come with me. I'll show you Brusts!"

We walked around the corner. Frau Baumgart was working in her rock garden.

"See, Dieter," he whispered. "Always she is out here. Watch now, she won't even look up." We walked up to the fence. "Hello, Frau Baumgart," Manfred said. "Dieter and I came to talk to you."

"Ja, that's nice, boys. How are you today?"

Manfred was right. She kept right on bending over, digging in her garden, and never looked up. Manfred poked me in the side and motioned with his head "Look," he whispered.

Her breasts looked like they were going to fall out of her dress. *I can't look!* I turned and ran home. Mutti held out her arm and stopped me as I came through the front door.

"What is this hurry?"

"Nothing. I just wanted to get home is all. I didn't do anything. Can I go to my room, bitte?"

She laughed and shook her head. "Sometimes I don't understand you."

82

11

"I'm home early." I walked into the kitchen, but no one was there. I looked in the living room and the bedrooms but they were empty. I heard something in Vati's study and opened the door. Mutti and Ruth were lying on the floor in the corner with a blanket over their heads. I tiptoed up behind them.

"Mutti! Ruth! You're listening to the radio again!"

They whipped the blanket off. "Sh-h-h, Dieter." Mutti clicked off the radio sitting on the floor between them and scowled at me. "This is dangerous, Dieter," she said. "You know what will happen to us if anyone finds out?"

"Ja. I do."

"Then don't talk so loud."

I bent down beside them. "What are you listening to?"

"From England. The BBC says Deutschland is having bad times. That we're losing many soldiers."

"Losing? England says that?" I stood up. "Lies. Jew lies."

Ruth shook her head. "Nein, Dieter. The news of the war is different from what our stations say."

"And you believe?"

"Listen for yourself." Mutti pulled my hand. "Sit down here."

"Nein!" I pulled away. "I do not listen to foreigners. You shouldn't either, Mutti."

"Don't be so silly, Dieter." She turned the radio on again. "Hear for yourself."

"I can't. It's wrong. You can be arrested." I bent down to turn it off and Mutti caught my arm.

"Dieter! What is this? You tell me what I can do?"

"Someone will tell the authorities, Mutti. You could get in trouble."

"And who will know I am doing this but you?" She stared at me. "You don't say you will turn me in, do you?"

"Nein. But if I did, it would be for your own good."

"Ja," Ruth said. "For our own good. Hah! Who has taught you such nonsense?"

"No one. I just know. That's all."

Mutti pushed me away. "You just know so much. Go out and play and leave us alone to listen. We won't tell Vati what you did, and I can trust that you won't tell anyone what we did. I am right, ja?"

"Ja."

They pulled the blanket back over their heads. I left and went to my hideout to think.

Dieter with Wolfgang in back yard
Buddel Kiste, 1941

12

"Ja. He said Americans are warmongers, helping England, and they should be careful or we will invade them, too."

"And you believed him?" Vati sat up on the edge of his chair and stared at me. "You think Deutschland is going to invade the United States?"

"Ja, I do. The Führer won't let them to help England."

"I would not be so quick to believe your Gruppenführer. America is very powerful. We would have a hard time crossing the ocean for an invasion."

"Deutschland is invincible, Vati. If the Führer decides to go there, nothing will stop us."

"All right. If you say so." Vati went back to reading his newspaper.

I sat back on the sofa and thought about going across the ocean to fight. "I was just thinking, Vati. The Americans, if they fight us, what will happen to Herr Wise? Will he fight us, too?"

"I hear America doesn't want war," he said from behind the paper. "I do not find out too much, but bits and pieces, they add up." He turned a page. "I hope America does not want to join the war."

"Then why do they monger and send guns to England?"

Vati put down the paper and smiled. "Monger, as you

say, they don't. Sending guns—that has to do with treaties and politics and friendships between nations."

He reached into the wastebasket next to his chair and pulled out an envelope. From his inside coat pocket he took out a pen.

"Look here," he said. I sat on the arm of his chair and watched as he drew a circle.

"This is your friend Manfred. If he was in a fight with a gang of boys—these dots are a gang —he might ask you—this circle is you—for help. But what if you don't really want to fight? Maybe you could help Manfred in a different way. You find a big dog, like Herr Oberstrand's Doberman Pinscher—this square is a big dog—and carry the dog to Manfred. That way you would help your friend, but you would not be in the fight. Verstehst Du?"

I nodded.

"Countries, they ask help of other countries. In Spain, Hitler sent the Stukas. Now Deutschland asks Italy to fight with us, and Russia not to fight. England asks America, and America sends to England guns."

"But that's why I hate England—and America, too. The English kill Deutsche and America helps them. Everything American is bad—their music, their books, their movies— "

"So you think my friend Herr Wise is bad? Sit down here." I sat on the footstool in front of him, and he put his hands on my shoulders. "Listen to me, Dieter. I've known Herr Wise even longer than I've known your mother. A good and loyal friend he is. He invited you to America. He sent me books. He sent you cards for your wall."

"But if he fights us? You would still be his friend?"

"He doesn't fight us, Dieter. He is not a soldier. We are not at war with America."

"The Gruppenführer says we will be, and he is never wrong."

Vati picked up his paper and leaned back in the chair. "Perhaps he will be this time."

86

13

"Mein Gott!" Mutti's voice came from the living room.

I stopped short in the doorway. Mutti sat on the couch, rocking back and forth. "Nein, nein, nein. We can't take any more." Vati sat beside her.

"Was ist los? Is she all right?"

Vati motioned me to sit down. "America has declared war on Deutschland," he said, pointing to the radio. "We just heard it." He rubbed Mutti's back.

"See! The Gruppenführer was right. I told you so. I told you we would fight America."

"Ja, Dieter. Your leader was right. I was wrong."

Mutti looked up at me. "America is much bigger than Deutschland. They have more soldiers and more money . . . There's no way we can win."

"Perhaps that is not a bad idea, Lis. Hitler has gone too far."

I glared at him. "Too far? We have to sacrifice." I clicked my heels together. "That is the job of the new order."

Vati looked disgusted. "Something you learned in the HJ? Or did this come from school?"

"Karl . . ." Mutti looked up at me. "Dieter, this is not the time for such words."

"The Americans are lazy. And Siegfried says they are all drunkards. They can't match Deutsche soldiers."

Vati smiled. "Always it is Siegfried, or Manfred, or someone else with knowledge. Your parents you never listen to. There is a reason, ja?"

"I am Deutsch, loyal to my Führer. To be Deutsch means to be invincible."

He reached over and shut off the radio. It was quiet but for a few sounds of Ruth putting dishes away in the kitchen.

"You are ten years old. Ten! What do you know of sacrifice and war? To wear a uniform and march at Potsdam for the Führer's birthday, you think that makes a soldier?"

"We are the future of Deutschland," I yelled. "We are the hope of the Vaterland."

Vati jumped up, his fists clenched. I stepped back and held my arms up for protection. "Look at yourself, Dieter. You strut and crow to an empty barnyard. You have no fear because you are in your own living room. But when I jump up, you cringe. Because I am bigger. And more powerful." He sat down. "So you will understand, that is what war with America will be. Being attacked by someone bigger and more powerful than Deutschland."

"No country is more powerful than Deutschland."

"Karl. We can't talk . . . "

"Ja, we can talk, Lis. I care about my family. Even this baby Führer." He walked across the room and turned around, pointing at me. "Look at him, Lis. Listen to him. Have you listened to him? Ja? You have heard this every day. How he struts. Still he wears that uniform."

Mutti sat me down on the sofa and walked over to Vati. She put her hand on his arm. "Karl. Bitte."

Vati shook his head and took Mutti's hand off his arm. He stepped away. "This is what you want him to be? Vicious and mean?"

Mutti looked like she was ready to cry. "You are both . . . Ach, I don't know, Karl." She shrugged. "How can we change . . . Dieter, do you have to carry on so? Why don't you . . . " She stopped and just looked at me, then at Vati. "I cannot stay in here," she said, walking to the door. "You are both too stubborn."

"Now, see what you've done. Your mother is upset."

You're the one who upset her, not me.

Christmas Eve morning Wolfgang and I ran to the living room, each trying to be the first to open the biggest and last flap on the Advent calendar hanging on the window. I won.

"Schnell, Dieter. Open it." Wolfgang danced around, jumping up and down. "Show me."

I pulled the flap just a little bit and stopped.

"I want to see. I want to see it."

I opened it a little bit more and stopped again. "What if I decide I won't open it any more? What if I never open it?"

"Mutti, Dieter won't open the last window."

"Ja, I will," I hollered. "I was only fooling." I opened it the rest of the way and there it was: the sunlight behind showed three angels above the crib with the Baby Jesus. Joseph and Mary were there, and sheep and cows and a donkey and a camel.

We closed all the little flaps and then opened them again. "Tonight the Weihnachtsmann comes. He's only going to leave toys for good boys. I told him some of the bad things you've done this year." I laughed. "Maybe he'll only leave you a switch."

"I don't want a switch! I've been good. Mutti and Vati said I've been good." He ran out of the room and down the hall. *He's a pain in the neck sometimes.*

"What is this, Dieter?" Ruth came into the living room and stood before me. "You told him the Weihnachtsmann might leave him a switch?"

"I was just kidding, Dicker. He won't leave a switch."

"That's better," Ruth said. "Now you boys get out of here. You can't come back in until tonight. Go someplace else to play."

We walked past Ruth, and she shut the door. "Crybaby," I whispered as we went to the kitchen. "The Weihnachtsmann leaves coal for crybabies."

Ruth pinched my ear. "You should know better, Dieter. It's Christmas. Maybe mean older brothers get nothing."

Wolfgang, Vati, Mutti, Dieter
December 1941

"We're going out now, Dieter." Ruth handed me my jacket and mittens. "I'm taking Wolfgang for his walk, and you come with us."

"It's time, ja?" I smiled at Ruth. "We have to take a long walk, don't we?"

Ruth nodded and winked. "Ja, a long one."

We walked slower than usual toward the S-Bahn station. From there we walked down to the lake, and onto the ice. We ran and slid, slipped and fell. Ruth laughed when we fell, and we laughed when she fell. By the time we reached

90

the bridge over the Teltow Canal, Wolfgang was having such a good time he didn't want to go home.

"Komm' schnell," Ruth said, pulling on his sleeve. "It's almost six o'clock. We need to be home."

Mutti held the front door open. "I thought you were going to be late." We ran in, panting, and stood in the hallway while Ruth hung up our coats and I tried to catch my breath.

"It's six o'clock," Mutti announced. "Time for Christmas." She opened the doors to the living room.

"It's beautiful. And I can smell it." My eyes were on the tree in the corner by the window. I took Wolfgang's hand. "Look," I said as we walked in the room. "There's a thousand candles on it this year, Mutti."

"Not quite, Dieter." Mutti laughed, and Ruth joined her.

"It just seems like that many when we light them," Ruth said. "Sometimes I wonder why we don't have a fire."

Wolfgang stood in front of the tree. "I can see myself in the balls." He turned around and smiled. "I look funny."

"You can see the candles in them, too."

"Ja, I can see candles, too. See, Ruth." Wolfgang pointed to a silver ball. "See the candles?"

"It looks like fairyland, ja?" Ruth had a big smile. "Just like a picture in a magazine."

Wolfgang looked around the room. "Where's Vati?"

"He'll be here soon, don't worry."

He's in the next room, in his red suit and white beard and a pillow puffing up his stomach. The door opened suddenly and there was the Weihnachtsmann. Wolfgang hung on to Mutti's leg. "You can't be afraid," she said, and laughed. "Here, he probably has something for you." She turned him around and led him toward Vati.

"I heard you were a guter Junge this past year. Is that true?"

Wolfgang nodded. "Ja, ja! I was a good boy!"

Vati handed him a present and he tore open the wrapping. "Ach, look! A new dog!" He jumped and jumped. "I got a new dog."

It was a toy dog, on little wheels and a string to pull it, the same dog he got last year. I knew, because I helped Vati repaint it a few weeks ago.

The Weihnachtsmann handed out more presents and left. When Vati came in, Wolfgang ran to him and told him he'd missed the Weihnachtsmann. Vati said he always seemed to miss him, and he looked over at me and winked. I winked back, feeling very grownup. We showed Vati our presents, and he acted surprised. He gave Mutti a pin to wear on her coat, and Mutti gave him a red plaid scarf. They kissed each other and we laughed and clapped and sat in the middle of wrapping paper and ribbon. Finally Ruth and Mutti blew out the candles and we went in the dining room and had supper. Later Vati turned the handle on the Laterna Magika, and we watched the same film from last year, airplanes flying in jerky motion.

14

"Nobody can stop our soldiers!" I whispered. "See how fast our tanks move?" The woman in front of us turned around. "Sh-h-h-h."

"Excuse, please," Mutti said. She turned to me. "This is the last time I'm asking you not to talk in the theater," she hissed. "We won't bring you again if you don't stop."
You'd think they would cheer, but nobody does.

I walked between Mutti and Vati on the way home. Vati clapped me on my shoulder.

"That was a movie you liked, ja, Dieter?"

"Ja."

"Ja? All you say, is ja?"

"Jawohl, mein Vater."

"Hear him, Lis? What has he to be angry about?"

"I told him we wouldn't bring him if he didn't stop talking out loud." Mutti took my hand. "Is that it, Dieter?"

I pulled away. "Nein."

"What is wrong then, please?"

"Nothing." *You ought to know what's wrong.*

Mutti stopped under the street light and turned my face toward her. "I was only upset when you talked during the newsreel. Now we can listen. You didn't like the movie?"

"Don't fish for his answer, Lis. Nothing is wrong, he says. Then we assume nothing is wrong."—*But something is wrong, Vati!*—"Manners like this he learns in the HJ? You think if his grand and glorious Gruppenführer asked him a question he wouldn't answer?"—*He'd know why I was mad!*— "He tells us Frederick the Great is his hero. We take him to see a movie about his hero, and this is how he acts."

"I did like the movie. Danke."

"Well, he can speak after all. Danke, Dieter, for joining us in conversation. You see, Lis. Our boy can be polite if he wants to."

We walked along and I listened as they talked. *They don't even mention the battles or the victories. It's like they didn't even watch.*

Wolfgang and Peter were asleep when we got home. After I took a bath I went into the kitchen to say goodnight.

Vati sat at the table. "Want to share my apple before you go to bed?"

"An apple at night? Nein."

Vati laughed. "I thought the same way one time. It's good. You should try it." He cut a slice and slipped it from the knife blade into his mouth. He chewed a minute, then smiled. "See? Look how happy it makes me." He cut another slice and offered it to me. I shook my head.

Mutti walked over from the stove with a cup of tea and sat down. "We enjoyed your company tonight, Dieter. Whatever was bothering you, it isn't anymore?"

"He said nothing was wrong, Lis. Remember?"

I slid into a chair opposite them. "Well, there was something wrong."

"You *were* the right one, Lis. There *was* something wrong, even if he said there wasn't." Vati shook his finger at me. "How can we know this, Dieter, if you don't admit it when you're asked? Tell us. What made you so cranky?"

"And impolite," Mutti added.

I folded my hands on the table. "On the newsreel. Why aren't you excited about the Wehrmacht's victories? If I'd seen that in school, everybody would clap and yell. Even the teachers."

Vati looked serious and put his knife down. He rested his elbows on the table and his chin on his hands. For a moment he didn't say anything. Finally he leaned toward me. "You think we should yell and applaud war?"

"Ja." I nodded. "Ja, I do."

"And that it is appropriate to yell and applaud pictures of killing?"

"Ja."

"And dead soldiers you liked looking at?"

I didn't answer.

"Ja, Dieter? Dead soldiers look good to you?"

"If they're our enemies, they do."

"Come here, Dieter." He motioned me around the table. I stood in front of him and he took my hands. "Mein lieber Sohn, what has happened to you? Tell me, so I can understand, why you think this war is good."

"For a new world order. Because Germans are the master race. We are meant to rule. And . . . " *What are the other reasons?* "And . . ."

"Enough. Too much, in fact." He pulled me right up next to him, his face close to mine. "Do you have any idea what it is like to die?"

"Karl . . . "

"Nein," I answered. "But I would be brave."

"Do you have any idea what it is like to kill another person?"

"Karl, enough . . . Don't—"

"Nein, but I'd kill him before he killed me."

"Ach Du Lieber." Mutti's hands flew to her mouth. "Karl, enough. No more, bitte."

"You remember what those soldiers' bodies looked like?"

95

"Ja."

"I would look like that if I were a dead soldier. A rotting corpse who—"

"Karl! Stop that!"

"A rotting corpse who has a wife and a family. They would have nothing but a medal to look at, instead of a husband and father. You think that is wonderful? You think that is something to applaud?"

I stared back at him. "Nein, I guess not."

His hands moved up and tightened around my elbows. He pulled me to his chest. "Your HJ talk makes me shiver. No longer you have feelings. And you're not even eleven years old."

I pushed myself away and stood up straight and tall. "The Führer deserves our feelings! Then Deutschland!" I clenched my teeth.

"Karl!"

His hand stopped just short of my cheek, and he grabbed my shoulders and shook me. "The Führer deserves to be shot! Better for the country if it was his body you saw tonight. Then I would applaud."

"Mein Gott, Karl!" Mutti rushed over and put her hands over Vati's mouth. "We're the ones who'll be shot. I don't care whose war it is. I want my family safe. All of them." She started crying. "You promised. You promised."

Vati slumped in the chair. "I'm sorry, Lis. I cannot take this anymore. You asked me to say nothing, but his heart is stone. Rather I would die."

Mutti pushed me away. "See this, Herr Steiner? You cause the family pain. Are you proud?"

Vati put his head in his hands. "I have no power, Lis. In my own house I can't speak. I can't teach my child to be kind. I can't keep him from hate. Upstairs is Frau Witte. The HJ is down the street. Overhead are bombers. In Berlin is his glorious Führer. Where does a father rule?" He slammed his fist on the table and stood up. "To your room, Klaus Dieter Steiner," he yelled. "Stay the way you are. Fill yourself with lies and hate until you explode. But do not say these things to me. Ever again." He pulled away from Mutti and stalked out of the kitchen. Mutti looked at me with narrowed eyes.

"You heard him. Get to bed. Now!" She followed him to his study and slammed the door behind her.

I waited a moment before I left the kitchen, then went down the hall and put my ear against the study door. They talked too low for me to hear much except my name now and then. I went to my bedroom and walked over to my desk and pulled out my pocket notebook. I flipped to the next-to-the-last page. Under *Listening to BBC - Elisabeth Drescher and Ruth Schuber, 31.3.42* I added, *The Führer should be shot. Then I would applaud. - Karl Drescher, 13.4.42.*

15

Helga stood near her front door, watching the workers carry lumber from a truck into the house.

"What are they doing, Helga? Building a bigger house?"

She laughed. "Nein. They're building a bombshelter under the basement."

"Under the basement?"

"Well, I mean deeper than the basement. Come see what they're doing."

The workers had dug a hole through the basement floor, maybe one meter deep, and there was another hole in the outside wall toward the backyard. "Why is that hole in the wall?"

"That's going to be the emergency exit."

Later, at suppertime, I told Mutti what I had seen.

"That must cost a lot of money, Mutti. And the workers look like they're soldiers. How come soldiers work for the Ludwigs?"

"I don't know. Maybe they have connections."

"Connections?"

"In the government. Maybe they know someone. But that's not our business, is it?"

Two weeks later, the bunker was finished. Herr Ludwig invited us over to see it.

It was like a big grey box sitting right in the middle of their basement, with a heavy steel door with a special lock and a tunnel to crawl through going out to the backyard. At the end of it was another steel door.

"Ja, Herr Ludwig," Vati said. "This is very safe."

Herr Ludwig showed him the generator for the bunker's air supply. "See. We have everything. If ever we have a bad raid, you come over. We have enough space." He smiled at Mutti. "For all."

"Danke, Herr Ludwig. You are a generous man." Vati shook his hand. "But I hope this gets little use."

Ruth leaned over me, shaking my shoulder. "Schnell! Get up and get dressed. Didn't you hear the sirens?"

Squinting, I rubbed my eyes and yawned so hard I heard my jaw bone crack. She threw my clothes at me and left. *I don't hear any sirens.* I looked over at Wolfgang's bed, but he was already gone. I scrambled.

Mutti waited at the door. Peter was asleep in her arms.

"Schnell! We have to get to the cellar! Come now, Dieter. You take too long."

Now I was awake. By the time I got downstairs, Ruth and Wolfgang were already sitting on their chairs. Next to them was Frau Witte and her husband. Mutti looked at me.

"Did you pull the shades tight on your window?" I started to shake my head.

"Get back up and do it. You know we get fined if Herr Schultz sees any light from the street."

I ran all the way back to my room and turned off my lamp on the night table.

By the time I got back to the outside door of the basement, I heard the faint sound of planes. I stopped and listened. *They're getting closer. And there are more this time!*

99

When I sat down next to Mutti and Wolfgang, my heart beat a lot faster. I was excited, nervous, scared. And wide awake. I looked at Peter still sound asleep. *That basket's getting too small for him. How can he sleep through the loud cracks of the flak?* I looked at the small alarm clock in the corner. *Almost midnight.*

In half an hour it was quiet. Minutes later we heard the all-clear signal. "I'll carry Peter." Mutti handed him to me and I went upstairs.

"Look! Look at the sky!" Wolfgang pointed to the east. "It's pretty."

Beyond Ludwigs' house, toward the city, the sky glowed red just above the tree tops.

"That is not pretty," Mutti said. "Those are fires in the city, and people must be hurt. Back to bed. Say your prayers for them."

16

I felt like Wednesday was never going to come. I tried to stay away from Vati all day Sunday and was glad when he left in the morning. I'll be gone for a couple of days, he said when he kissed Mutti goodbye. *Gut! Now he won't pick on me.* Mutti and Ruth spent more of their time listening to the BBC. They didn't seem to worry at all. *What's wrong with them? How can we win the war if people don't act responsible? That's what the Gruppenführer said: "We have to act responsible."*

I stayed in my room and pretended I had homework. I lay on my bed and stared at the ceiling. *I'll just stand up when my turn comes and tell him: "My mother and Ruth listen to the BBC and my father said he would clap if the Führer was killed." Everyone will shout, and the Gruppenführer will tell me I am brave.* I closed my eyes and saw myself at the front of the room next to the Gruppenführer. *"Here is a loyal Deutscher. See, he is not afraid. He does not shirk his duty. Heil Hitler, Pimpf Steiner. You will be rewarded."* I smiled to myself. *What will I get? Maybe a medal. With a ribbon to wear around my neck.* I was so excited I couldn't lie on my back anymore. I rolled over and hugged my pillow. *"Pimpf Steiner, you are pre-*

sented with the . . . " what will it be? Like an Iron Cross?
"The Führer sent this to you personally . . ." — no, I stand
in front of the Führer. "Danke, Führer. I am happy to be of
service to you and the Vaterland. Heil Hitler." I rolled onto
my other side and rearranged the pillow. *"You are the bravest Hitler Junge in all of Deutschland. You are—"*

"Dieter! Can you not answer?" Mutti stood in the doorway.

I shoved my notebook between the blanket and sheet.

"Supper is ready. Your father is back early."

"I'll be right there. In a minute." As soon as she shut the door, I took the notebook and put it far back in my desk. I walked into the dining room and sat down.

"You had a good day, Dieter?"

"Ja, Vati."

"I brought you something." He handed me a small package.

"Danke." I put it next to my plate and helped myself to a potato.

"You are not going to open it?" Vati looked at me over his glasses. "Usually you tear the paper off."

"I'll look after supper."

"If you wish."

Mutti wrinkled her brow and motioned to the package. "Open it," she mouthed.

I put down my fork and took the string off the package. I unfolded the paper. I picked up a big HJ belt buckle. "Danke, Vati. It's wonderful."

"A HJ buckle, Karl? You bought a . . . "

"It's better than any I've ever seen, Vati. I'll wear it tomorrow night. Danke."

"I know you don't understand why I am against the HJ, Dieter. While I was gone, I realized I can't change your mind. You will have to discover these things for yourself. I hope before it's too late. So, in the meantime, I do not like to fight and argue with you every day. We have our differences, but I love you very much. Can we declare a truce?"

"Ja, Vati. I don't like to fight with you, either. We will have a truce." *But I have to turn you in, Vati, for your own good. Then they can teach you what's right to think.*

"What a buckle, Dieter. Where did you get that?" Siegfried reached over and felt the buckle. "It looks like real silver."

"My father brought it back from a business trip." I looked at it again. "It's the best buckle I've ever seen."

We walked down the stairs at the Hitler Youth building and fell in line. We marched to our seats and sat down. I felt in my pocket for my notebook. The Gruppenführer walked in.

"Achtung!" he shouted, and we stood up. "Heil Hitler!"

"Heil Hitler!" we answered.

"I will go down the rows. Report to me, please. What have you heard this week?"

My heart beat so fast I thought my head would explode. Josef turned in the butcher. He said only the Jews should be rationed. The Gruppenführer said that would be good, but the butcher should accept rationing as a way to help the war effort. He copied down the man's name. Heinrich said he saw a man and a woman dressed in black who could have been Jews going into the Catholic church on the corner. He watched and when they came out, he followed them to the S-Bahn and they talked to Frau Steuben at the tobacco shop. He thinks they were spies. The Gruppenführer wrote down the information and said Heinrich was very brave. "Next row," he said. "Anyone with information in this row? What about you, Pimpf Steiner?"

I couldn't breathe. I felt my face get hot. "My . . . my . . . "

"Speak up! What are you saying?"

"My father. Karl Drescher. He said . . . " *I can't do this!*

"Your father said what, Steiner?"

"He said . . . he said . . . He said he does not like to fight and argue with me."

"And you think that is bad enough to report?"

I nodded.

"Pimpf Steiner says his father does not like to fight and argue with him, and he thinks that is bad enough to report. Hitler Jugend. Is that bad enough to report?"

"Nein!" they all yelled.

"See, Pimpf Steiner. That is not bad enough to report. That is *nothing* to report. Comments about the Führer or the Party—only then you report. You have much to learn."

I felt my face get red as everyone laughed. "Jawohl," I said. "I will learn." I was happy when the Gruppenführer finished with the rows and I could sit down again.

Siegfried leaned over to me. "That was a dumb thing you did, Dieter. I'm walking home with Hans tonight." *I don't care. I'll walk home by myself.*

When I got near the corner of Griebnitz Strasse I heard someone running. I turned around just in time to be hit in the face. I fell.

"Look at the Juden-Junge. He can't even stand up."

"Jude, get up. Pimpf *Stein.* You think we don't know."

"My name's not Stein." I got up on my knees. "It's Steiner. I'm not a Jew." Someone kicked me in the back. "Nein! I'm not a Jew. Leave me alone." I tried again to get up. "Stop it. I'm not a Jew. Stop."

"Stein, Stein, Stein. Juden Scheisskopf."

"I am not!" I got to my feet. Everyone laughed. I couldn't see their faces.

"Scheisskopf. Du bist ein Scheisskopf."

Fists smacked my head. I tasted the blood from my nose. I swung at them. "I'm not a Jew. Leave me alone." *They'll finish me if I cry.* I bit my lip hard so I wouldn't scream. I fell again and rolled from side to side. "Nein! Nein!"

"Someone's coming! Run!" They ran off toward the lake.

"Was ist los?" A man gave me his hand and pulled me up. "Are you all right?"

"Ja," I said. "Danke. I have to get home."

"Should I walk with you?"

"Nein. I live close by." I brushed my uniform off and limped toward home.

I started crying as soon as I was inside our fence. I pushed open the front door. "Mutti! Vati! Help!" I walked down the hall without even shutting the door. "I'm hurt."

"Mein Gott! Look at him, Karl." Mutti pushed my hair back and looked into my eyes. "Are you all right, Dieter?"

"Lie here, son." Vati lifted me onto the sofa and pulled the lamp closer. "Let me look at you. Ruth, get some warm water." They stood around me, unbuttoning my jacket and then my shirt.

"Should we call the doctor, Karl? He could have a—"

"He'll be all right, Lis. He's just been in a fight." He reached for the washrag Ruth brought in. "Here, let me wash your face."

"Ow-w-w." I pushed his hand away. "Easy, Vati. It hurts."

"I know. I've been beaten up."

"You have?"

"Ja. Every boy has." He carefully wiped my face. "Look, Dieter. This is how much blood there is. That was some fight. What happened?"

"They called me a Jew."

"A Jew?" Mutti looked surprised. "You, a Jew? Who did that?"

"Some of the HJ."

Vati smacked his fist against his hand. "I might have known. You deserve it, Dieter. You spend your time with these savages who can only think—"

"Karl. We agreed."

"You want your son to be one of them? You think it is easier to say nothing? Look at him." He pulled the light closer to my face. "He is getting what I knew he would. Violence brings violence."

Mutti sat on the sofa beside me. "They called you a Jew?"

"Ja, they said my name was Stein. So they beat me up." I touched my eye. "Ow-w-w. Ow-w-w. This hurts. I'm not a Jew. They shouldn't beat me. I didn't do anything."

"Ja, but it would have been all right to beat you if you were a Jew? Is that what—"

"Nein, Karl."

"Ja, Lis. Ja. Tell me, Dieter. If you were a Jew, would it have been okay to be beaten?"

"Well, if I was one, I guess . . . . But I didn' t do anything. It wasn't fair."

"That is my point, Dieter. You didn't do anything. What if you were a Jew and didn't do anything. Would it have been all right to beat you? Just because you were a Jew?"

He's right. Why would you beat someone who didn' t do anything? "Nein, Vati. It's not all right. But Jews do things. They steal our mon—"

"Ach, Scheisse, Dieter," he yelled. "How can you be so stupid?"

Mutti put her finger to her lips. "Sh-h-h-h, Karl. He's been hurt. Don't use this time to—"

"This is exactly the time to use, Lis." He pushed Mutti's hand away. "When he hurts. When he feels. Perhaps now he can understand." He turned back to me and looked hard into my eyes. "That's what you've been taught. In school. At the HJ. At the theatre. Everywhere they tell you the Jews are vermin. They lie. They steal. They cheat. It is no wonder you believe. But it is not true! You have just been beaten up because they think you're a Jew. See how a Jew feels? Do you still think it is okay to say those things?"

I shook my head.

"Gut! Then this bad time has something positive come from it. You have learned a lesson. Sometimes, Dieter, experience is the hardest teacher of all, but its lessons we never forget." He picked me up from the sofa. "You have become a man tonight. You have thought for yourself." He sat me on my bed. "I hope you never forget tonight. I do not think you ever will."

I was lame the next day, and my whole body ached. My eye was black, and my lip swollen. Mutti kept me home from school. In the afternoon I sat with her in the kitchen while she kneaded the bread dough.

"Was my real father a Jew?"

Her eyes opened wide. "Nein. What a silly boy. Why do you ask that?"

"Then why did you divorce him?"

Her words came slow, as if she wanted to make sure I understood everything. "Our marriage did not work out. It was not a happy one."

"Is my name really Stein?"

"Nein! Of course it isn't. You're name is Steiner. It is not a Jewish name. And your father is not Jewish. Now, does that settle this?"

"Ja, Mutti. Now I know."

She wiped the flour from her hands and put her arm around my shoulder. Her voice turned soft.

"Children are often mean. Those boys must be very stupid! Ignore them."

It was hard for me to go back to the meetings, but I did. Vati convinced me that just by showing up I proved I was brave and they would probably leave me alone. He was right.

17

For the first time I questioned my attitude about Jews. I thought they must have done *something;* why else would they be treated like they were. And if they didn't do anything, why didn't they all get together and make an army and fight back? Or why didn't they just leave and start their own country? I read the newspaper and watched the newsreels and war movies. I listened to the Gruppenführer, and my teachers, and Hitler and Göbbels on the radio. I felt the wings of angels when I sang *"Deutschland Über Alles."* I couldn't feel this good about the new order if we weren't doing something right. Still, I had a nagging doubt about the brutality, and my heart hurt when I saw the yellow stars the Jews were made to wear. "Never look at the star," Mutti said. "It is an embarrassment to have to wear it. Look in their eyes and smile."

"But if someone sees me smile . . ."

"Then look in their eyes and do *not* smile. But do not look at the yellow star."

"We have something to tell you, Dieter," Vati said. "Sit with us a minute."

"Is it another baby?"

"Nein!" Mutti said and laughed. "Three boys already . . . "

Vati smiled and patted Mutti's hand. "Not another baby, Dieter. Sit down. I will explain."

I sat on Vati's footstool.

"My company has told me that I must join the Party. If I refuse, I will be drafted."

"The Party?" *A black uniform with leather boots.* "You will be in the SS?

"Dieter!" He pounded the arm of his chair. "Why do you say such things? Never will I join the Party!"

"But you said you had to—"

"Did you listen? I said join the Party or . . . ?" He leaned forward. "Or what, Dieter?"

"Be drafted?"

"Ja. Now you are listening." He sat back. "I prefer the Wehrmacht to the Party."

"But you'll still have a uniform." I imagined the medals on his chest. *Like Manfred's father.*

"Ja, I will wear a uniform."

"When? Soon? How soon will you join?"

Mutti reached over and put her hand on my shoulder. "Let him finish."

"Danke, Lis. Dieter. I will join nothing on my own. I will wait. I will wait for them to come to me, just as you did with the HJ. Perhaps I will be luckier than you." He reached for Mutti's hand. "I do not want to leave my family. But anything is preferable to joining the Party. They are all idiots."

"You should not say that, Vati."

"In my own home?"

"Karl. Enough. Dieter understands that you would rather join the Wehrmacht." Mutti looked at him, and he stared back at her. He got up and walked to the window.

I followed him. "Then when will you get a uniform? Can I tell them in school that you're joining the Wehrmacht?"

109

He turned around. "See, Lis. I told you the HJ has . . . Nein. I am not going to say anything more. I have done what I can. At least he is not a Jew hater anymore. Now it is just the British and Americans."

"Danke, Karl."

"Dieter wants me to be a soldier. He will get his wish."

I nodded. "Ja, if you won't join the Party. At least you'll be fighting for Deutschland, like Manfred's father. And you'll have medals and a gun."

Mutti shook her finger at me. "Vati will have to leave us. This you want?"

"But he'll leave us to fight for the Reich, the greatest glory any Deutscher can have." *Mutti ought to be proud.*

Vati shook his head and pointed upstairs. "The HJ. And that woman. I am no competition. Even after they beat him up—"

"But it was just some who were bullies. Not all of them. You always said I should just be mad at the bad ones, not all—"

Mutti pushed me toward the door. "Find Ruth; see if there is help she needs from you."

A month later Vati received his induction notice.

"I report to the Lichterfelde Army Barracks." He took off his glasses and smiled at me. "Soon, Dieter, I will be a soldier."

Vati in a uniform! "I will be proud of you, Vati."

He handed the letter to Mutti. "Herr Rheinholdt wasted no time in notifying the authorities. And they have wasted no time in making me appear. Two weeks is all I have."

Mutti threw the notice on the kitchen table. "Men with families should be exempt. Stupid rules we live by now." She wiped her eyes and went to the stove. "What will we do, Karl?" she asked in a low voice. "How will I manage with the boys?"

110

Vati walked over and put his arms around her. "You have Ruth to help. And Dieter is old enough to take my place."

"Ja. I will help."

"He is just a boy, Karl."

"I'm almost eleven, Mutti. I'm practically grown. I can fight for Deutschland in a few years myself. I've even been on maneuvers."

"See, Lis, he is almost a soldier himself. The HJ has taught him to fight fires, to forage, to use a gun. He hates his enemies. Is that not wonderful?" He kissed the top of her head. "You will need his help."

Mutti buried her face against Vati's shoulder. "Ach, Karl."

"Sh-h-h, it's all right, mein Schatz. Someone will win, and then we will be together again."

"Deutschland is going to win!"

Vati scowled. "He still thinks hate deserves to win. Isn't that nice that I leave my family to fight for such mentality."

"But we are going to win, aren't we?"

"Come here, Dieter." He pulled me close to him and Mutti. "You are so sure, so confident." He squeezed my shoulder. "Be this strong for your mother."

Mutti made the best out of the next two weeks. She made jokes of everything and told us lots of stories. Every time Vati was near she hugged him. But at night, after I went to bed, I heard her crying. In the morning she was all smiles again.

I kept a calendar in my room and marked off the days to his date to report. Soon I could tell everyone my father was a soldier. I wished it had been the SS, but the Wehrmacht was better than nothing. The important thing was he would wear a uniform. I could finally be as proud as Manfred.

The day arrived. Ruth got us up early for breakfast with Vati. My mother bustled about, going in the bedroom and closing the door behind her, then opening the door and calling my father in there. A short time later she'd come back out, her eyes more red than the time before. When it was finally time to leave, I was dressed in my uniform and ready to escort my family to the place of induction.

We took the S-Bahn to Lichterfelde-West, six stations from Babelsberg-Ufastadt. My father wore an old brown jacket and trousers. I carried his little suitcase for him. I felt sure the other passengers knew where he was going.

"Where's your big suitcase?" Wolfgang asked.

"At the barracks they will give me a uniform and boots and a coat. Anything else I don't need."

"And a gun you will get too?" Wolfgang's eyes widened.

"Ja, I am sure they will give me a gun."

My mother turned her head and looked out the window. Vati reached over and patted her hand.

We got off the S-Bahn, and Mutti and Vati pushed Peter in his Kinderwagen while Wolfgang and I followed behind. Their steps slowed as we neared the barracks' gate. I saw big, four-story buildings behind a row of pine trees. My father pointed out that half of the roof and a part of the top floor of one building were gone. He said it must have been hit by a bomb. My mother said Mein Gott! Was it safe for him to be there? They looked at each other and began laughing.

A soldier with a rifle over his shoulder stood guard at the gate. He took the orders Vati handed him, read them, and pointed toward a smaller building inside the fence. My father put his suitcase down and asked Wolfgang to guard it while he went in and reported. Wolfgang stood very straight, kept his head up, and looked straight ahead. "Ich bin Soldat," he said. In a moment Vati came back.

"I have five minutes," he said, looking at his watch.

He pulled my mother to him, and they hugged for a long time. Then he whispered something to her, and she shut her eyes tight. She didn't want to turn him loose, but he finally put her arms down at her sides and gave her one more kiss.

He lifted Wolfgang and squeezed him so hard he gave a little squeak, then he picked up Peter and did the same to him. Turning around, he looked at me.

"For you, Dieter, I have something special to say." I stepped in front of him and stood at attention.

"You are now the oldest man in the family. To help your mother, your brothers need a good example, ja?

I nodded. "Jawohl."

My father smiled. "I expect you to be that example."

"Jawohl, mein Vater."

"You keep these two in line for me, ja? Promise?"

"Jawohl! I promise!"

A big grin spread across Vati's face. He shook his head and told my mother that sometimes he didn't know where she'd found me. He promised to let us know as soon as we could see him again.

He gave Mutti one more quick hug, picked up his little suitcase, and disappeared behind the guard house.

18

The phone rang at ten in the morning. Mutti ran for it and spoke for a minute. "Everybody get ready!" she said, a big smile on her face. "Vati can see us! Schnell!" She looked at the S-Bahn schedule on the table next to the phone. "We can make the ten-twenty if we run. Ruth, you come with us this time."

Still a block away from the barracks, I could see a group of soldiers standing at the fence. Vati saw us and started waving. We ran toward him. Even Ruth, who pushed Peter's Kinderwagen so fast his head was back and he was laughing.

Wolfgang and I reached Vati first, and Wolfgang climbed on the fence. "Come out, Vati. I want to see you."

Out of breath, Mutti reached us. Vati kissed her through the chain link.

"I only have thirty minutes, Schatzi. This is my lunch time."

Ruth held Peter up to the fence and he giggled. "Vati. Vati," he said. He held out his toy. "Whistle. My whistle."

"Ja. A whistle you have, Peter. Can you blow it?"

Peter put it in his mouth and tried to blow, but it didn't work for him. He took it from his mouth. "Whistle," he said, holding it out to Vati. "Whistle."

"You will learn. When I come home you will know how

to blow it, my beautiful little boy." Vati tickled his chin, and Peter scrunched his shoulders and laughed. "You take such good care of him, Ruth. Danke."

"Tickle me, Vati. I want to be tickled." Wolfgang pressed his face against the fence.

"You are too big to get to. Here, hold my fingers." He put his hands against the fence, and Mutti locked her fingers into one hand, and we held his fingers on the other.

Wolfgang started jumping. "Did they give you a rifle, Vati? Have you shot a Russian?"

"Nein, not yet." Vati laughed. "I do not think I will be shooting. They are training me to be a radio operator. It is new to me, but interesting."

Mutti smiled. "A radio operator? Ja, that's good. Maybe they won't send you to the Front and you won't have to—"

He put two fingers through the fence to her lips. "Sh-h-h, Lis. We cannot count on that." He nodded toward the other soldiers. "Everybody here is nervous. No one tells us where we will be sent. Or how soon we go."

"Maybe Russia?" Wolfgang asked. "In school we talk about Russia."

"Oh, nein, Karl." Her smile was gone. "Not Russia."

Vati shook his head. "You know as much as I do." He looked at me. "Dieter, are you making your brothers behave? Are you being the man of the house?"

"Jawohl! I make sure they—"

"He is bossy, Vati. He makes me do things you never did."

"That's my Dieter." He winked at Wolfgang. "When I come back home I will be boss again, all right? We'll have to—

"You do not have any idea when you go?" Mutti interrupted.

"Nein. Some of us asked, but they do not say. And they give us no time to think."

"Will you shoot a cannon?"

Vati, behind fence of Wehrmacht barracks.
Fall, 1942.

"Shush, Wolfgang." Ruth took him off the fence. "Let them talk. Come play tag with Peter. You, too, Dieter."

"But I want to stay—"

"Komm,' schnell," she demanded. I looked at Vati, but he was looking at Mutti, so I went along with Ruth. Peter waddled around and Wolfgang kept trying to run back to the fence and Ruth kept making me catch him and bring him back.

"Let them have some time alone."

"They can talk with me, too."

"You don't understand. They want to be alone."

What are they talking about that I can't hear? Why

116

don' t they want to talk with me? I looked back at the barracks, wondering what they were saying. Vati was talking
right into Mutti's ear, like he was telling her a secret. *Maybe
Vati is going to be a spy . . . Ja, my father is a spy!* I smiled
in their direction.

"Ja. I do understand, Ruth." I smiled and nodded. "I know."

"Vati's time is up, boys." Mutti waved us closer. "Come
tell him goodbye."

We ran back. Vati shook our fingers through the fence
and kissed Peter's cheek.

"I am really proud of you, mein Vater." I saluted him.
"Heil Hitler!"

Vati returned my salute. "Danke, Dieter. I am proud of
you, too." I moved back and made Wolfgang get away from
the fence so Mutti would be there alone. Vati stared at her
for a long time, then he kissed her for a long time.

"Karl, Liebling, call as soon as you know if we can see
you next weekend. Please?"

"Ja, ja. I will. I have to go now!"

He walked away fast, turning once to wave at us.

Frau Witte was waiting for us when we returned. "Frau
Drescher, it is an honor to your family that Herr Drescher
wears the uniform of the Third Reich. If help you need, tell
me. The Party does not forget those who sacrifice for the
Führer."

"Danke, Frau Witte. We will manage. Dieter is a big help."

"Ja, such a fine boy he is." She smiled at me. "The hope
of Deutschland's future. Wolfgang, too. Even Peter. Aryan
angels they are."

"Danke, Frau Witte. Excuse me, but I must go in." She
walked past her and opened the front door. "We have things
to do, boys."

I smiled at Frau Witte. *Why doesn't Vati like her?*

117

When Vati finished his training, he came home on furlough. We climbed all over him. Wolfgang wanted to see Vati's gun, and Vati said he couldn't bring it home, and besides, he did not like guns. I wondered if he had been on maneuvers, like I had. Ja, he said. I've been on them, and I did not like carrying so much on my back. Did you ride in a tank? Wolfgang asked. Nein, Vati said, and I hope I never do; they are dangerous things to be in.

I looked at him and felt so proud. He looked as good as any picture Manfred had of his father. And he didn't even have any medals yet.

I smiled at Vati. "We will win the war if my Vater goes to the Front." He blinked, and with his finger under his glasses, touched the corner of his eye. "Danke. I am glad you are proud of me, Dieter." He looked at Peter playing on the floor. "I am very lucky to have such fine sons. Come give me a kiss, Frau Drescher. You deserve the credit."

Mutti laughed and slid onto his lap. They kissed a long time. Finally, Vati looked up at me. "Why don't you boys go with Ruth? Dieter, take Peter and Wolfgang with you." He shooed us toward the door. "Your mother and I want to talk some in the bedroom."

Mutti giggled. "You are so handsome, mein Karl," she said, kissing him again.

In November Vati said he would be home on leave shortly, but he wasn't sure when. He would call as soon as he found out. I made a list of things I would talk to him about. I wanted to know what the Wehrmacht was really like. I could not decide which I wanted to join: it or the Party. I needed to know about parades and what things I could learn in the Wehrmacht. Frau Witte had already told me the reasons to join the Party, but since Vati hated it so, I wondered if maybe he had good reasons. I added to my list every day. Already it was two pages long. Wolfgang kept track on the calendar, and he kept making Ruth count the days X'd out.

But Mutti was the one he asked most often. "How many more? When will Vati be here?" One Sunday, for at least the fifth time, he ran up to Mutti. "Did Vati call, yet?"

She turned around fast. "Nein, he did not. And do not ask again! I will let you know when he does!" Wolfgang ran past me and out the door.

I tried to think of something nice to say. "When Vati comes home, we won't argue at all. And we will leave you alone."

She covered her mouth with her hand. "Ach Du Lieber! Bring your brother back in here, please."

He was crying when I found him. "Mutti wants to see you," I said.

"I don't want to see her."

"Ja, you do, Dicker." I wiped his face with my hand. "She wants to talk to you." We walked back in the house, and Mutti smiled and picked him up.

"I am sorry I yelled, Wolfgang," she said. "I did not mean to. Nothing have you done wrong. This waiting for Vati to call makes me nervous. Can you understand?"

Wolfgang shook his head. "Nein. I didn't do anything wrong."

Mutti laughed. "Ach, you are right. Why would you understand?" She hugged him tight.

"I understand, Mutti." I put my arm around her. "I don't mind if you are mad at me."

She turned her head and wiped her eyes, then turned back around. "I am sorry, boys. I should not cry. Be brave, your father said. I have to be brave." She hugged us. "I love you both. We will get through this together."

Wolfgang leaned back. He put his hand on her chin and made her look at him. "You won't get mad at me anymore?"

"Not unless you do something bad, ja?"

119

Wolfgang nodded. "If I do something bad. Ja."

"Forgiven then?"

"Ja, Mutti," he said and slid off her lap.

Friday passed. The phone didn't ring. Late that night another air raid came, but the bombers passed over us with only the sound of flak and the rumble of bombs exploding far away.

In the morning Mutti's face was pale, her eyes red-rimmed with dark shadows underneath. The morning passed, and the phone didn't ring.

Outside, it was cold and wet and foggy, but I took Wolfgang and Peter into the backyard.

"Don't bother Mutti," I told Wolfgang. "She's waiting for Vati to call, and she's upset. You stay out here with Peter; I'll go see if she needs me."

As I walked into the living room, Mutti was on the phone. *Vati!* I waited, but she didn't say anything. Finally she hung up the receiver and without saying anything, walked over to a chair and slumped into it.

"What's wrong, Mutti?"

She stared straight ahead but didn't answer me.

"Did you talk to him? Can he see us?"

Ruth came in and sat next to Mutti. She put her hand on Mutti's arm. "Was ist los, Frau Drescher?"

It was so quiet I was afraid to breathe. Finally, after a long sigh, Mutti looked up and stared past both of us.

"He was shipped out yesterday," she said in a dull voice.

Ruth put her arms around her. "Ach! Where?"

"To Russia, I know it is."

She stood up, and Ruth stood up with her. They hugged and tears rolled down Mutti's cheeks. "Danke, Ruth. You stay with the boys, please." She walked toward her bedroom like she was very tired and shut the door behind her.

For the first time I was afraid for my father.

The atmosphere inside our apartment that day matched the fine mist falling outside where everything looked wet and gray and cold. Mutti finally came out just about dusk and sat at the dining room table. I stood at the window, staring into the yard and thinking about Vati on the front lines, fighting in the snow. A blustery wind blew the last brown leaves off glistening black branches.

"We forgot to cover Vati's rose bushes," I said.

Mutti sat nearby, but she didn't answer. I turned around and looked at her. "Before the snow comes, shouldn't we do it?"

"What? What about snow?"

"Vati's rose bushes. We didn't cover them yet."

"Oh." She stared straight ahead, past me, out into the yard. "Ja," she said. "If you say so." *Did she hear anything I said?*

A couple of weeks later, I came home from school and heard Mutti whistling! *Vati's home?* I dropped my bookbag and hurried to the living room. Mutti was just dusting furniture and whistling to music on the radio. She stopped when she saw me and picked up a paper from the table.

"Here. I've read it over and over." She smiled and handed me a letter.

From Vati! I sat on the floor and read.

He was on a freight train, somewhere in eastern Poland. Nobody knew their destination, but everyone was sure that they would go deep into Russia.

"Please send heavy mittens and earmuffs and socks, anything warm you can find. It is very cold on this train, and they say it is going to be worse when we get into Russia."

At the end of the letter he listed some postal numbers. If things are sent to those numbers, he said he'd get mail from us eventually.

"Quickly now, Dieter. Do your chores. We will write

121

letters tonight and mail them tomorrow, and I will start knitting for Vati." Her cheeks were red, and she looked happy. Already she had put paper and pens on the table. "We have to hurry because Christmas is only two weeks away. Even if the package does not reach him in time, he will like our letters. Who knows how long for him to get anything!" The words bubbled out of her.

That evening was quieter than usual. All of us sat and wrote our letters. I wrote small so I could say a lot, and my fingers were stiff when I finished. I explained everything I was doing—at home, in school, and in the Hitler Youth. I told him I hoped he killed a lot of Russians.

Wolfgang drew a picture of each of us. Even Peter scribbled with one of Wolfgang's colored pencils, drawing lines and circles and filling up three pages before he got tired and went off to play with his toys.

Knitting needles clicked in Mutti's and Ruth's hands.

"What are you making first?" I asked.

"I am starting the socks, Ruth is doing a scarf."

"Ta-ram tam tu-u, da-ram da-da . . . " Mutti sang along with *La Traviata*, her favorite opera, the one Vati liked. *Always* she sang along with it, keeping time with her own sounds. *Always* I hated hearing it. But tonight her voice reminded me of Vati listening to it with her. *It's just like he's here.* I watched as she moved the knitting needles back and forth and twisted the yarn in her hand. "You sound pretty, Mutti."

"Danke, Dieter. Ta-ram tam tu-u, da-ram da-da . . . "

Tonight I don't mind it at all.

Slowly, the number of air raid warnings increased, and the radio became the most important item in our house. As soon as enemy bombers were spotted crossing the English Channel, the program was interrupted by a steady whistling sound, followed by an announcement: *Bomber formations are sighted over the Channel on a southeasterly course.*

122

Possible targets are Hamburg, Bremen, Hannover, and Berlin. A few more minutes of music, then an update on position and direction of the bombers. If they continued in an easterly direction past Hannover, or southeasterly from Hamburg, we could count on Berlin to be the most likely target, and we'd run to the wine cellar.

In ten minutes we'd hear the rumbling sound of bombers and the sharp cracks of antiaircraft artillery.

But every now and then, the enemy tricked us. Bombers flew into Germany, straight toward Berlin past Hannover, and we scrambled into the cellar. Our fighters concentrated around the city, ready to meet them. Suddenly the bombers turned straight south and bombed targets in Central Germany, cities without adequate fighter protection. Within the hour we were back upstairs, breathing easier and hoping for at least some sleep, when the radio signaled yet another bomber formation heading straight toward Berlin, just when many fighter planes were busy elsewhere. We learned not to take anything for granted.

My fear of the wine cellar became stronger each time I had to enter it. I didn't like sitting there, watching the ceiling, wondering if the walls closed in on us, or if it was my imagination. I wasn't sure what scared me more: the bombers or being in the basement.

"Mutti, if a bomb hits this house, you think the ceiling will hold up?"

She let out a short, tense laugh. "Well, we hope so. But nobody knows for sure. And we really don't want to find out, do we?" From the far corner I heard Frau Witte chuckle.

Looking at the ceiling, I felt a tight knot in my stomach. *What if we're buried down here? It would be like being in a coffin. That's it, a coffin!* I shuddered and looked at the goose bumps on my arms.

123

A few nights later, just before another raid, I stopped at the outside door to the basement.

"Mutti, let me stand here, just inside the door. Bitte?"

She stared at me for a second. "Why?"

"I'll watch the sky, and when they get close, I'll come in and let you know."

Herr Witte heard me as he walked past us. "Not a bad idea. You are our sentry."

"All right, Dieter. But you do not go outside." She shook her finger at me. "Is that clear?"

I nodded. I felt better by the door, staring up at the black sky and listening to still distant rumbles of bomber engines and flak. The thin beams of crisscrossing searchlights came closer but not straight at us. Relieved, I ran into the wine cellar to report.

"They're not coming over us this time. I think they're going in over Spandau."

"Good boy," said Herr Witte. "But we wait for the clear signal."

I went back to the door; the searchlights fascinated me. They looked like giant spider webs catching enemy planes. While I watched, they caught one! A tiny silvery speck in the center of a dozen beams of light. It was surrounded by flashes of exploding flak. Suddenly, I saw something new— clusters of green lights fell slowly from the plane. *Like green candles.*

"Come out quick! You have to see this. Schnell!"

Mutti was at my side immediately, followed by Herr Witte. They saw it just before the green lights disappeared.

"What was that?" I was out of breath from excitement.

"Target markers, Dieter," Herr Witte answered. "Dropped from the lead plane to show the other planes when to let their bombs go. It does look like Spandau was the target." Flashes of explosions lit up the sky in that direction, followed in seconds by rumbling sounds, but soon it was quiet again.

"You know what that looked like, Mutti? Fireworks on New Year's Eve with thunder and lightning, all at once."

"It is nice you can think of something pleasant while we are being destroyed." She shook her head. "I do not have that pleasure."

One week before Christmas, a second letter arrived from Vati. Mutti tore it open. She had tears in her eyes as she read. She held the letter to her lips and wiped her eyes. "I have to get back to my knitting." She handed me the letter.

Vati's writing was scribbled, uneven and shaky, on two crumpled pieces of paper torn out of a notebook.

In Russia we are, but we do not know where exactly. No one could read the signs at the stations. The cold is terrible. We do not have enough warm clothes. The tip of my nose is black and I do not dare touch my ears for fear they will shatter. My fingers and toes are numb all the time.

Please send something warm for me to wear.

I miss you all. Never will I leave my family again. War is good for no one. If it was warm, it would be no better.

I gave it to Ruth and went looking for my mother.

She stood at the window in Vati's study, staring into the front yard at the snow falling. She wasn't crying, but her face had changed to a hard mask. Her arms hung at her side, her hands balled into fists. I touched her shoulder. She reached out and pulled me close.

"I didn't want for Vati to hurt, Mutti. I just wanted him to be a soldier." I started to cry.

She kissed my head and hugged me tight. "It is not your fault, Dieter. It must be God who hates us." For a long time she held me until, finally, I couldn't cry anymore.

We were cold. It was cold inside, much colder outside,

125

and the only place for a little warmth was the kitchen stove. The rest of the apartment gave us shelter from icy winds, nothing more. Mutti bundled us into the warmest clothes she could find, even when we didn't go outside, and in every room we could see our breath.

Mutti took us to the movies sometimes to keep warm, but we wished we hadn't gone. Newsreels showed dead Russian soldiers on battlefields, frozen into strange-looking figures and half-buried by snow. Our soldiers, with their heads pulled deep between their shoulders, stumbled past them. Horses with thick crusts of ice around their mouths pulled heavy artillery. *What's happened to Vati's nose and ears?*

On the radio, Josef Göbbels appealed to us. "Support our heroes in their fight for the Vaterland and their loved ones, to save them from our murderous enemies! Take all the warm winter clothes you can spare to official collection stations. Your sons, fathers, and husbands need them in Russia."

Mutti and Ruth knitted all the time, often until late at night. Even in the basement during air raids. Two pairs of heavy mittens were ready, Mutti finished the second set of earmuffs, and Ruth was at the end of a scarf—all made of heavy wool. The package was made up. Wolfgang drew a picture of a horse and Peter scribbled circles. Mutti and Ruth and I wrote letters. This time, we all went with Mutti to mail it.

"Vati will be surprised, won't he, Mutti? He doesn't know we can send him so many things."

"Ja, Wolfgang. Vati will be excited when he sees all we send. He will be happy to read our letters, too."

"And my picture."

"Ja. Your picture."

"And he will finally be warm," I added. "So his ears won't shatter and come off."

"His ears come off? Mutti, will Vati's ears come off?"

"Nein, Wolfgang. They just felt that way to him. Now he will get the earmuffs. And not a moment too soon." She shivered. "As cold as we are, I cannot imagine what it is like for him."

Frau Witte considered Göbbels' radio appeal an order and demanded all the warm clothes we could spare. Mutti gave her Vati's old overcoat and some trousers. "I should hope that children's clothes are exempt?"

"Why? Dieter is tall enough already. His clothes could be sent."

"Dieter's clothes are being worn by Wolfgang. I need them for him, ja?"

"I will take what you have, then, Frau Drescher. Perhaps later you will have more." She turned and left.

Mutti thumbed her nose at the door that closed behind Frau Witte. "Ja, of course I will have more, and I will be sure and give them to you, Frau. Ha!"

Later in the afternoon, watching her come back with an armful of clothes, Mutti whispered to Ruth. "That woman is crazy. She thinks clothes will win the war!"

If the war is going as good as Herr Göbbels says, why would soldiers wear civilian clothes?

I stared out the window for a long time, missing the fun Wolfgang and I used to have in the snow. We'd take our sled, go to the woods behind the garden store across the street, find our favorite hill, and play for hours. Vati came with us on weekends, sometimes with Mutti. When we got back inside the warm house, Wolfgang's cheeks turned red like a clown. We never minded the cold then.

Suddenly, I felt like crying. I missed Vati.

"You at the window!" Mutti yelled from the hallway so

loud I jumped. "The sirens you didn't hear?" she said. "What are you looking at? Get downstairs!"

I pulled down the black window cover and followed her to the basement.

"Were you daydreaming up there, or what?"

"Nein. I was thinking about the things we did in the winter, the fun we had over there in the woods. And with Vati."

"Your father is doing something much more important now." Frau Witte's sharp voice came from the far corner of the wine cellar. "You should not forget that."

Mutti touched my arm. "We all miss it. And we will do it again. Look at the good things we have. Over our heads is a roof, glass is in all our windows. We are healthy, we—"

"But how long is this going to last, all this bombing, and no shoes, and a cold house?" I glared at Mutti as if it were her fault. "And I want to get out of this coffin!"

Mutti stood up in front of me. Her finger jabbed at my face, almost touching my nose.

"I do not want to hear you use the word coffin again. Ever. I do not want to hear anything from you right now. That is clear?" She sat down again, breathing heavily and still staring at me.

I was afraid to move, scared to look at anybody. *Why can't I say coffin? That's what this is.*

"Look, Mutti," I hollered from the hallway. "I have a new map of eastern Europe so I can color all the places the Wehrmacht is. It shows Russia." I hurried to hang up my coat and rushed in the living room with my prize from school. "Look!"

Mutti was slumped at the table, crying. Next to her sat Frau Witte.

"Mutti, was machst Du?" She didn't look at me. "Mutti? What's wrong with Mutti, Frau Witte?"

She slid a letter to me. "Read."

128

19

In the East, Feb. 10, 1943
It is my responsibility to inform you of tragic news. I hope that you, dear Frau Drescher, are strong enough to accept it. Your husband died a hero's death on February 7, 1943, caused by a bullet from Russian sharpshooters into his head.

During the evening of February 6, my company conquered the village of Belo-Skelewatyj on the Don River and defended it against heavy Russian assaults, which included sharpshooters. One of their bullets hit Karl's head.

Immediate First Aid by his comrades and Medics came too late for him. His wound was so severe that he died instantly. It will be small comfort to you that he suffered no pain. Karl was recovered, brought back, and buried in his final resting place next to his fallen comrades in the Heroes' Cemetery at Krasnodom.

Karl arrived at my company with a relief-transport about one month ago. Despite being in heavy firefights immediately upon his arrival, he was a very brave soldier. His quiet and determined personality quickly won our admiration, and his sudden death left all of us extremely sad.

Enclosed are pictures of you and your dear children,

part of his personal belongings, which show your family's happiness.

The loss of your husband, and father of your children, is surely devastating to you. But you must be proud that he gave his life for the Freedom and Greatness of the Fatherland!

With deep Sympathy,

I started to read it again, but the writing blurred as my eyes filled with tears. I put it back on the table quietly, afraid to make any sound at all. Mutti's hand opened and closed on her crumpled handkerchief. Her other hand was a fist with white knuckles. I felt like I was going to choke.

"This war is crazy!" Mutti suddenly yelled, pounding the table with both hands. "Adolf Hitler is crazy! We are all crazy!" She put her head back and shut her eyes tight. "This war we cannot win." She opened her eyes wide. "We will all be dead," she screamed. "Everyone. All of us." She hit the table with her fist. "Verdammter Idiot. I hate the Führer!"

Frau Witte stood up so fast her chair toppled over with a bang. Her hand shot straight at Mutti, her finger hitting hard at Mutti's shoulder.

"One more word against the Führer, and I will see that you never say anything again," she shouted. "The Party has places for your kind. They will take you all."

"Don't threaten me or I—"

"Nein, Mutti. She will report us."

"He is right," she said. "Listen to him." She left, slamming the front door behind her.

Mutti slumped back in the chair and covered her face with her hands. She sobbed until her whole body shook. Ruth came in and sat down. She reached across the table and patted Mutti's arm.

"I sent the boys outside for a while, Lis. They can play out there, and we can be alone. Later you can tell Wolfgang."

Mutti took my hand. She held it so tight it hurt. My insides churned. *Vati. I love you, Vati.* I wanted to hit something. *I hate this war!* I heard Wolfgang yelling outside.

"I'll see what they're doing, Mutti." I grabbed my coat and went in the yard.

Wolfgang was teasing Peter and laughing at him. I pushed him into the snow. He got up and ran at me.

"Now I get you, Dieter," he said, and laughed.

"Stop your stupid laughing! Don't you know Vati's dead? He won't ever come back?" I raised my hand to smack him. "You idiot!"

"Vati is dead?" His eyes were big. "How is Vati dead? Vati is dead?" He started to cry.

What am I doing? Dicker doesn't know. How can I do this to him? I reached for his hands and pulled him up to hug.

He pushed me away. "Vati is not dead. You're not telling the truth. He is not dead."

"Ja, Dicker. He is. He was killed in Russia."

"I hate you!" he screamed. "I don't want Vati dead." He pounded me with his fists, but I wouldn't let him go. I started to cry myself. "I'm sorry. I didn't mean to yell. I don't know what I'm doing, I don't know anything anymore."

It was quiet, and the cold air turned our breath into thin clouds. Peter patted my sleeve. "Ach, Peter. Vati's dead."

"Vati?" He stooped and picked up some snow. "Play. Snow." He put it in my face and giggled. I hugged both of them, and Wolfgang and I cried while Peter patted our faces.

When we went back inside, Mutti and Ruth hadn't moved from the table. Mutti's eyes were red and swollen, but she was not crying anymore. She balled up the handkerchief and smoothed it out, then balled it up again.

"Children, this is the saddest day in my life," she said. "Your father gave his life for us. Never forget that." She looked straight at me. "You are now the oldest man in this family, and you have to help us all. I hope you can do that."

I nodded. "Ja, Mutti. I will take care of you." *Vati can't be dead. What's going to happen to us? He can't be dead.*

Mutti looked away. "Oh, Karl," she murmured, tears rolling down her face. "I hope you got the earmuffs and you were warm."

A month later Ruth brought home from the Post Office our package to Vati. He'd never gotten it. Mutti put it under her bed.

Father's grave at Krasnodom, Russia
February 1943

EIN FEUERWIND

The bombing was constant, around the clock, and indis-
criminate in its choice of targets. The central area of the city
was systematically laid to waste, and whole sections of the
northern and eastern part—the blue-collar areas of Berlin
—were more flattened with each attack. During the night,
swarms of British bombers dropped hundreds of tons of in-
cendiary bombs on the city. While thousands of firefighters,
many of them Hitler Youths, tried to contain the hellish blazes
during the early-morning hours, American bombers followed
with a rain of high explosives. This deadly cycle was repeated over and over.

Word of a new type of bomb, a Luftmine, spread quickly
through our neighborhood. The detonator of the air mine
was timed to explode at a certain height above ground level,
resulting in a concussion blast that flattened everything within
a specific distance. If you were unlucky enough to be caught
in its radius, your internal organs, like lungs and eardrums,
exploded. I had grown accustomed to the usual bombing,
but when I heard of the Luftmines, I became terribly scared.
I asked Mutti if she thought the rumors of it were true.

"How would I know if that's true? How could anyone
know that? Do you know anyone who lived through one?"

"No, but why are they—"

"I would not worry about it, Dieter. If a bomb hits you, believe me, you will not feel a thing. It will not hurt. You will be in heaven really quick." Mutti chuckled. "You will never know what hit you."

"I don't think that is funny."

"You are right, Dieter. It is not funny. Sometimes that is the only way I can deal with my own fear. My fear for you and your brothers. My fear for myself. And Ruth." She smiled a little smile. "Your father. He is the one who told me to look at troubles with humor. Sometimes humor is the only thing I can muster."

Near the end of July, British bombers attacked Hamburg four straight nights. State Radio said the attacks caused heavy damage and loss of lives. Everyone spoke of Feuerwind. Now there was something else to be afraid of.

"Ein Feuerwind must be terrible," Mutti said after she spoke with Frau Engelbert about Hamburg. "She says it is like you are in hell with the devil. There were so many fires, all at once, and the winds became so strong everything was sucked up."

"People even?"

"Ja, people even. And animals. Everything."

It sounded awful, and I shuddered at the thought. "Why do they do this to us, Mutti? We're not soldiers. We don't shoot at anybody. Why does everybody hate us? What did we do?"

Mutti shrugged. "You don't remember, ja?" She looked at me expectantly.

"Remember? Nein. What should I remember?"

"How you used to hate? How Herr Beidermann taught you in school about the Jews? And the HJ? Remember Vati warning you?" She crossed her arms. "He was right, you know." She looked past me. "He was always right. Now we are the ones who are hated."

We sat there for a while. I thought about firestorms. And Vati. And I did remember hating everybody. Now I was being punished.

"Go get Wolfgang and get some cardboard," Mutti said suddenly. "Or sheets of wood, if you can find any. We have to nail these windows shut."

Because I feared them so much, I wanted to know everything I could about firestorms. The stories were all the same.

There was no oxygen, and you suffocated. They didn't happen often, but when they did, the winds sucked everything toward the center of all the fires at cyclone speed, and the temperature reached fifteen hundred degrees. People, animals, wood, and even the asphalt on the streets was incinerated. I heard stories of people and animals—even horses—flying horizontally through the air, engulfed in flames. In Hamburg more than thirty thousand people died after those four days of bombing. Most of them were women and children. Then another firestorm in Magdeburg killed more than twelve thousand. Magdeburg was small compared to Berlin. When would it be our turn?

The bunker didn't seem so safe anymore. I couldn't think of anyplace I'd be able to hide. I imagined what it must be like to be on fire and flying through the air. I dreamed of exploding, and one time when I woke up, I was sorry it was a dream.

I wanted dying to be over.

20

After Vati was killed, I didn't have to attend the Hitler Youth meetings with the regularity that had been required. This pleased my mother. Every time I didn't go meant she didn't have to worry about my not making it back. Berlin had become a favorite target of the Allies. As Germany's capital, it was headquarters for all branches of the military. Large factories important to the Nazi war machine were located there. And, as one of the most densely populated places in the country, it covered an immense area and was highly visible from the air. It was also where Adolph Hitler spent most of his time.

Germans had always been proud to live in Berlin, with its multitude of year-long cultural and sporting events, its nightlife, its thriving business climate, and its rich history that spanned hundreds of years. Now it was a curse, a place to get as far away from as possible. Berlin's death and destruction erupted every day and every night.

At first the bombers searched out specific targets—factories and railroad yards—and hit them with a fair amount of accuracy. Now the bombing appeared more random, as if it made no difference what was destroyed. The center of the city, with its concentration of banks, foreign embassies, museums, and theaters, was slowly obliterated. Many streets, lined with burned-out hulks of buildings and mountains of rubble, became impassable. The war had become a very unwelcome way of life, and any diversion seemed a good one.

"Look at this," Mutti said. "A letter from Tante Gertrud. I cannot believe it got through. I am so happy to hear news." She sat down at the kitchen table and opened the envelope. "Over three weeks ago she wrote this." She read a little bit, then turned to me.

"Dieter, Tante Gertrud wants to know if you would want to come visit her for a week."

"In Bautzen? Ja. I would like to go."

"She thinks you might like to get away from all the bombing for a few days. The problem is you need a permit to get a ticket."

"I can't take a trip?"

"Not without a permit." She thought a moment. "Frau Ludwig, maybe she knows how to get one. I will ask."

"Ja, Mutti. They have connections. Generals have been going into their house."

Mutti laughed. "Then she will know how to get a permit. I will ask her right now."

She came back smiling. "She will get you a permit, but it might take a few days."

"Will you be all right? If the neighborhood is attacked, what will you do without me?"

"Such a worrier you are." She reached over and rumpled my hair. "We have been lucky so far. We will be all right. For a few days you are going is all. You deserve a rest."

I gave her a big hug. "Danke, Mutti."

A week later Frau Ludwig brought the permit and the ticket. Mutti and I rode the S-Bahn to the Anhalter Bahnhof, the major train station.

"Look at that!" I pointed out the window to the blocks of bricks that had been apartment buildings. "The apartments. They are all gone."

"That is war, Dieter," Mutti said quietly. "Our whole world is being destroyed. I am happy your father is not here to see what has happened." She wiped her eyes. "He loved Berlin so much."

Blackened shells were all that remained of some buildings. The sun shone through the holes that used to be windows. In some places buildings still burned from yesterday's or last night's attack, but there were no firetrucks around. People hurried by with their heads down, not even looking at the fires.

"Look, Mutti. The trees are burned, too. They're just stumps."

"Sh-h-h, Dieter." Mutti had turned her face from me and looked straight ahead. No one in our S-Bahn compartment talked. Like Mutti, they didn't even look out the windows. They sat like she did, staring at nothing. I wondered if our block would soon look like this.

"Look at that soldier, Mutti," I said as we entered the Anhalter Bahnhof.

She pinched my arm. "Do not stare like that, Dieter. It is impolite."

"I can't help it. He looks like a mummy." His head and face were completely bandaged, with small holes for his eyes, nose and mouth. His arm was in a sling and he limped.

"Wounded are all over here. The greatest respect you can show them is not to stare." Mutti pulled me along fast, zig-zagging through and around clusters of people, most of them soldiers. Some, missing legs, hobbled on crutches. Still others had only one arm. Some pushed themselves along in wheelchairs. I was afraid I was going to cry and coughed so

I could cover my mouth, squeeze my eyes shut, and wipe away the tears, all in one motion.

Before I realized it, I was on the train. I pushed my way to a window to wave goodbye to Mutti, and for just a moment I saw her run alongside the train, waving a white handkerchief. I waved back, but with so many people crowding around the window, I knew she didn't see me. "I love you, Mutti," I yelled. "I love you."

"You are a good son." I turned around and saw a white-haired old man in a big overcoat standing beside me. He patted my shoulder. "She will be proud of you," he said. "You are a brave one to go off by yourself. Have you gone alone on the train before?"

"Nein. This is my first time. But I'm not afraid. I'm a Hitler Junge."

He shook his head and sighed. "So old our Kinder have become. No time you've had to play."

"Only babies play. I can fight for the Vaterland if the Führer needs me." *Who wants to be a baby? I'm the man in my family. I can take care of myself. Old people don't know that we can do anything they can.* I stood up very straight, trying to look like I did when I wore my Pimpf uniform. I hoped no one else on the train thought I was young.

The train crawled out of the city. *Why did I want to leave Berlin?* I already missed home. The old man put his hand on my elbow.

"How far are you going, son?"

"To Bautzen, to see my aunt. First I have to get to Dresden."

"To Dresden, ja? I get off in Dresden. I will help you there to find your train to Bautzen."

"Danke."

He sneezed and pulled a big handkerchief from his pocket. "This cold weather; it chills me. I think I will try to take a nap standing up." He folded his arms across his chest and leaned against the doorway. "Shake me if I start to fall."

I watched the old man as he slept, leaning from side to side, catching himself with a jerk of his head when he started to fall, then just as quickly, he was asleep again. When he finally woke up, he rubbed his eyes and looked at me. "When you get old, you sleep all the time, even standing up." We rocked along with the clackety-clack of the wheels, leaning back and forth into one another as the train lurched along. No one talked. No one smiled. I was hungry, but I knew it would be a long time before I ate.

We pulled into Dresden just before dark.

The old man stretched and tugged out his big gold watch. He opened the cover. "So many hours to cover a hundred and seventy-five kilometers," he said, shaking his head. He snapped the cover shut and stuffed the watch back into his pocket. "When the war is over, the trains will run on time again."

My legs hurt from standing all day in that cramped compartment. The old man disappeared, lost in the crowd. *It's a good thing I didn't wait for him to help me.* I found the track for a train to Bautzen and climbed aboard.

Few people traveled east any more, so I sat for the first time since leaving Berlin. In just one hour I reached Bautzen.

I called Tante Gertrud from the train station, and she came to meet me. When we reached her small apartment, I went to bed. I lay there, smelling the clean sheets, hugging the pillows.

Where am I? Was there a raid and I'm dead? For an instant I'd forgotten where I was, but there was Tante Gertrud, standing in the doorway.

"So finally you wake up, Dieter. Almost twenty hours you slept. I have Sauerbraten for you." She smiled. "Will that get you up?"

"What time is it? Mutti will be worried. I have to call."

"I got word to Berlin already. Your mother knows you are here and safe."

"Danke. But what time is it?"

"Almost five. Time to eat now."

I filled myself up on supper. In a few hours, I was ready to sleep again.

Where does that moaning come from? From far away, like in something covered up, I heard it. *And crying. Tante Gertrud has ghosts!* I pulled the cover close around me, held my breath, and listened. At first all I heard was the thump of my heart. *There it is again.* I sat up to hear better. *Those are* people *moaning and crying.* The sounds rose and fell, like a chorus. Suddenly, someone screamed, but it was faint, as if it was deep inside something. I fell back into bed and pulled the pillow over my head. *Who's screaming? What is this?* I waited a moment under the pillow, then pulled it away and listened again. The moaning continued. My heart beat so fast I felt it in my neck, but I was too scared to get out of bed. As the moans continued, I knew they had to come from across the street. With one hand holding onto the bed, and without putting my feet on the floor, I reached out and pulled the curtain of the window closest to me.

Across the street was a building. In the dark it appeared to be at least four or five stories high. Big spotlights shone on a wall that was topped with barbed wire. *A prison. But what are they doing to people in there?* The moaning came in waves, drifting across the street to my window. I shuddered and felt goose bumps on my arms.

There was a knock on the door.

"Ja?"

Tante Gertrud opened the door and came in. She sat on the edge of my bed. I stared at her, afraid to say anything.

141

"Dieter, I should have told you about the noise from the prison, but I am so used to it, I did not think. At night it sounds much louder."

"But what are they doing to those people? Are they hurting them? I heard children crying." I grabbed her hand. "Are they hurting people over there?

She shrugged. "Who knows? It has always been a prison. We see trucks go in and out of there all the time. That's all I know." She smoothed the covers. "Try and go back to sleep now. Here, I will shut the windows."

I tried, but I couldn't sleep. Even with the windows shut, I lay there and waited for the noise. And then I cringed when I heard it. *Who is it that's moaning? Traitors? Criminals?* I shuddered again and put the pillow over my head. *This is worse than living with bombs and flak and shrapnel in Berlin. I want to go home.*

"Time to get up, young man." Tante Gertrud stood at the door holding a glass. "Here. For you," she said, handing me tomato juice.

I sat up. "Danke." I took a sip and gave it back to her. "I had terrible dreams last night, Tante. I don't remember them, but they were nightmares. I'm still tired."

"Was it the noise, Dieter? From the prison?"

Then I remembered. "Ja, it was. That was real, wasn't it? You came in and shut the windows." She started to leave. "But why?" I asked. "What are they doing in there?"

She turned around. "We only guess. We ask no questions."

"Isn't there anyone who knows?"

She turned her head and listened. I listened, too, but didn't hear anything. She sat down on the edge of my bed and folded her hands in her lap. "Margot, my friend, she lives two doors away. The other morning we drank coffee, and she said she could not stand it anymore. She was going to the police and find out about the crying." She looked

142

away. "I have not seen her since. Nobody has seen her. She is not at home, her cat was not fed, her stockings still hang in the tub." She started to cry but quickly stopped and stood up. "Chances like this we should not take—talking about this." She put her finger to her lips. "No more can we talk, Dieter."

"But what do you think happened to her?"

Tante sighed and shook her head. "No more talk like this."

"But can't you ask what happened to her?"

"Ask?" Her voice rose. "You foolish boy. You do not know asking is verboten?"

"Sh-h-h, Tante," I warned. "Someone will hear."

She paid me no attention. "You do not know there is no freedom in Deutschland? That Deutschland is doomed?" *She can be reported.* She sank onto the bed. "You poor boy," she said, and reached for me. "You have seen so much and been through so much. Nothing a child should do. You lose your father. Who knows how long your house stands?" She rocked me back and forth. "Where did God go? I wonder sometimes, what will save us?"

I knew then I wanted to go home. "School starts soon again," I said. "I think I should go home now."

Tante stopped rocking and looked down at me. "I understand, Dieter. You can go tomorrow if you like." She kissed the top of my head and stood up. "Get up and we will spend our last day away from here. I will show you Bautzen."

After I dressed, I looked out the window. The prison building facing us was five stories. *Those must be windows.* Along the side of the building were sheets of something, like metal or wood, that slanted from the bottom at a sharp angle upward. *But if they're windows, you couldn't see much sky from them.* I stared at the building a long time, trying to imagine what went on inside. Finally I turned away and caught sight of myself in the mirror. I felt different, but I didn't look different. *I've seen a real prison and heard pris-*

143

oners in there. Maybe traitors. At least they deserve it. En-
emies of Reich! That must be who they are. But children?

"Dieter, your breakfast. It is getting cold."

I left and went to the kitchen. The red-checked tablecloth looked brand new and all the dishes matched. The bis-
cuits and bacon tasted so good. I chewed slowly, knowing I
wouldn't eat like this for a while.

"If I can remember this taste, maybe when I eat the terrible food at home, I can pretend it tastes good. Like yours!"

Tante smiled. "Blessed are the children," she said. "What
would we do without them?"

That night I was too excited to fall asleep. I lay there
and thought about the train ride home, and how Mutti would
be so glad to see me. *Will Helga—*

The roar of trucks startled me. I looked across to the
prison. The large iron gate was open, and gray Army trucks,
their headlights thin slits of white, rumbled out onto the street
one after the other. *Sixteen. Are there people in them? Where
are they going?* Everything was quiet over there. I shivered
and pulled the blanket up over my head.

Bright sunshine awakened me, and I packed to go home.
We left early in hopes of catching a train going toward Berlin. We found one, and I said goodbye to Tante Gertrud.

"I enjoyed our visit, Dieter, although it was short. I hope
you can come again."

"Ja, Tante. Sometime I will," I lied.

I used the S-Bahn, the Underground, and buses to get
close to home. In the few days I'd been gone there'd been
more bombs and fires. I walked fast, not even stopping to
look. I was just one or two kilometers from home now.
People poked through the smoking ruins.

When I got in the yard, Mutti ran out and swept me off
the ground in a terrific hug.

144

"These are happy tears," she said, crying. "You are safe and you are home."

"I was lonesome. And homesick, too." I held on to her like I was Peter. "I promise I'll never go away again without you or Wolfgang or Peter."

"Do not worry, Dieter. We will not let you leave us again."

How nice it was to walk with my very own mother back into my very own house and see my very own brothers and Ruth. Even when the sirens wailed, I didn't mind. I was home in my very own city, Berlin.

21

By the fall of 1943, the Farmer's Markets in and around Berlin had turned to wasteland. Daytime bombing raids had reduced the trickle of fresh vegetables to nothing. It was rare to see a farmer's horse-drawn wagon from the surrounding farmland pull into a suburban street. When one did, in minutes the wagon was mobbed by a hundred women, children, and old men. Those close enough to the farmer outshouted one another, holding up wads of paper money, watches, jewelry, anything of value, to catch the farmer's eye and be rewarded with a head of cabbage, or a few potatoes or carrots. I saw one woman offer an expensive-looking Persian rug. Her reward? A small basket of eggs. Money meant nothing anymore, and no one wanted it. Especially the farmers. Store shelves were mostly empty, and ration cards were needed to buy anything at all.

At home we made a game of hunger. When a night raid came late, lasting into the early morning hours, we didn't go back to sleep. Instead, we sat up and hatched our plan for the morning. Mutti was our chief planner.

"Dieter, it's your turn to try Foltner's for coal and wood again. Wolfgang, you and I have to be at Müller's. I heard that they might get a delivery of margarine and fish. And

Ruth, could you take Peter and go to that vegetable store on Ufastrasse? Maybe they'll get something this morning. Peter can catch up on his sleep. He always dozes as soon as he is in motion."

Before dawn we were ready. Mutti waited for Ruth and Peter to leave, then took Wolfgang by the hand. "Schnell, Kinder. Before the line is too long we must be there. And you, Dieter. Here is the ration card and some money. Take your sack and the wagon. Get anything you can. We are almost out of coal."

Many mornings, when the wind was right, the air was thick with smoke from the fires in the city and all around us pieces of ash fluttered to the ground. Occasionally a fire truck rushed past, but we heard little and smelled even less. By the time I reached my designated location, it was still dark. Usually a line had formed already. I thought how lucky the people were who lived nearby. November was cold, and some of the people on the long line jumped from one foot to the other, slapping their arms on their sides to keep warm. Others sat on boxes they'd brought, while some of the very old sat on the ground. If there were twenty to thirty ahead of me, I was just about certain to go home empty-handed. But Mutti was never angry when that happened. "Do not feel bad," she'd say, and give us a long hug. "We will try again tomorrow." Happy were the times when there weren't a great many ahead of me. Whatever I got that day was always worth the wait.

Once a month a single store received a small shipment of bacon. We could buy no more than one hundred twenty-five grams per family or ration card. Mutti herself went to that store, no matter how far away it was. She wasn't even bothered if she had to sit through an air raid on the way there, for this was the ultimate treat. The bacon trip usually meant no sleep at all the night before; she had to be among the first in line. Once home, she stretched a fifty-gram chunk of that delicacy to the last drop of fat. She'd shave off one, sometimes two thin slices, chop them into tiny squares and fry them until a small puddle of grease accumulated. On days when we had a few potatoes, she boiled them soft, then sliced them into the bacon grease, and that meal was the highlight of our week. When at last there was only the rind left, she pressed this into a pan until it was almost burned dry. Too soon that chunk of bacon was a thing of the past.

22

I did not look forward to Christmas. Mutti carried Vati's picture with her every time we went to the basement, or to Ludwigs' bunker. This would be the first holiday since he was killed, and she seemed to be more nervous as the time drew closer.

Between bombing raids she found things for Wolfgang and me to do. We shoveled snow from the veranda, and then from the steps to the sidewalk, and then she wanted us to do the sidewalk as well, and even, sometimes, the neighbor's sidewalk. I wrote letters to Oma and Opa, and Wolfgang and I together swept the floors, looked for firewood, and polished the door handles. Wolfgang had a hard time with the handles.

"Mutti, the wood is splintered. Why should I do this?"

She smiled. "It keeps your mind busy, Wolfgang, does it not? When you are done with the doors, you can clean the bathroom sink again. And the tub."

"But Mutti, we never have time to take a bath. You make me wash in the bucket. What reason is there to clean the tub?"

"I have just told you to clean it. That is enough reason."

She was right. The cleaning kept us busy, and nothing

stayed clean for long. As bombs exploded closer to the house, large cracks appeared in the ceilings in every room, and a fine white dust settled on floors and furniture. There was always work to do.

"Schnell, Dieter. The walk. It needs to be shoveled." Mutti handed my coat to me. "Wolfgang is out there playing. You and he can make quick work of it if you work together."

"It's cold this morning, Mutti."

"Ja, it is cold. You know a better way to warm up than with a little work?" She smiled while she waited for my answer, knowing I couldn't disagree. "Besides, even though there's a war, the city says we have to keep the walks clear."

"They don't still give notices, do they?"

"Ja, they do. Frau Kundert said she got one."

"But I want to read. If you get a notice, why can't you tell them Vati's dead and we can't—"

"Can't what? Take care of ourselves?" Mutti sat down on the sofa beside me. "Never we use Vati's death as an excuse not to work." She shook her head and smiled. "When you were little, you liked to shovel snow. Now that you have to, you look for ways to avoid. Wolfgang will probably be like that, too." She rose and went to the window. "Look at him, pushing his little shovel around." She tapped on the window pane and waved to Wolfgang.

"See, for him it's fun. For him it's a game. It makes life go on in spite of the war." She came back and sat beside me. "We do not live like civilized people, Dieter, so when we get the chance, civilized things we do. Like keeping the walk clear. It may not be much—"

"I think it's much. I think it's a lot."

"Enough, Dieter. You are the man of this family, not the head of it. The walk will be shoveled. By you. Now."

I nodded, put on my coat, and went to the basement for the snow shovel.

"Let's make an igloo, Dieter." Wolfgang had a pile of snow almost one meter high in the front yard.

"Can't. I have to clear the walk. You have fun while I work."

"Then can I have your snow?"

"Ja, Dicker. You can have my snow." I pitched the snow over the fence into the yard, and he shoveled it as fast as he could onto his big pile. I stopped and leaned on my shovel. "Why don't you clean off the steps and the front walk? Then you'd get your own snow."

He grinned. "Ach, ja, Dieter! Then I'll have my very own snow." He hurried to the top step and began pushing the snow onto the next one.

I worked my way down the sidewalk. *Who cares how it looks? Did Mutti mean I was lazy? I'm not lazy. I don't like foolish work is all. But she's right about getting warmed up.* I stopped and wiped my face with my sleeve. I glanced up and saw a soldier walking toward us on our side of the street. His right arm was in a sling, the empty sleeve of his overcoat flapping by his side. I stopped shoveling. I strained to see him. *He looks like Vati!* I held my breath. "Vati?" I cried out, and ran toward him.

I stopped short as he reached out his good arm to me. "It's Uncle Willie, Dieter." He gave me a hug. "I wish I could be Karl for you." He kissed the top of my head, and we walked back to the yard.

"You're not Vati!" Wolfgang said. "You said it was Vati, Dieter. You lied."

"It's Uncle Willie. I couldn't help it. He looks like Vati."

"You are Wolfgang? You have grown up! So big you are. Both of you."

Wolfgang's lip turned down. "I knew you weren't Vati.

151

Vati's dead. He's buried in Russia. Mutti told me that. So you couldn't be Vati."

Uncle Willie squatted down to talk to him, and I ran to the house, yelling as loud as I could. "Onkel Willie ist hier! Mutti, Onkel Willie! Komm' schnell!"

Mutti came running from the back of the house, a big smile on her face, and raced out the front door and down the steps. Uncle Willie grabbed her with his good arm. Wolfgang and I stood there as they hugged. Mutti cried and laughed all at once.

"Do not just stand there with your mouth open, Dieter. Take the bag inside." Mutti pulled Uncle Willie toward the steps to the front door.

"We sit in the kitchen, Willie. It is the only warm place in the house. You want something hot? I can make some coffee, but it is thin coffee, not very strong. Your beard looks frozen. You are cold? Tell us, you hear news from the family? What happened to your arm? Are you back for good? You can stay with us, ja?"

"Stop now, Lis." Uncle Willie held up his hand. "Slow, please. I am not back for good. I wish I could be."

Mutti's smile disappeared. Mine did, too.

"A bullet hit me, here, below my elbow. I can't fire my gun. Two weeks convalescent leave I have. Then I report back to my unit. I can't stay any longer than that."

A piece of wood crackled in the stove, the only sound in the kitchen. I knew we were all wishing the same thing: that we could be together for a long time.

Mutti broke the silence. "We hear the Russians are pushing our troops back. Maybe you won't be able to find your unit. Maybe they have gone back too far. Or in another direction. Then you would have to stay here."

He laughed. "Nein, Lis. That is not the way it works. I report in Berlin first. I am a deserter if I don't. You know

152

what they do with deserters now." He nodded toward Wolfgang. "And details I don't want to go into."

Mutti and Ruth stood up. "Aren't you hungry?" Ruth asked. "Something to eat we can scratch together."

"Nein. But I am—"

"Show me the bullet, Uncle Willie." Wolfgang pulled at his sleeve. "Where did it hit you? Did you shoot him back?"

Uncle Willie smiled. "Nein, Wolfgang. I did not shoot him. And I can't show you the bullet. Or the hole it made. My arm is in a cast, see?" He rolled up his sleeve. "But you can write your name on it before I leave."

"I can't write yet, Uncle Willie."

"Then you can draw me a picture. How would you like to do that?"

"Ja. I will draw a picture. Of a soldier. And a gun."

"Ach, we have so much war," Mutti said. "Even the children. They think of nothing else."

We made it as comfortable as possible for him, but he didn't like the air raids. They made him nervous. He hated the sound of the sirens, the bombers, the explosions. He became very restless, although for the next several days no bombs hit anywhere near us.

Christmas Eve came. Uncle Willie went into the woods with me to cut a tree, and I dragged it back and set it up. In spite of the cast on his arm, Uncle Willie helped Ruth with the decorations. At six o'clock Mutti opened the doors and Wolfgang, Peter, and I walked into the living room. Peter ran to the tree and stretched to reach a candle.

"Nein, Peter." Mutti grabbed him. "They are hot. They will burn you." She bent down and picked up a box sitting next to Vati's picture. "This is for you, Peter. Sit with me, and I will open it for you."

Mutti sat down and put Peter in her lap. "You can help me," she said, and Peter pulled at the paper.

153

"Hund!" He looked at Mutti and smiled. "Peter's Hund."
He slid off her lap and put the toy dog on the floor. "Peter's
Hund," he said, holding onto the string and pulling it around
the room.

Wolfgang looked up at me. "That was my toy."

I nodded and put my finger to my lips. "Sh-h-h. Don't
say anything," I whispered.

Wolfgang squatted and looked at the tree. "Don't I get
something, Mutti? Isn't there something for me?"

She laughed. "Of course, Wolfgang." She reached behind the tree and brought out a package tied with twine.
"The Weihnachtsmann did not have any pretty paper or ribbon. Enjoy anyway."

He sat on the corner of the sofa. "Dieter. Look!" He
held up three writing tablets and two red pencils. "And a
rubber eraser."

"Ja, Dicker. That's a fine gift." I turned to leave.

"Not so fast, Dieter. There is something for you, too."
Mutti handed me a little package. "You are the man of this
family. You need to carry this with you."

I sat down and undid the string and folded back the paper. *A picture of Vati.* "Danke, Mutti." My eyes filled with tears.

"Thank the Weihnachtsmann. He brings things, you
know." She nodded toward Peter.

"Ja. You are right. The Weihnachtsmann."

I went to my room and brought back two packages.
"For you, Mutti, and Ruth, too. The Weihnachtsmann did
not forget you."

"For us?" Mutti looked at Ruth. "What have we?" They
sat side by side and slowly opened the packages. "Mein
Gott!" Mutti said. "Where did this come from?" She held
up a blue scarf. "Where?"

"Look at mine, Lis." Ruth held up a green one. "They
are silk." She put hers on her lap and ran her fingers over it.
"Silk, they are, Lis. We have silk scarves." She stood up and

draped it around her neck, twirled it around her face, and smoothed it out again around her neck. "So soft, so beautiful it is. Danke, Dieter."

"The Weihnachstmann, Ruth. Remember?" I smiled and motioned toward Uncle Willie.

Mutti looked at him and grinned. "Ja, Soldat. Even the Weihnachstmann wears a uniform. Danke."

"We need music in this house," Uncle Willie said. "Karl would not want the second day of Christmas without some joy. You know that is true, Lis. For the second day. Let us have some fun for the children. And for you."

"But I . . . don't know, Willie. It is not Christmas without Karl."

"Ja. But it is the way Christmas has to be now. For the boys? Life is hard enough anyway." He took her hand. "You know how Karl would feel. He would not want you to make them unhappy."

"You are right. Karl enjoyed the holidays." She laughed. "You win. We will celebrate."

She sent me to the cellar for a bottle of Vati's Boxbeutel and she unpacked three of her champagne glasses. Wolfgang and I waited until the glasses were almost empty and then I sneaked a swallow.

"Nein! Dieter! You want to be a drunk?" But Mutti was only joking, and I pretended to be drunk and staggered around the living room. Wolfgang laughed. "I want to be a drunk, too," he said, and Mutti let him pretend to finish her glass of champagne. He staggered around behind me, finally falling on the floor.

Uncle Willie pretended he was a policeman, and he arrested Wolfgang and me and put us in jail in the corner of the room. Then Ruth said she was going to get us out, and she tiptoed up and opened the imaginary jailhouse door, and we ran to the other side of the room.

All of us were laughing, and Uncle Willie said, "Wind up the Victrola, Dieter, and put on a record. I will punish this beautiful girl who let the prisoners escape by making her dance with me."

I took a record from the album and cranked the Victrola. The music began, and Uncle Willie held Ruth's hand as they danced around the living room. Wolfgang and I cheered and danced around beside them, jumping up and down. When we came close to the table, I said, "Mutti, dance with Dicker and me," and she held out her hands, and we jumped in circles around the room. Mutti smiled and sang along with the music.

The sirens! Bombers! Explosions rattled the floor.

We spilled into the hallway. "Here, Wolfgang, between us." Uncle Willie pulled Wolfgang down between Ruth and himself. I scrambled to find a space near the double door to the living room and hit the floor. I covered my head. *Where's Mutti?* For the fraction of a second, I heard the rumbling swoosh of a bomb.

In terrifying slow motion, the top of the door bulged inward and dust and splinters shot out around us. The ceiling cracked and chunks of plaster crashed to the floor. Jagged cracks swept out from the door handle. The door exploded and the lock and handle smashed into the wall above my head. *Scheisse! If I'd been standing up* . . . One of the double doors ripped from its hinges and crashed on top of us. I buried my head under my arms, waiting for the ceiling and walls to topple. They didn't.

Carefully, I looked up. *Ow-w-w-w.* I rubbed the back of my head. A stinging pain shot through my neck and down my right arm. My ears hurt.

"Dieter." *Gott Sei Dank. At least I can hear!* "Where is the flashlight?"

"Mutti? You are all right?"

"Ja, I ran in with Peter. It was worse out here. Where is the flashlight?"

"I will find it." Everyone was coughing. I spit plaster dust and wiped it from my eyes. *Why does my arm hurt so?*

"Wolfgang, Uncle Willie. You are all right? And Ruth?"

"Ja," Uncle Willie said. "All safe. Wolfgang is fine. He was here, between Ruth and me." He coughed and cleared his throat.

I pushed parts of the door off my back and groped in the darkness for the flashlight. *Here it is!* The beam fell on the thick layer of plaster dust that filled the hallway.

"Ach! Look at this," said Mutti. "We could have been killed."

I looked at my arm under the light. It was stuck with long, thin splinters.

"Over here, Dieter. Bring the flashlight."

"In a minute. My arm is filled with splinters." I carefully pulled one out. "Ow-w-w-w, it hurts."

"Careful, Dieter. That can be dangerous. Wait for the lights."

"I can't Mutti. They hurt more in than they do coming out." I pulled another one. And another. I felt the back of my head where something had hit, but my hand brought back only a little blood.

Wolfgang whimpered.

"You are all right, Dicker. You are alive, and Uncle Willie said you are all right."

"Ja, but I am scared."

"Me, too, Wolfgang. And I am a soldier."

"But you aren't supposed to be scared."

"You never get used to it, Wolfgang. Do not even try." Uncle Willie crawled past me to the front door. "This door is smashed, too," he said. "Come. Go outside for fresh air."

We followed him out, still coughing. The sky was red, but our house still stood. So did Ludwigs' and the house on our other side. *Again!*

Mutti held Peter in her arms and sat down on the top step. Ruth sat down next to her and rested her head on her knees.

"That is our Christmas present: We are all here. What a gift for you, Weihnachtsmann Willie!"

"You are brave people. But I cannot stand any more of this. I feel safer in a foxhole. I am going back tomorrow."

Mutti reached her hand out to him. "Your arm, Willie. It has not healed. Don't be crazy!"

"They will find something for me to do, Lis. I cannot stay here. This place isn't safe. It is hell."

He left the next morning.

Uncle Willie,
1941 photo

23

"Mutti! There is an officer to see you. A Major." I ran up behind her in the kitchen. "Maybe he knew Vati. You think he knew Vati?"

"A moment, please, Dieter." She put the glass on the counter and the dish towel beside it. "I know no officer. I'll see who it is."

I followed her to the door. The Major's back was to her when she opened it. He turned around.

"Elisabeth!"

"Hans! A surprise to see you." Mutti stepped back and looked at him. "My son says you are a Major! I might have known." She held out her hand. "Come in. Too cold it is out here." He walked in, and she motioned to the living room. When he reached the door, he stopped and bowed and she went in ahead of him. "Sit with us," she said. "I'll fix coffee."

"First, tell me of Karl. How is he?"

I stepped close to Mutti. "My father's dead. He was killed at Stalingrad."

"Lis. I am sorry. So many were killed there." He took her hand again. "I am so sorry. Poor Elisabeth." He looked at me. "Can you be Dieter?"

"Ja, Hans. You remember him?"

"Not at this size, I don't. You are the one who liked to draw."

I looked at him, but his face meant nothing. "Ja, I draw. And I am a Pimpf, too."

"I must assume your father was not happy about that. Karl never liked the military. Remember the arguments we had? Guns and brawn I argued, Karl forever talking about policy-making and brains." He smiled. "Raucous times those were."

Mutti laughed. "Ja, they were. At each other you shouted, as if the loudest one was right. Dieter, if you had been older you would have learned from them how senseless arguing is. Particularly with your father." Mutti shook her head. "So little sleep I got when you two talked all night."

Major Graubert smiled. "Pleasant times they were, Elisabeth. I shall miss them. And Karl."

"The coffee I should start," Mutti said, turning and going toward the kitchen. "Get acquainted with Dieter."

Major Graubert, assigned now to the Potsdam barracks, took it upon himself to look out for us. He stopped by often with canned goods, a welcome bounty for a table that saw little variation from its meager day-to-day fare. And he drove a military motorcycle. That alone would have been enough to impress me, but it was also equipped with a sidecar. To ride in a sidecar with a Major! I felt as if I were a soldier myself and imagined standing up and reviewing the troops from it. If I ever joined the Wehrmacht, I would have to be an officer.

Berlin was being systematically destroyed from the air. Fires in the city were so widespread that the night sky never darkened anymore, staying such a bright orange color that we could read the newspaper outside. During the day, the sun couldn't break through the smoke. It was like wearing darkly tinted sunglasses all day. When the winds came from the direction of the city, a fine rain of ashes fell.

These circumstances tended to demoralize Berliners. My mother mentioned how sad everyone looked and sounded. "Impending doom is written on their faces," she said. Yet according to radio and newspapers, despite "occasional re-arranging and withdrawals of our armed forces for strategic reasons," a German victory was inevitable. Especially, the reports stated, along our frontlines in Russia. But the rumors, based on tales told by wounded returning soldiers, were otherwise: that large units of Wehrmacht were fleeing in utter disarray; that they were giving up and becoming prisoners; that they were being killed by the thousands.

Mutti shook her head. "I just cannot believe anymore that Deutschland will win. This terrible bombing of Berlin and all those other cities . . . " She twisted the handkerchief in her hands. "Every day the Ruhr area is being smashed. Where will they make the ammunition?" She sighed. I didn't know if she expected me to answer or not.

24

Two waves of bombers struck Berlin around midnight and we spent the whole night in Ludwigs' bunker. But our routine could not be broken. Frau Ludwig had set her alarm clock so Helga and I could get to school.

We walked together out to the yard into a thick fog.

"It's strange, Dieter. What's wrong?"

We stood in the middle of the yard and listened. "I hear birds! Listen."

"And no ashes! There's no ash today!" Helga rubbed her hands together. "And smell! There's no smoke."

She was right. The wind had shifted.

"It feels like a holiday, Helga. Like nothing to worry about. After Deutschland wins, it will be that again. *What did the Gruppenführer say?* "The sun will shine on the Master Race."

"I like sometimes the way you talk, Dieter." Helga smiled a big smile.

Now the day is *perfect.*

We started toward the S-Bahn. "Look," I said, "Frau Baumgart is working in her garden. She never comes out anymore. Everyone must feel this is a special day."

Helga stopped and caught my arm. "Do you think something is going to happen? Something bad?"

"You mean the bombers?"

She nodded.

"They'll be back. When the fog goes."

She stooped and picked up a handle of a broken teacup. "Ja. I know they will."

"We can still have fun for now. Let's pretend it's like it used to be." I grabbed her arm. "Let's see how many things we can find from here to the S-Bahn." We ran down the sidewalk, laughing, looking for good things in the litter that covered the street.

"I've got a red button," I yelled, holding up a button from a woman's dress.

"Here's a blanket pin." Helga showed me a large pin. "This is bigger than your button. Whoever finds the biggest thing is the winner."

"What if I find a good piece of shrapnel? I can trade that in school. That's worth more than anything."

Helga put her hands on her hips. "Dieter, you know what I mean."

We poked through the trash and rubble all the way to the trains. When we got there, I had to agree that her treasures were better than mine. We left everything, except my pieces of shrapnel, in a pile by the corner of the S-Bahn before we went to our schools.

By noon the fog was gone and my classroom was warmed. Finally I could take off my coat. Without an air raid, the day dragged. When I finally left, I walked slowly, just to feel the peace and quiet. *All day without a raid. Just like it used to be.*

I crossed the street so I could walk past one of the big estates owned by a Party official. *Vati never liked Herr Schopenhauer. 'Loyal weasel Schopenhauer.'* I picked up a stick and dragged it along the pickets.

As I got closer to the gate, I heard voices up ahead. I looked through the fence and thick bushes on the inside.

They're prisoners! And guards! I dropped my stick and stepped back quickly to the sidewalk.

I walked fast and looked straight ahead. *They didn' t see me, or they'd have hollered by now.* When I got near the end of the fence, I slowed down a little.

"Ps-s-s-st. Don't stop. Keep walking."

I jumped at the sound of a man's voice coming from the shrubs. I glanced toward him.

"Nein! Don't look at the fence! Keep walking! Look at a piece of paper ahead of you. Take it and keep going."

A few steps ahead of me, a tiny piece of paper appeared between the pickets. I grabbed it and forced myself to just keep walking. *Links, rechts, links, rechts.* I wanted to turn around and see if anyone saw me, but my heart beat so loud I thought they'd hear it. *They'll shoot me in the back! Links, recht, links, recht. Slow, like nothing's happened.*

When I was far enough away, I ran, the piece of paper tight in my fist.

"Mutti," I yelled. "Mutti, where are you?" I ran into the kitchen and stopped short.

"Ach, Dieter, was ist los? Frau Witte and I are having coffee. Are you all right?"

"Ja, I'm all right."

"Then what's the big hurry, Junger Mann? You're out of breath."

"I was . . . it just . . . We had a full day of school. Still no bombing."

Frau Witte put her cup down. "The stupid Americans. They have not enough planes," she said. "We have shot them down. Roosevelt will be sorry. The Führer will take care of him."

"I have something to show you, Mutti. It's in my room."

"Do I need to see it now?"

"Ja, Mutti. It's about school. You have to see it."

"Well, if it is important I will look. Excuse us, please."
She poured another cup of coffee for Frau Witte. "A moment is all, Frau Witte. Then I'll be back."

When we got to my bedroom, I shut the door.

"What is it, Dieter, why are you so nervous?"

I gave her the piece of paper. "A prisoner gave it to me," I whispered.

"A prisoner? Ach, mein Gott! Where have you been?"
She opened the tightly folded note.

"He pushed it through Herr Schopenhauer's fence. The one Vati didn't like. You know, the one he called a loyal weasel."

"Look," Mutti held the opened note. "It's written on toilet paper." She read it. "He wants to tell someone he's healthy," she whispered and gave it to me to read.

I squinted at the tiny writing. *112 Marien Strasse 5. Etage Ich bin gesund* it said. "Do you know where that is?"

"Not yet, but we'll find out. Let's hope there aren't too many of Marien Strassen in Berlin. Go on with you now. I'll get back to Frau Witte."

After Frau Witte left, I heard Mutti and Ruth talking in low voices in the living room. I listened for a minute, then walked in. "A Konzentrations-Lager? What kind of camp is that?"

"Sh-h-h, Dieter!" Mutti looked at Ruth. "I need to tell him so he won't ask others." She turned back to me. "They keep prisoners there."

"Like the prison in Bautzen, across from Tante Gertrud's?"

"Not so *loud*, Dieter. Sit here, between us." She patted the middle cushion on the couch, and I sat down. "Ja," she said, "but worse. Terrible stories we've heard, but how much is true . . . " Mutti shrugged. "How can it be? Why would they make Jews and gypsies prisoners? Move them away,

165

ja. Maybe for their own good, but make them prisoners? It makes no sense."

"In Berlin is there one?" I whispered.

"Tell him what you heard, Ruth."

Ruth leaned closer. "Frau Mettelmann told me this morning that her niece told her there is a large camp north of Berlin, in Oranienburg. People say it is one." She shook her head and shrugged. "But who knows? Nobody can get close to it."

"Maybe it is a rumor only," I said. "Maybe it is a place for spies. When places are well protected, it means they are important to the war effort. The more protected and guarded, the more important they are. I learned that in the HJ."

"Sh-h-h, Dieter. Do not be so loud."

"I'm not loud. Why do we whisper over this? What secrets do we have?"

Mutti crossed her arms. "Frau Witte should hear us? This is something you want her to know we talk about? Don't ever forget: We cannot trust that woman. No one can we trust but ourselves. Karl was right. It has happened like he said it would."

We found two Marien Strassen on the map. One was in the northern part of Berlin, the other closer, in Lichterfelde.

"We'll start with the closer one. If it's not the right one, we'll go to the other."

"In one day? What if the bombers come? Remember how long it took me to get the tickets at Anhalter Bahnhof."

"All the chances you've taken and you worry about the bombers now?" She crossed her arms and scowled. "If Vati had been that man and he'd given a note to some boy to bring to me, you would have expected him to be afraid?"

"Nein, Mutti. I wasn't thinking about his family."

"I know. You were thinking about yourself." She held my face close to hers. "Strange things we do in war. We survive. We look out for ourselves first. That's survival. But sometimes we have to think of someone else. This is one of those times."

I nodded.

"All right. We have to try to get this message delivered."

We had no problem getting to Lichterfelde, but from the S-Bahn station it was a long walk to Marien Strasse. Getting close to it, we could see already that it would be difficult, if not impossible, to find number 112. Long rows of burned-out buildings, mountains of still-smoldering bricks and piles of twisted steel beams were all that was left of Marien Strasse. Next to the door opening in a piece of outside wall we spotted an almost melted metal sign, Number 114. On either side of this pile of rubble were more piles of rubble. "Nothing lives on 112 Marien Strasse any more," Mutti said.

The other Marien Strasse was more than sixteen kilometers away. We walked many of them, but for a few stretches we rode the S-Bahn and the Underground and a bus.

"Ach, my legs hurt," Mutti said, leaning against a building and rubbing her knee.

"Mine do, too. We've been gone almost four hours. And my feet hurt."

Mutti smiled at me. "We don't make too good soldiers, do we?"

"Not in this wind and rain. Now it's turning to snow." I turned into a doorway and hugged myself. "I'm freezing."

"Vati felt like that, too, remember? Come along. We have to keep going."

An hour later we stood in front of an apartment building, Marien Strasse 112. It must have had six or seven stories at one time; now the two top floors were burned out.

"Let's hope this is it, Dieter. I can't walk too much longer."

We went inside and climbed the stairs. The stairway smelled like cold, wet ashes, and small puddles of water

167

made the stairs slippery. We rested on each landing to catch our breath.

Finally we reached the fifth floor. The door to the apartment was made of large wooden boards nailed together. There wasn't even a handle. On the wall at the left of the door was a small, rusty metal plate nailed above a doorbell. The name *Wegert* was in black letters.

Mutti looked at me and nodded. I knocked on the wooden boards. Nobody came. I knocked again, louder. Now we heard someone coming.

"Wer ist da?" *She sounds old.*

"Frau Drescher," Mutti whispered into the edge of the door. "From Babelsberg we come. My son is with me. A prisoner gave him this note for you."

A heavy chain banged against the other side, then the door opened a little. An old woman peered through the opening. Mutti held the note to the crack. The door opened wide.

"Komm' rein, schnell!" We rushed inside. "Did anyone see you come in the building? Or on the stairway?" the old woman whispered.

"Nein," Mutti said, shaking her head. "Nein."

The woman wound the chain around a bolt in the door frame, grabbed my hand, and pulled me through a narrow hallway into a living room. Mutti held my other hand and followed us.

"Sit." She pointed to two chairs. "Sit here. Please. Can I see this paper?"

Mutti gave her the note. The woman stared at it for a long moment. *It's only a few words. Why's she taking so long to read them?* Mutti stared at her hand and twisted her wedding ring, and the woman kept looking at the note. *Why doesn't she say something.*

Her hands shook and the note went back and forth like the wind was blowing it. Her cheeks were wet and tears dropped onto her dress.

Finally the woman sighed and looked up at us. She stood up slowly, reached in her pocket and pulled out a handkerchief. She pressed it against her eyes.

"Where did you get this, please?"

"You tell, Dieter. He gave it to you."

When I finished my story, the old woman gave me a long and gentle hug. Her cheek felt damp and cold against mine.

"Danke, junger Mann. That is my husband." She gave a little sob and covered her mouth with her hand as if to stop any more. "They took him right from our store downstairs. Over four months ago, and I hear nothing." She dabbed at her eyes. "I thought he was dead, that they killed him."

"Downstairs was our shoe repair shop. For more than twenty years we owned it. We were comfortable. We had good customers. Many Jews were our customers. Then Kristallnacht and they left." Frau Wegert fidgeted with her handkerchief as she talked.

"Across the street lived a Jew. He lived with his parents. Always they brought their shoes. One day he asked if he could stay here a few days. 'My parents, they are old, and don't want me there when it's their turn to go,' he told my husband. Karl, my husband—"

"That's my father's name," I interrupted.

She looked up and smiled. She looked at Mutti. "Your husband, he is Karl?"

Mutti nodded. "Ja," she said.

"And your husband, Karl. He is all right?"

"Nein, Frau. He was killed at Stalingrad."

The old woman patted Mutti's hand. "Gott. You were brave to come here to give me news of my Karl." She wiped her eyes again.

"My Karl. He's such a good man. When he let the Jew stay here, I warned him. 'Saving Jews is not your job,' I told him. 'What did a Jew ever do for you?' but he wouldn't

169

listen. 'Someone has to risk,' he said. 'God has asked me to.' Imagine. A Christ-killer God asked him to save? He was crazy. Ach, my poor Karl." Tears ran down her cheek. She wiped them away and put the handkerchief in her lap and smoothed it open. She kept her eyes on the cloth as she folded it neatly into squares.

"The Jew, he stayed in the back of the store for three or four weeks and helped my Karl. He never left that—"

Voices in the hall. Frau Wegert stopped whispering and held up her hand. *At least two people.* We stared at the door and waited. I tried to hold my breath so I could hear. The voices faded away. "They have gone downstairs," Frau Wegert said. I breathed easier.

"I was telling—ja, I remember. They came and took Karl and the Jew. The SS. They broke everything downstairs. Everything, ruined. Someone had told the authorities. Like that, my Karl was gone." She wiped her eyes again. "Thirty-eight years married. Who is a friend? Who can we count on? That Jew! He shouldn't have helped that Jew."

"But you are safe, Frau Wegert." Mutti smiled at her. "At least you are still here."

"I went for food that day. I was lined up all morning. They were gone when I came home. Neighbors told me." She started crying again. "Because he helped that Jew. A customer he helped."

Mutti stood up, motioning to me. "We have to go now, Frau Wegert. It will be difficult to get home before dark."

Frau Wegert rose and took our hands in hers.

"Danke. The greatest gift you've given me. At least I know Karl was alive two days ago. Never will I forget you. Danke." She hugged me. "Viel Glück," she said and we followed her to the door. We left quickly after making sure no one was in the hall. The heavy chain rattled behind us when she closed her door.

25

We tried to live in as normal a fashion as was possible in spite of sirens and running for cover and coming out again with all-clear signals and rationing and fires and death notices. I went to school as often as I could, checking at the S-Bahn on my way to see what sections of the system were out of service and which trains were running. The tracks were often repaired with phenomenal speed, and by noon sometimes the system was back to normal.

At school we began the day standing at attention, saluting, and singing *"Deutschland Über Alles."* We sat at our tables, listened to our lessons, and, if the alarm system wailed into operation, we covered our heads and ran for our lives. Because of the bombing raids, I rarely remained in school more than three or four hours on any given day.

Some of us had taken to moving our lips, pretending to sing but making no noise. As more of the boys joined this small and relatively safe act of defiance, Herr Stuben became aware of the diminished vigor of our national anthem. One morning he sneaked up from the back of the room and stood directly behind Hermann Wachter, who was ahead of me and to my right. Hermann's mouth moved, but I knew he made no sound.

"So, you have no voice, Herr Wachter?" the teacher shouted in his ear. Startled, Hermann clamped his mouth shut and stared straight ahead. Everyone stopped singing.

"Surely someone with no voice for our anthem will have no cries when he is whipped." Herr Stuben grabbed Hermann's collar and forced him to the front of the room. "Lie down," he ordered, pointing to a chair. "On your stomach." Hermann lay across the seat and grabbed the chair legs. He squeezed his eyes shut. Herr Stuben reached for the Rohrstock and held the bamboo rod over his head with both hands.

"Remember, Herr Wachter, you have no voice." Down came the rod on his rear—once, twice, three smacks. Hermann winced each time, but his lips had disappeared between his teeth and he said nothing.

"No voice is there?" He hit him again and then again. "Where is your voice, Herr Wachter? Is it *here?*" and he crashed the rod across Hermann's shoulders.

"Ja, ja, ja. I have a voice."

Herr Stuben stepped back and stood the Rohrstock on the floor against the wall. "Then stand up. At attention. And sing like a loyal Deutscher is supposed to."

Tears streamed down Hermann's face. He stretched out his arm in salute and sang. His arm shook and his voice shook and I looked straight ahead, neither right nor left, right past Hermann, right at the blackboard. I shook too.

We kept to our lessons the rest of the morning, afraid to be the next ones to feel the rod across our backs. When a few minutes before noon the alarm rang out, bombs or not, I welcomed the chance to leave. I bolted for the door. Down the steps I flew and then outside. When I reached the schoolyard, the flak was already close by. I listened for the bombers. They were getting closer. I ran as fast as I could, turned the corner of the building to run onto the street, and smashed into a soldier. I fell down. I grabbed my book bag as the soldier helped me up.

"I'm sorry," I mumbled and started to run on, but the soldier held tight. Trying to jerk my arm away, I looked up. It was Hans Graubert.

"Schnell, my bike is up here," he yelled. "I will get you home!" I took off behind him, running to keep up. "I heard at the barracks that a large bomber formation is heading for Berlin," he shouted over his shoulder. "It is the Americans."

"The Americans? In the daytime?"

"Ja. Americans."

We were out of breath when we reached his motorcycle.

"There's no sidecar. Where will I ride?"

"Right here, behind me." I jumped on and grabbed on to his belt. We roared away over the cobblestones so fast I was afraid I'd die from falling off. I wrapped my arms around Hans' waist as tight as I could.

"Don't be scared," he shouted. "I won't let you die."

We swung around the corner onto Potsdamer Strasse. "Our best chance is this way. They are going to bomb the tracks." He pointed to the S-Bahn and railroad tracks on our right, not more than a hundred meters away.

Seconds later came the horrifying whoosh and explosions. Sharp pains stabbed my ears. I wanted to cover them up, keep the pain out, but I didn't dare let go of Hans. He wrestled with the cycle as blasts of air lifted it off the ground and threw us forward. I managed to look back. Hell was following and gaining on us. Flying toward us was a huge wall of smoke and flames, tree branches and chunks of concrete. We seemed to crawl ahead in slow motion. *This is it. I'm dying.*

As suddenly as the explosions began, they stopped. *Nein. I am already dead.* I felt the sharp, stabbing pain in my head again. *If I'm dead, why does it still hurt? But I can't hear*

173

the cycle. Hans stopped and pried my hands from around his waist. He dragged me into the ditch alongside the road. With the pain pounding in my ears. I pushed my body as tight to the shaking earth as I could. When finally the all-clear sounded, I moved and began to cry.

"My head hurts." I touched my ears and felt something warm and wet on the left one. Hans pulled out a handkerchief and wiped the side of my face. The handkerchief was covered with blood.

Hans' mouth moved.

"What? I can't hear you."

He got up close to my ear. "Can you hear me now?"

"Ja, I think so. But my head hurts."

"You are cut," he shouted. "Something hit you. Probably shrapnel." He patted my back. "Your hearing will return soon. Do not worry."

By the time we finally climbed out of the ditch, I could hear again. Smoke and dust surrounded us. Some sunlight filtered through the smoke and made houses and trees, even the grass, look milky-orange. The sound of the bombers and the flak had faded toward the city. I stood there, safe and alive, but I couldn't move.

"You are all right now, ja?"

"Ja."

"Then come along. We are almost at your house."

I didn't move.

"Schnell, Dieter. We have to go. Don't worry, I will drive slow." Hans tugged at my arm, but I still wouldn't move. "Dieter, what is wrong? Why won't you go?"

"Could they have bombed our house?"

He hugged me. "Nein, Dieter. They are after bigger things. The family is safe." I gave in and he helped me back on his cycle and we started home.

174

"See, Dieter. Your house. It is still here."

I jumped off the cycle and ran toward the back of the house, forgetting the pain in my head.

Mutti was in the back yard with Frau Ludwig.

"He saved my life, Mutti. You should see how he drove the cycle." She grabbed me in a big hug.

Wolfgang and Peter ran up behind her. "Blood is on Dieter," Wolfgang shouted. "He's been shot!"

"Ach Du Lieber. Where?"

I pointed to my head.

"Such blood and I did not notice? Was ist los?"

"He's been shot, Mutti. Dieter's been shot!" Wolfgang danced around me. "Show me, Dieter. Show me the bullet." Peter started to cry.

Hans put his arm around Mutti. "He is all right."

"He needs a doctor?"

"Nein. It is nothing serious, Lis. It looks worse than it is. One of those Schweine missed the railroad tracks and hit the street behind us. It is nothing. We are just a little shell-shocked." He pulled out a cigarette, struck a match, and lit it.

Mutti grabbed his hands. "Well, Major Graubert, if it is nothing, why do these shake so?"

He smiled. "War does that to you. As Karl used to argue, war destroys the spirit." He kissed the top of Mutti's head. "I am on my way."

I gave him a quick hug. "You saved my life. Danke, Major."

"My own as well, you know." He bowed to Mutti. "Auf Wiedersehn, Lis Drescher. The war waits for me."

We never saw Hans Graubert again.

June 6, 1944

I ran down the steps to the basement. Mutti and Frau Hermann were hugging each other, jumping up and down, laughing and crying, all at the same time, but with almost no sound. Mutti grabbed me and whispered in my ear, "The Americans. They have landed in France!"

"They've lan—" but she covered my mouth with her hand.

"Sh-h-h, Dieter. Frau Witte, you know. This is a bad day for her. Hah!" She smiled. "I hope she has many." *I never saw her eyes twinkle before.*

We paid no attention to the roar of bombers overhead. "They do not want us today," Mutti said—and went outside. The women were in their yards, smiling and hugging each other. Ruth waved at Frau Kleiner, and when she came over, she started crying.

Ruth put her arms around her. "It will soon be over, Marie," Ruth told her. "Heinrich will be coming home."

"If only you are right . . . " Frau Kleiner wiped her eyes. "I miss him so." She stepped back and started crying again. "What if . . . What if he does not come?"

"Nein, Marie. Don't think that way." Ruth took her by the arm. "Come in and sit. We will have coffee and talk."

They started to the house but stopped short when they ran into Frau Witte.

She had been standing by the side of the house, behind the big evergreens and stepped out now in front of them. She looked mad, as usual. All the women in the yard stopped talking. Frau Witte put her hands on her hips and glared at them.

"What is this loud talk of France?"

The women stood still and did not answer. But instead of going home, as they usually did when she arrived, every one of them, including Mutti, put their hands on their hips, and stared hard back at her.

Frau Witte turned, and this time, she went home first.

26

"These are the last fresh vegetables from the garden. Eat them slow and enjoy, please."

Mutti spooned two small potatoes and four pieces of green beans on my plate. She counted out the same for Wolfgang. On Peter's plate she put one potato and two pieces of green beans. There were two tiny potatoes left and the ends of the beans. She divided them with Ruth.

"Chew very slow, and you will think more you are eating."

Wolfgang scrunched up his face. "But it's not more, Mutti."

"But you will fool yourself by chewing slow."

"I don't want to fool myself."

"Then you do not, Wolfgang. You chew fast and swallow it whole, and have it gone."

Wolfgang ate fast. "I'm finished, Mutti." He stood, but Mutti motioned him back in his chair.

"Ja, you are finished," she said. "Now you will sit here and watch the rest of us finish."

"I don't want to."

Mutti smiled. "I know, but watching us finish you will do."

He put his elbows on the table and rested his chin on his hand. He stared at us as we ate our potatoes and beans. I didn't swallow a bite until I chewed it into mush. Wolfgang squirmed.

"Can't I go now, Mutti?"

"Do you see any of us finished?"

"Nein, but I—"

"Then you will sit." Mutti put her fork down and wiped her mouth on her napkin. She took a sip of water and put the glass down slowly. She picked up her fork and cut off a tiny, tiny piece of potato and put it in her mouth. She smiled at us and chewed. And chewed some more. And some more.

Ruth and I copied Mutti. I tried hard not to laugh. All of us chewed in slow motion and Wolfgang twisted and turned in his chair.

"Now, Mutti?"

She didn't answer.

"Mutti! Now?"

She kept chewing.

"Answer me, Mutti, bitte."

She swallowed. "I am sorry, Wolfgang. You know we shouldn't talk when our mouths are full."

Ruth looked like she was ready to burst out laughing, and I could not help myself. I laughed out loud.

Wolfgang glared at me. "What is funny?"

Mutti smiled. "It is enough. We were having fun is all."

"It takes you too long to finish." He stood up. "Can I go now, Mutti? Bitte."

"Ja, you can. You should learn to eat slow. A long while it may be before you eat again like this."

"There is no more food?"

"There is more food, but sometime there may not be."

"What do we eat then? When there is no more food, what will we eat?"

Mutti reached over and patted Wolfgang's hand. "Whatever you and Dieter find for us."

Mutti and Ruth were skinny now, with dark shadows under their eyes. Their fingers were thin and bony and their eyes were always red. I looked just as bad. Wolfgang laughed at my skinny legs and said I looked like a scarecrow.

He was right. Even the birds would be scared of me.

We spent more and more time sitting in Ludwigs' bunker. Mutti knitted and Frau Ludwig read while overhead was the low drone of the bombers. They paid no attention to the sounds of flak and muffled explosions.

"Isn't it amazing how fast they rebuild the S-Bahn after each raid?" Mutti said suddenly. "And how many of the buses and streetcars still run? A surprise that must be to the Americans and the English."

Frau Ludwig put her book down. "Ja, I imagine that it is." She smoothed the wrinkles from her dress and laughed. "To be bombed so much and still have a rail system that works. I wonder if they would be able to keep their trains running. Although I am Russian, I have lived here many years. I have the greatest respect for the Deutsche people. They handle adversity with such courage."

Mutti smiled. "Danke, Frau Ludwig." She turned and looked at me. "See, Dieter. Deutsche manage to get through trouble. Remember that."

The flak stopped. The planes were gone. Mutti put her knitting down on the bench beside her. "Let's go and see what our house looks like."

We went upstairs and through the hallway. Just before I went down the steps from Ludwigs' front door, I glanced behind me. Two large wooden crates stood in a corner of the first room, the one with the fireplace. *Why are they packing now?*

In the backyard I saw a piece of shrapnel on the ground ahead of us. I ran over and grabbed it.

"Ow-w-w!" I dropped it and looked at the cut on my hand.

Mutti grabbed my hand. "Mein Gott, Dieter! Where is your brain?" She wiped the cut with her handkerchief. "You know they are sharp. And they are always hot when they first hit." She shook her head. "Sometimes I think you are too dumb to be my son." She smacked my rear. "Inside. That cut needs to be washed. You do not need an infection."

The radio woke up all of us in the bunker. *"Large enemy bomber formations have entered Deutsch air space in Schleswig Holstein on an east-southeast course. Possible targets are Luebeck, Schwerin, and Berlin. Take necessary action at once."*

"Schnell, Wolfgang, let's play sentry. We'll go outside and listen." He followed me up the stairs. As we went outside, I looked in the room with the fireplace. *Three crates. And a big canvas bag.*

It was early morning and the sun was just up. We stayed outside until we saw the planes. "Americans," I shouted, and we ran back to the bunker. The door clanked shut behind us.

"They're coming straight at us," I announced. "Americans—and a whole lot of them this time." I was talking to nobody in particular, but everyone looked at me. I sat down next to Helga.

The sound of the antiaircraft batteries dug in a few hundred meters from us across the Teltow Kanal came through the walls of the bunker and rattled the coffee cups. "They're close by," I shouted.

The heavy rumbling grew louder. "There must be hundreds of them this time," I said. We watched the ceiling. My heart beat hard, but I hoped Helga couldn't tell. "There are no close ones," I whispered to her. "They won't hit us. I know we're safe." Helga slid closer to me. I tried to breathe slower. *I'm the oldest male here. I have to be strong.* The noise of the bombers grew faint but flak was still heavy and no one moved until it stopped. I went to the door and opened it.

"When they come in from the west or southwest, they fly off to the northwest after they're finished," I told them. "I'm going up to the attic to see what's happened." A quick look outside the door showed nothing unusual, so I went up to the second floor and finally another stairway to the attic. Next to the chimney was a small window that the chimney sweepers used to get out on the roof. I opened it and looked toward the city.

As far as I could see, the eastern sky was darkened by such big clouds of ugly brown smoke that already the sun was gone. *It looks like late afternoon. If the wind picks up and blows from the east, we'll be covered with ashes.*

I heard voices in the back yard, and Wolfgang crying, but I couldn't see them. *What's happened?* I climbed through the little window back into the attic and ran down the stairs two steps at a time.

Helga and Mutti and Ruth and Frau Ludwig, Wolfgang, too, stood together in a circle. Helga turned around and looked at me. She said something to the others and put her hands over her mouth. The others looked toward me and stood aside when I got close. Wolfgang was still crying.

"Look, Dieter. Putzi's hurt." He pointed to Mutti.

Mutti held Putzi in her arms. "She is dead, Dieter."

Wolfgang started jumping. "She can't be dead! Her eyes are open! She's not dead, is she, Dieter?"

I took her from Mutti. She was warm, but she was dead. "Ja, Dicker. She is dead."

She'd been hit in the back. I held her up by my face and felt her soft fur against my cheek. I turned away so no one could see me. "I love you, Putzi," I whispered in her ear. "I love you very much. I didn't want you to leave me, too."

Helga touched my arm. "Shrapnel hit her, Dieter. See?" She showed me a jagged piece of metal with blood on it. Helga wiped tears from her cheeks. "I'm sorry, Dieter. Don't cry."

182

"I don't cry." I turned away from her. "I'm busy now. I can't talk. I have to bury her." I looked around. *By the Buddel Kiste.* I laid her carefully on the ground. Wolfgang looked at her and sobbed. "You can touch her, if you want," I said. He squatted beside her and stroked her head. "We will make a cross for her, ja, Wolfgang?"

"Ja." He hiccuped a sob. "We will make a cross for Putzi."

I dug a hole, long and deep enough to fit her. She looked so small in there. I started to shovel in the dirt.

"Nein! Don't throw dirt on her. She will be dirty." Wolfgang tried to dig it back out.

I took his arm. "We have to, Dicker. That's what burying is. We have to put dirt over her so no one can hurt her again."

"Like Vati? Is that what happened to him?"

"Ja. That's what happened to him."

Wolfgang knelt down and together we pushed the dirt and filled up the hole.

"She was a good cat." Wolfgang smoothed the mound of dirt. "Why did they kill her?"

"Because they want to kill all of us. They want to kill Deutsche! The Russians killed Vati and now the Americans killed Putzi." I thought of Herr Wise killing Putzi. "There is something I have to do. I'll be right back."

I walked to the house and went straight to our bedroom and pulled out the bottom drawer of my dresser. I groped in the empty space. *Here it is!* I opened the dingy yellow envelope and took out my American flag. I unfolded it. *I thought this was wonderful! How stupid I am.* I scrunched it up in my fist. On the way out I stopped in the kitchen and took a couple of matches from the stove.

"What are you doing, Dieter?"

I didn't answer. I bent down and put the flag on top of Putzi's grave, struck a match, and touched it to the edge of

183

the flag. It flared, slowly at first, then, as the flames spread over it, the sides curled and the red and white stripes and those little white stars blazed away.

I shook my fist at the sky. "Ihr Schweine!" I screamed. "You killed her."

I stomped the ashes into the ground above Putzi. "Ihr Schweine!" I cried again. "I hate you all. Herr Wise, too!"

I sat down on the ground and buried my face in my knees.

"Ihr Schweine," cried Wolfgang. I looked up. He shook his little fist at the sky. "I hate you, too," he said.

I grabbed him and pulled him into my lap. We cried and cried, like a dam that breaks and can't be fixed.

27

"Dieter, I have to ask you to go to the city tomorrow. You will do that, please?"

"The city, Mutti? It's dangerous to go there."

"I know. A lot I ask of you, but for a long time I have been thinking that we should get Peter out of here." She reached over and patted my hand. "Only four he is. He deserves to grow up somewhere besides a bunker," she said in a soft voice. "Children are still permitted to leave. He can go with you, but I cannot take him."

"Where would he go? How do we get there? My trip to Bautzen was awful."

"To Würzburg, to Grandmother and Grandfather. No bombs are there. There are no factories in Würzburg. Maybe they won't bomb that city."

"But that's a long trip, Mutti."

"Ja, I know. But you have experience already. You can do it. As soon as it's safe, go to Anhalter Bahnhof and try to get the permit and two tickets."

"But school, how can I—"

"They don't care anymore, Dieter. As soon as possible, you go. I'll try to get word to school that you're taking your little brother out of the city. They will understand. It will be all right, don't worry."

We decided to wait for a rainy and overcast sky. Heavy rain seemed to keep the bombers from coming. At least, sometimes. A few days later as we listened to the radio early in the morning, there was no word of bomber formations heading for Berlin. I took off for the S-Bahn station.

Again, to reach Anhalter Bahnhof by S-Bahn and bus took all morning. I got there and joined a block-long line of people waiting in the cold drizzle. The line moved fast, and in another two hours I had permit and tickets and just enough money to get me home on whatever public transportation I could find.

On my way back to the nearest S-Bahn station, I walked through streets with gaping holes where six- and eight-story apartment houses once stood. Surprisingly, on each block a few buildings still stood, their doors and windows blown out by concussions and replaced by wooden boards and cardboard. These buildings were next to completely gutted structures, as if invisible steel domes had protected them. Hundreds of paper scrap notices covered walls and the few remaining tree trunks, tacked there by survivors looking for family members and friends, or announcing to searchers that *"The Schmitt family is safe in Beltzen,"* or *"The children of August and Maria Schultz have found refuge at No. 1121 Else Strasse."*

I pulled my head down deep into my coat collar. My eyes were watering and my hands freezing. I held tightly to the permit and tickets in my pocket. My name was on the permit but not the tickets. They could be a welcome escape for anyone else.

I was still a ways from the S-Bahn station when the sirens started. Everyone deserted the street immediately. I followed some people to one of the still-standing buildings nearby where I joined a small group of women huddled at the entrance to the basement, their scared eyes searching the gray sky. The sound of the approaching bombers became rapidly louder as an old man, apparently the Block Warden, came up the stairs.

"Schnell!" he commanded. "Down here, now!" Just then the sound of exploding bombs reached us, and we rushed down the stairs.

In the light of the candles, I saw that the ceiling had been reinforced with heavy lumber the size of railroad ties, held up from the floor by two steel beams. I looked around. There was only one door at the top of the stairs leading directly to the street, the one I'd just come through. I stood near the steel beam, where I could see the door. *Another coffin.* We huddled and waited for the blasts to reach us.

The floor began to vibrate as the explosions came closer. *If this place is hit . . . Mutti will never find me if I'm buried under tons of bricks . . . Nobody will find any of us again.* The bombers were just above. Explosions crashed on top of us, and I held my hands over my ears to stop the stinging pains in my ears from the waves of concussions. I looked up at the ceiling just as a jagged crack rushed from one support beam to the other, and pieces of mortar fell from the opening crack. *I can't die in here.*

Blasts of air blew out the candles. I could still see a little with the light from the door at the top of the stairs. I felt sand in my mouth. A woman screamed and stumbled toward the stairs, pulling away from the Block Warden when he tried to stop her.

"Nein!" he cried. "It is not safe!"

She didn't stop and was almost to the top when a huge explosion slammed her backward. Her body crashed to the bottom and folded in half against the steel beam beside me. Something rolled and stopped at my foot. *Her head!* I was so numb I couldn't move. A woman covered her with a newspaper and pushed me away. "Go!" she said. "At least we give her privacy."

187

Everyone was screaming. I looked up at the door. Some light was visible, but chunks of concrete and rubble blocked the opening. I pushed through the screaming people to the bottom of the stairs.

Suddenly, a loud voice cut through the noise.

"Everybody quiet! We're not buried. We're not dead. There is enough space at the door to crawl out one at a time when this is over. Put something over your mouth and nose until we can get out," the voice commanded. It was *my* voice.

The explosions were farther away now, and vibrations weren't as strong as before. The crack in the ceiling widened, and pieces of concrete and bricks continued falling through it. Then I heard voices from outside. I tripped and fell up the steps until I could stick my arm through an opening in the rubble.

"We are here," I yelled and waved my hand. "Help us get out."

People outside moved the concrete and wood, and I crawled out. The street was filled with smoke and dust. People stumbled about, some going in circles, as if they were blind. My eyes watered and itched. I coughed and coughed.

"Here they are, Mutti." I handed her the permit and tickets.

"Such a raid on the city. Many buildings collapsed the radio said." She hugged me. "But you are safe. That is all that matters."

Nein! It is not safe! "Ja, Mutti. That is all that matters." I saw the woman shoot backwards and fall next to me, the blue woolen gloves she had on, and her head rolling toward my foot. "Ja, Mutti. That is all that matters."

28

Mutti packed a small suitcase for Peter. The less baggage we carried, she said, the easier it would be to find space on a train. According to her latest information, Würzburg was still untouched by any major bombing raids. It still seemed a safer place than Berlin. She went with us to Anhalter Bahnhof. She checked the schedules and came back to us.

"A train that goes toward Dessau and the Harz Mountains leaves in a few minutes. At least that is in the general direction you need to go."

"Ja. That will take us there. Schnell, Mutti. We will have to run for it. Auf Wiedersehn."

Mutti hugged Peter, and he started to cry when I pulled him to go. "Don't cry. We have to go. We'll have fun."

He held on to my coat as I pushed our way into a car.

"We can't sit, Peter. It's too crowded. You stay right here, in front of me." The train started moving, and I saw Mutti running alongside, waving. I waved back, but I knew she couldn't see me. Peter was surrounded by legs and bodies and held my hand in a tight grip.

"I want Mutti. I want to go home. I want my Mutti."

"Ja, Peter. But we have to do this. Be good."

We pulled onto sidings several times to let other trains pass us toward Berlin. Some of them were loaded with military equipment, tanks, artillery. Some of the cars were full of troops.

Four hours later we reached the Elbe River near Dessau.

"Get out! Everyone out! Take cover away from the tracks." We climbed down and ran away from the tracks as a large enemy bomber formation flew eastward.

"Are they going to bomb us, Dieter?"

"Nein. I don't think so. They're already past us and nothing came down. They'll bomb somebody else. Don't worry."

"How much longer to Oma's? My legs hurt."

"I don't know. Maybe you can get a seat when we get back on, or you can sit on the floor."

But we didn't board the train again. The bridge ahead was destroyed and we had to walk across a makeshift bridge of an endless row of pontoon boats. In the distance we could hear the sound of exploding bombs.

I held on to Peter's hand and helped him keep his balance on the bridge. "Schnell!" someone cried, just as we reached the middle of the river. "Run. Quick."

I picked Peter up. When we got to the other side, we faced a steep, sandy embankment. "We have to climb, Peter. Here. Run ahead of me. I'll boost you up."

"Are we going to die?"

"Not if we climb. Schnell."

He pulled himself up, and I pushed him. "I can't, Dieter. I can't go up anymore."

"Get on my back, then." I crouched, and he climbed behind me. *At least he's not heavy.* Alongside us old men and women tried to climb. They left their baggage and struggled to make it to the top. *I wish I could dump this suitcase, but Mutti would be mad.*

After about ten minutes, I reached level ground again. I was out of breath. "We made it, Peter."

"Ja. We made it."

"Next time don't hold my neck so tight."

"I didn't want to fall."

"Ja. I know. You were good, Peter."

A man in railroad uniform stood atop a wooden crate. "Keep going along the tracks for a couple of kilometers. Another train should be there sometime today."

"My legs hurt, Dieter. I can't walk. You have to carry me."

"I can't carry you anymore, Peter. It's too hard to carry you and your suitcase. We'll have to sit here and wait." I put him down and sat down beside him. The ground was cold and wet with patches of snow, but I didn't care. I was happy to sit awhile.

"I want to take a nap."

"Nein. You can't. We have to make that train. If we stay here we will freeze."

"I don't care. I want to sleep." He started to cry. "I want Mutti. I want my mother."

"Don't be stupid! Mutti's not here. We have to go." I pulled him to his feet.

The line of passengers was shorter. *Maybe now we'll get a seat.* We walked along the track. There was no one ahead or behind us for fifty meters or more. Peter stumbled alongside. *It's like we're the only humans in the world.*

Already I'm homesick, and I'm not that far from home. I looked down at Peter. *He's so little. He doesn't even know what's going on. I will get you there, Bruder. I promised Mutti.*

An hour later we reached a large crowd of people and another uniformed railroad man. He pointed us toward the end of a long line of people.

"Stand there and wait."

"Can you tell us—"

"You heard me. Do as I say!"

191

I shrugged and moved to the end of the line and put the suitcase down. Peter flopped onto it.

"Get up, Peter. It will crack. Then Mutti will be really mad."

"Nein. I want to take a nap. I'm tired."

"Get up!" I pushed him off the suitcase. "Stay and guard—"

"You're mean. I don't like you anymore, Dieter. I want Mutti." He slapped my leg. "I don't want to go to Oma's with you."

"Look, Peter. You will break this if you sit on it. Then we'll have to leave it here, and you won't have any clothes. Is that what you want?"

He turned his back to me. "I want my mother."

"Listen. You stay here and guard our spot. I remember seeing a slab of wood back there. I'll bring it back and you can lie down."

"Ja." He crossed his arms. "I will guard our spot." He stood in front of his suitcase.

"Like a soldier, Peter. You don't let anyone get in front of you."

"Nein. No one here."

When I returned with the wood, it was just long enough for him to lie on. He closed his eyes and was asleep in minutes. A woman standing next to me gave me a heavy shawl.

"Put that around the poor Junge. He is going to freeze in this cold."

"Danke, but what will you do?"

"When the train comes, you can give it back to me."

I awoke, startled by the noise of the steam engine braking to a stop. *I slept standing up.* Some people had flashlights, and their beams jabbed into the fog around us. Peter's legs had slipped off the board and were wet and muddy. I shook him and he jumped up, wide awake.

192

The train was an empty, short one with a few passenger cars and two freight cars at the end. Everyone rushed to get aboard and find a space. Peter and I were near the front, and the crowd lifted the two of us into one car. I had to hold on to Peter and the suitcase and still keep my balance.

"Sit on the floor, Peter. There won't be seats. I'll stand close so nobody steps on you."

"How much longer until Oma's?"

"I don't know. Don't ask. It took more than six hours just to get here and we're not even halfway."

"It's hot down here. I want you to hold me."

"I can't, Peter. Shut up. Please shut up."

He gave me a dirty look and turned his face away.

I bent down and patted his shoulder. "Sorry, Peter. I'm as unhappy as you are. But I can't hold you." *I don't mean to yell. I hate everything right now. And it stinks so bad in here.*

We gained speed. I shivered from the ice-cold drafts from the broken windows. *I wish I was sitting on the floor.*

For three or four hours the train rolled along, again going right through several stations in smaller towns without stopping. Peter stayed on the floor, his head resting on his knees, asleep. I drifted in and out of short naps, standing up, jerking when my knees buckled.

Daylight finally appeared, together with the absolute silence of the passengers around me. A few words, short sentences, but then silence again. My legs were numb, but my feet throbbed.

With an ear-splitting screech of the wheels, the train suddenly stopped. I fell forward, along with everyone else. Luggage fell on us out of the overhead baggage nets. Outside people ran along.

"Get out of there. Find cover!"

Overhead I heard the high scream of fighter planes. I

yanked Peter out of the train and up an embankment. I ducked behind a large boulder next to a tree.

"On your stomach, Peter." I fell over him.

"I can't breathe, Dieter." He tried to push me away.

"Move, Dieter."

I rolled off him a little bit, covering him with my arm and chest. "I have to do this. I have to save you. Turn your head to the side. You'll get air." In moments the front of our clothes soaked up the wet, muddy ground.

"Cover your head, Peter," I yelled. "With your arms. Cover your head." Two fighter planes screamed toward the train from the front and fired. The screech of their engines hurt my ears. "Keep your head down."

Both planes pulled sharply up and into a wide circle. *They're coming around again. Did they see us? Will they fire on us this time?* "I'm sorry, Peter, but I've got to cover you. Breathe from the side."

The machine guns opened up again. Bullets hit metal and wood and ricocheted through the trees above us. Again, the two planes climbed out of sight, but this time I saw them fly to the west and disappear.

I pulled Peter up with me.

"I'm dirty," he said. "I don't want to be muddy. Mutti says I have to be clean for Oma."

"Ja, Peter. I'm muddy, too. We can't help it. Oma will give you a bath when we get there."

"I want to go home and take a bath."

"Genug, Peter. We have to do this." We started back toward the train. All around us people stumbled down the embankment along both sides of the cars. When we reached the ditch next to the tracks, Peter stopped.

"Are they sleeping there?" He pointed to five dead women and a little girl. Their blood melted the snow beside them.

"Nein. They are dead."

194

We walked a little way, and he stopped again. He pulled on my hand. "The woman is hurt. Help her." Stretched out ahead of us was the body of the woman who lent me her shawl. Blood flowed from the corners of her mouth and made a pool around her neck.

I picked Peter up, and we stepped over the body.

"We have to get back on the train, Peter, or it will leave without us. Hurry!"

"What about that woman?"

"We have to go, Peter." I lifted him to a woman in the train, then climbed up myself. Peter looked back at the woman in the ditch. I pushed him away from the door.

"Why can't she come with us?"

"She's hurt, Peter. She can't walk anymore. Somebody will find her and take good care of her and all the other ones." I pointed out the window. "Look at those pretty fields out there now. The haystacks have little white snowcaps on their tops. Can you see them?" He nodded. "Then let's see how many you can count."

"How much longer before we get to Oma's?"

"A little more patience you need, Peter. Maybe . . . half an hour."

"I like train rides. I want to do this again."

29

Stiff and aching from many hours of standing in that crowded train, Peter and I walked slowly toward Opa's apartment house. We saw Oma waiting for us when we reached the door to the apartment house. "Ach Du Lieber! You are so thin." She lifted Peter and kissed him. "Such a little hug for your grandmother?"

"Hello, Oma," he whimpered. "I'm too tired to hug. I want to sleep."

She put him down and gave me a quick hug. "Skin and bones, you are, Dieter. I feel your ribs!" Together we half-carried Peter up the six flights of stairs. Opa was waiting for us at the open door. "Feel his ribs, Heinrich. A skeleton. They both are."

He grabbed me in a big hug, then bent down and picked up Peter.

"We have time to fatten Peter, but Dieter . . ." He stepped back and looked at me. "He will take longer."

"We're so tired, Opa. All we want to do is lie down for a little while."

He patted my shoulder. "Ja. Of course, you poor children. Later, you will tell us of your trip. We are pleased you finally made it. While you two are sleeping, I will send your mother a card."

Emma and Heinrich Drescher
Oma and Opa
1941

"Don't you want something to eat, Dieter?" Oma stood beside me, smiling. "You must be starved. I have something for you in the kitchen."

"Already it's time for supper? How long did I sleep?"

Oma laughed. "Through last night's supper and today's breakfast and dinner. All yesterday and through the night you slept, and here it is now, three in the afternoon." She laughed again. "It is tomorrow, Dieter. You were exhausted. Peter, he still sleeps. Now get up and get something to eat."

I followed the smell of food to the kitchen and sat down with Oma and Opa. "This is a feast. Bread and sausage—and ham." I took a drink of milk first.

"Oma, this tastes funny. Is this real milk?"

"Listen to him, Opa. He thinks the milk is not real." She smiled at me. "Ja, Dieter, it is real. Fresh it is. From the farmer's cow this morning, not like you get in the city."

197

Peter came to the table, rubbing his eyes like he was still half asleep.

"Look at all the food, Peter. Wake up or I'll eat yours." I reached for the bread, but Oma pulled my hand back.

"Not so fast. Your mother warned that you were thin, but you look like skeletons. You cannot stuff yourself like sausages at first. You must eat very, very slow, and chew good."

"But I'm really hungry."

"I know you are, but you haven't had this heavy, rich food for a long time. Not easy for your stomachs to digest. Slowly you drink the milk, and eat only one sandwich for now. If your stomach doesn't feel funny, in a few hours you can have more.

"Don't you have any air raids here, Oma? No bombing?"

"None so far, Dieter. We have been lucky."

"You don't have to run for the basement all the time?"

"The plane flies over every few days. It drops notes on us but no bombs. To the shelter we still have to go when the sirens sound. This plane, it comes always at the same time, right after midnight. It drives us crazy."

"Notes?"

"Ja. Messages from the Allies. Propaganda garbage. Lies from the American gangsters. To convince us how bad it is."

"Schnell, children, time for the shelter." Oma shook me awake. I looked at the clock. It was just after midnight. We dressed and followed Oma and Opa down the stairs. The shelter was two houses away.

An air raid warden stood next to the entrance and motioned us to hurry into a tunnel straight down into the earth. When we reached the bottom, I saw we were in a huge wine cellar. Large barrels lined the walls, and water dripped from the ceiling. The only way out was the way we came in— one door.

"Oma, this place scares me. I'm going up to the door and stand there." I ran for the steps before she could grab my sleeve and hold me back.

I stopped next to the door opposite the warden. I took a deep breath of the clean night air and looked up at the stars. "Why are you up here?" he growled. "It is verboten to be outside during an air raid. I order you to—"

"It is a deathtrap down there," I shouted. "I'm from Berlin, and I have experience—"

His slap threw me toward the doorstep.

"I do not care where you are from! The orders here I give, verstanden? Get out of here."

I rubbed my cheek and went back downstairs.

"Why you cry, Dieter?" Oma put her arm around me.

"I'm not coming back here again. That man up there is crazy."

"Sh-h-h, Dieter. He does his job." She pulled me toward her. "You can afford to obey, ja? Even if you are a Berliner."

"All clear," the warden yelled. People moved toward the exit.

"I didn't hear the sirens, Oma. Are you sure it's all clear?"

"Down here we cannot hear. It is too deep. If he says it is all clear, it is all clear." She gathered us together, and we went upstairs and turned toward the apartment.

When we reached home, Oma and Peter went up first, then Opa, and I climbed behind him. "Opa, that wine cellar is under a house just as big as this one. If a bomb hits that house, anyone in the cellar will be killed. There's no other exit. That's a bad bomb shelter, Opa."

"Ja. You are right, Dieter, but that is the only shelter in this whole neighborhood. No other place we have to go."

"I won't go there again. It scares me. I'd like to be outside, where I can see what's going on."

199

He shrugged. "Your mother. She will not be happy if I let you stay out of the shelter. You think I want her mad at me, ja?"

"Mutti lets me stay out at home. She won't mind if you let me do it here?"

"Ja? You are sure?"

I nodded.

He shrugged again. "Ja, well, on the hill behind this house you could go. It is only a few minutes' walk. Tomorrow morning you look from the kitchen window. You will see it." He unlocked the front door. "We do not have bombing here so far." Opa's hand slowly stroked his mustache. "Let me tell you something that might explain all this." We sat down in the living room.

"Lately we have heard some stories that people talk about in this city. They say that Winston Churchill studied here at the University before the war. He likes our city so much he asked our Mayor to declare Würzburg an "Open City.""

"An Open City?"

"Ja, when you promise not to fight in it or defend it. Then the enemy won't bomb it. It is an open city."

"I wish he'd gone to school in Berlin." Opa laughed, but I was serious.

As soon as I was awake the next morning, I went to the kitchen window. *Ja, that's where I'm going when the sirens sound again.* During the next few days Oma or Opa took us down to the park to feed the ducks and the pigeons. It took just a short time to get used to the different sounds. There were no sirens or bombers flying above or rumbling sounds of exploding bombs. The sun wasn't covered by huge clouds of smoke from fires in the city. "This is so peaceful, Opa, that it makes me nervous."

He laughed. "That is why you brought Peter to us, ja?

Maybe you should stay here with him. There is room enough for you, too. Would you like that?"

"Ja, please, Dieter!" Peter begged. "We can feed the ducks every day."

"Nein, Peter. I have to go back to Berlin and Mutti and Wolfgang. Vati asked me to look after all of you when he left. That's my job. You will be fine right here with Oma and Opa."

Peter looked away and didn't answer.

I put my arm around his shoulder. "Don't be sad, little brother. I'll be here a few days before I go back. Sometime the war will be over and we'll be together again, all of us. You'll see. You'll have more fun feeding ducks than spending all day on a mattress in the basement."

"Karl would be very proud of you, Dieter. You are a good son and brother." Oma wiped her eyes with her apron. "Two boys I lose. First, Karl at Stalingrad, then Willie . . . " She shook her head. "This a mother should not have to do."

I had three or four days left before going back to Berlin. Peter and I spent time in the park feeding the ducks. "I might like living here, Peter. Everything is so clean."

"Let's live here. Mutti and Wolfgang and Ruth can live here, too. We will live at Oma and Opa's."

"We would have to find our own apartment. But it would be nice. Maybe after the war, when you grow up, we can move here."

The shrill sound of sirens changed everything in seconds. I grabbed Peter's hand and ran toward Opa's as fast as his feet could move. *An air raid during broad daylight in Würzburg?* People ran past us. Everyone looked scared. Opa and Oma were waiting for us outside.

I handed Peter to them. "I'm going up to the hill, Opa."

"Be careful! Remember. I do not want to have to write your mother."

"Ja, I will. And you stay near the door in that cellar if you can."

I was almost out of the yard when I heard Oma call. "Stay away from the airport," she said.

The airport? What airport? I kept running.

When I reached the top of the hill, I was surprised at how high it really was. Behind me the city had disappeared into the valley. All I could see was the Festung, the ancient fortress, far away on the other side of the river. I turned and continued walking, but much slower now. I was out of breath. *I don't see an airport.*

Along the road to my left was a high fence, topped by barbed wire, and to my right the hill sloped downward. A long, winding row of bushes bordered a wheat field below. I turned toward the fence again, and I recognized what Oma meant. Far beyond the fence were hangars. *Scheisse! Maybe this isn't such a good spot. It's probably a target.*

I walked faster, away from the fence, across the wheat field. *I must be a perfect target in these black clothes!*

The screaming noise of airplane engines stopped me—and my heart. I was frozen to the spot. Out of the valley below, at treetop level, an American fighter plane roared straight at me. In a second it passed directly over me and turned toward the airport, machine guns flashing. I ran for my life, downhill toward the row of bushes. Just when I checked to see where it was, the plane made a sharp circle around its target and flew directly toward me. *Mein Gott! This is it! Please God, let it be quick.* My feet felt like lead weights. *Can I make the bushes?* He was right behind me. I waited for the bullets. He passed low over me and banked to the left. He was so low I saw his head in the cockpit just before I dove headfirst through the bushes. I landed in the shallow icy water of a small creek.

But the bushes were no protection. *He'll see me. And I've got no place to run.* The plane made a much wider circle now, barely clearing trees, and came back in my direction. *Why's he doing this? Does he think I'm going to jump up and run again, and then he'll shoot? I don't care. I'm ready.* Suddenly, the pounding blood in my ears slowed and I was almost calm as the plane came toward me. *I will sit here like a duck and die. Goodbye, Mutti. I go to join Vati and Uncle Willie.* But there were no orange flashes from his wings. He did not fire! He came back over and banked again, passing over so low I saw his face. This time he looked right at me and smiled. He saluted, pulled up into a steep climb, and disappeared as fast as he'd come.

I was too afraid to move. I lay in the cold water for long minutes. My teeth chattered, but I couldn't move. *Why didn't he kill me?*

Finally, I got the courage to get up. I climbed out of the creek and started running uphill, toward the road. I ran all the way to Oma and Opa's.

"Oma! An American pilot saw me, and he didn't shoot! Can you believe that? I hid in a creek, but he saw me. He smiled. And he saluted me! He must have been an angel!"

"Hm-mph," Oma answered. "A Deutscher he must have been." She pulled me into the bathroom and ran warm water into the tub. "You get out of these wet clothes at once! Then you can tell Opa about Americans who smile at you when they bomb."

Two days later I was back up on that hill but much farther from the airport fence. My grandmother tried to stop me when the sirens wailed for the second time during broad daylight, but Opa understood.

"Let him go, Emma. He knows what he is doing. He won't take chances." I looked at him, grateful for his faith, and ran off.

This time I found the cover of an orchard. The trees had

203

lost their leaves, but I felt safe there. I leaned against a tree, looking at the sky, enjoying the peace and quiet while I waited for the planes.

At first it was just a humming sound, like thousands of bumblebees far away. I recognized the sound. A large bomber formation was coming from somewhere. In minutes the hum became the deep rumbling of heavy bomber engines. I'd heard it so many times in Berlin. My heart beat faster. *What if their target is the airport again? Am I far enough away?* I started to walk and search the sky, slow at first, then faster.

I spotted them! Three or four planes in tight triangles, a great number of triangles, big planes with four engines. *They're B-17's.* The lead plane was directly over me now. *Target markers!* The thin, white smoke flares came down in crazy zig-zag patterns. *Bombs!* Long lines of dots fell out of the first planes. I panicked, started running, then stopped.

Don't be an idiot. Those bombs won't hit near me. Remember the trajectory? They'll come down kilometers from here!

I looked toward the valley. *What if they hit the whole city? What about Peter and Oma and Opa?* The swooshing sound of falling bombs filled the air. I ran back up the hill to reach the road to the city. The ground vibrated. I reached the top of the hill and looked down.

Monstrous brown and black towers of smoke rose high above the city. Whole sections of buildings flew up with the smoke, then broke into small pieces and tumbled crazily back toward earth. On the ground huge sheets of orange-red flames lit the black smoke as each bomb exploded. I was scared and fascinated all at once. I was always hiding from the bombs. I'd never seen the fires when they happened.

I looked up. The sky was empty. *They're gone!* I was scared as I started running. *I've got to get back to the house. Please God, let them be alive. Peter should have stayed in Berlin!*

I was soaked in sweat when I got near the house. I turned the last corner and there it was, standing, untouched. *None of the houses are hit! What happened? Where did the bombs hit?* People were just beginning to come out of the house with the wine cellar.

Oma reached me first and gave me a long tight hug. "Gott Sei Dank. You are all right. Together we stay next time." She hugged me tighter. "I don't like being apart. It is too scary."

"But Oma, I'm scared in that cellar. I'd like to take Peter with me to that hill. Up there you can see everything, and you can go and hide."

"The cellar frightens all of us. Look at me." She pointed to her hair. "Dust is all over me. Dust from the ceiling. Some pieces of rock fell, too. Oh! how that cellar shook when those explosions came! We were scared. Believe me."

"Where did the bombs hit? Do you know? Did you hear?"

"The train station, we just heard. Maybe we will go and take a look after awhile, when we do not get in the way."

Later, Opa took Peter and me for a walk to the train station. The closer we got to it, the more houses were damaged. All their windows were blown out and most of the tiles ripped from the roofs. Thick smoke drifted above us, turning the sunlight into that eerie orange-brown.

"This looks just like Berlin, Opa." He stared straight ahead. He didn't answer.

Two or three blocks away from the station the rubble in the street stopped us. We watched silently as ambulances and nurses moved through the debris. An old man walked up to Opa and shook his hand.

"Heinrich, good to see you are all right." He shook his head. "The train station . . . A perfect hit. A few houses across the Bahnhof-Platz—direct hits. Good eyes those pilots have, ja?"

Opa looked very sad. "Ja," he said, "Or good luck it is they have." He sighed and looked very old to me—and very tired.

"Let's go home, Opa. The smoke, it's making me cough." We turned around and walked a few yards when I stopped abruptly.

"Opa, is this the only train station here?"

"Ja, Dieter, it is." His eyes widened. "And I know what you are think—"

"How am I going to get out of here? I have to go back to Mutti and Wolfgang!" I felt totally helpless and afraid, as if I was going to cry, but I swallowed hard.

Opa patted my shoulder. "Do not worry. They will repair the tracks."

I remembered how fast the S-Bahn tracks in Berlin were repaired after each bomb attack. *Maybe they'll know how to fix them here as fast.* We kept walking. I wanted to get back to Mutti, to Wolfgang, to our house. Soon!

Two days to go! I felt uneasy and anxious to leave. I'd heard on the radio that Berlin suffered major air attacks again and that the death toll was high. *Are Mutti and Wolfgang and Ruth all right?* I wanted to be with them. At the same time I felt guilty leaving Peter. But since the city itself hadn't been bombed, maybe he was safer staying in Würzburg. *That's why you brought him here.*

Oma went to check the train schedule. She looked serious when she returned.

"They are repairing two tracks. By tomorrow some trains will leave. Ja, they are leaving, but nobody can say how far any of them will get. We do not want you to go on any train that goes to nowhere."

"Oma, as long as there's any train going, I'll find my way. This isn't the first time I'm doing this, you know? I'll get to Berlin somehow, don't worry, please?"

My grandparents looked at each other for a minute, then Opa put his arm around Oma. "Emma, Dieter is not a child anymore. He does not even talk like a thirteen-year-old."

"You'll do just fine, Peter. Those ducks down there will really get to like you when you feed them every day. And as soon as I get back to Berlin, I'll write you a card, all right?"

He nodded, smiling just a bit through the tears that welled up in his eyes. I had given him a long hug, then turned quickly because I didn't want him to see me cry. Opa walked me to the train station. We waited for over an hour, sitting on a makeshift bench in the middle of piles of bricks and rubble. I convinced him that I'd be fine, that he could go back home. Then I sat there by myself, with my suitcase, waiting.

It turned dark, and I still waited. Because of the black-out, the few lights around the station were covered with black tape, leaving only a thin slit open. Time crawled.

"Achtung, Achtung! All personnel leave the station immediately. Follow the signs to public shelters. Enemy bombers approaching!" People all around yelled and screamed at each other.

My good luck on the hill was still a fresh memory, and I ran quickly, bumping into people on my way. When I thought I was at least two blocks away from the station, I slowed down and looked for some signs. Someone grabbed my sleeve and pulled me inside a doorway.

"Get downstairs with the others!" It was a man in an Army uniform, a gun in his hand. I didn't argue.

This was a regular basement, but I didn't have time to worry about it—the droning of bombers was already loud. Explosions followed, the floor shook, dust rained from the ceiling. Children cried. Then the sudden rumble of a bomb, for a fraction of a second, sounded like a huge truck had tumbled out of the sky. My head was under my arms as if they would protect me from a crashing ceiling. A dull thud, *but no explosion.* We raised our heads, slowly, in disbelief. A dud it was. Another angel with me?

At the all-clear I followed the others up the stairs. Out on the sidewalk, I saw flames licking out the top windows of the next house. I stumbled across the street, then through the park in front of the station house. Walking fast, my foot struck a mound of dirt and I went down, face first, suitcase flying. Momentarily stunned, I lay there a minute to catch my breath, then braced my hands to push myself up. I was lying against something metallic. I was halfway to my feet when I screamed and scrambled out of the hole. I'd been leaning against the unexploded bomb! A man in uniform ran toward me.

"A bomb! Right there! Don't fall on it!" I pointed and ran back toward the station.

I got on the first train. I didn't know where it was going, but two days and several train changes later I reached the end of the line at Magdeburg on the Elbe River, a hundred kilometers west of Berlin. From that point the tracks leading to Berlin were destroyed. I walked the rest of the way, occasionally getting a ride on a crowded bus by hanging on to the side of it.

30

Mutti and Wolfgang were fine. So was the house and most of the houses around us. Potsdam had been bombed several times, and our S-Bahn station burned to the ground. But the trains were running, although on nothing which could resemble any kind of schedule. No house in our neighborhood suffered any direct hit, but a few huge craters showed the near-misses. The closest one to us, perhaps a hundred meters away, was filled with smelly water, a result of a bomb ripping the water and sewer pipes. When the wind blew from that direction, the stench made us gag.

"Aren't they going to repair that, Mutti? We don't have any water, and the toilet doesn't work. How long has it been that way?"

"Two nights. They said that it will be repaired soon."

"What are you doing without a toilet?"

"We dug a hole in the backyard, behind where the rabbit cages were. We put a small barrel there."

"The toilet is a barrel? Where the playhouse is? Mutti!"

"Wolfgang plays there often? Nein. We spend all our time in the basement. A toilet is more important than a playhouse. We're lucky to have found a barrel. Welcome back to Berlin!"

Since I was in Würzburg, Mutti and Wolfgang and Ruth spent most nights in Ludwigs' bunker. "The bombs are bigger, more powerful, than they used to be," Mutti said. "Our basement is no protection if one of them hits the house."

"The bunker, with all of you, isn't it crowded?"

"We fit, Dieter. Frau Ludwig is nice to invite us. And we don't have to sit with Frau Witte."

"Is Helga still with them, or did they send her away, too?"

"No, she's there. She asked how you were."

My heart skipped. "Can I go see her?"

Mutti smiled. "Ja, go see your girlfriend."

I went at once. Frau Ludwig opened the door wide. "Hello, Dieter. I see you made it back. I suppose you want to see Helga?"

"Ja, bitte."

Helga came running into the kitchen. "I'm glad you're safe," she said. "I was worried." She took my hand. "Come outside. Tell me about the trip."

We walked together into her yard, still holding hands. She looked prettier than she had when I left.

"Wasn't it scary? The bombs here we're used to, but you were away, in a new place." She smiled a big smile. "I missed you."

"I missed you, too." We sat down on the back steps. "You know, an American plane tried to shoot me. I had to run, like this." I ran around the yard, looking up at an imaginary plane. "He came after me! Bullets whizzed right by my head so I jumped in a creek." I slumped back on the steps. "He came real close, so close I saw his face. But he couldn't hit me. I was too fast. So here I am."

"You're a hero!" Helga clapped. "My cousin Rheinhold was close to a bomb when it went off, but I don't know anyone who's been chased by a plane." She gave me a quick kiss on my cheek. "I'm telling everyone you're my boyfriend."

My face turned hot, and I knew it was red all over. I tried to stand up, but Helga yanked me back down beside her. She unbuttoned her jacket and held it open. "Do you like my new blouse?"

"Like your blouse?" I looked at the silky blouse she wore. "Ja, of course I like your blouse. It looks real . . . nice." The heat in my face was unbearable. I wanted to turn away, but I couldn't stop imagining what it would feel like to touch her.

"I just wondered if you liked it. I like it myself." She pulled her shoulders back, then pulled the bottom of the blouse downward so it was tight over her breasts. I was afraid I'd faint.

"Now tell me more about your trip."

I tried, but my voice was shaky. All the while I talked, telling her about the train ride, and seeing Würzburg being bombed and falling on the unexploded bomb, I kept my eyes on her breasts, the outline of her underwear, and I remembered that day we had looked at each other. I leaned closer and closer to her, so close I could smell her. My face was inches away from her chest when the sirens blasted into the moment. Startled, I lost my balance and reached out to catch myself against her. *I touched them!*

"Dieter! Get to your bunker!" Mutti sounded like she was right behind me, but she was hollering from the backyard and the sirens were screaming, and I'd just touched Helga's breasts! Helga smiled at me. She stood up and quickly tucked her blouse in and buttoned her jacket. "Next time don't pinch, Dieter."

My hands tingled as I ran toward home. The alert lasted half an hour, but it seemed like minutes to me. When the all-clear sounded, my hands, palms up, the hands that had just touched Helga's breasts, were still resting on my knees.

Mutti and Wolfgang came back from Ludwigs' house. We stood near the door to our basement for a while and

211

watched the steady rain of ashes from the fires in the city. After each bombing raid, the huge fires created a tremendously powerful updraft.

"Look, I can get the letters again." Wolfgang ran around the yard, scooping up pieces of paper blown from the northeast. "Come get some with me, Dieter."

"Nein. I don't want to get my hands dirty." *They just touched breasts!*

"Hah!" Mutti said. "When did you become so fastidious, Herr Steiner? Help your brother clean the yard."

I looked with him and found an invoice from a store in Bernau in the far northeastern suburbs of the city, more than fifty kilometers away. I picked it up with two fingers and took it to the pile. Wolfgang brought back as many as he could find and spread them on the veranda where he tried to match them up into a whole letter.

"Look at this," Mutti said. "Here's almost a whole letter. 'Dear Vati, Mutti and I miss you so much,' she says. 'Come home soon. Mutti cries after Hans. Love, Sonja.' Look at her writing. Just a Kind she is. Is she alive? Dead? And no one left to care. Everything scattered. When does it end?" She rested her head on her knees. The letter she'd been reading dropped at her feet, and Wolfgang ran over and picked it up.

I patted her arm. "Don't worry, Mutti. We'll make it through all this together."

She looked up. "You are right, Dieter. We cannot give up. Vati would want us to be strong. We will be strong for him."

I felt tears coming, but I swallowed hard and fought them back. I was supposed to be the man of the house now.

The daily, and nightly, ordeal of staying alive, the hunt for something to eat, the scrounging around for heating material to keep us warm at least for an hour—all of it was

212

taking its toll. We did not have much time left over to think of Vati or of anybody else. Frau Kundert came over from time to time and begged for any scraps of food for her old cat. "I have to try to keep him alive," she said. "When everything else is gone, I want to hold on to something that loves me."

Our basement, as well as Ludwigs' bunker, was cold and damp all the time. For several days I felt a slight pain in my ears. Not a bad pain, just an annoying pain. I didn't say anything to Mutti. I didn't think she needed anything else to worry about.

But the pain got worse.

"Why are you holding your ears all the time, Dieter?" she asked me several days later.

"I don't know, Mutti. Maybe it's the noise. It makes them hurt worse. When I hold my hands against them the pain isn't so bad."

"How long have you had that pain? Come here." She used the flashlight to look inside one ear.

"I can't see anything. Exactly where does it hurt?"

I pointed behind the ear, very gently pushing into the slight indentation there. Then her finger touched the same spot.

I screamed. "Not so hard, Mutti! That really hurts bad!" She pulled her hand away.

"Frau Ludwig, can we get some hot water going? I think we better put some heat on his ears." They hurried upstairs and were back a few minutes later with two steaming hot rags.

The inside of my head felt like it was on fire when Mutti tried to hold the hot rags tight to my ears. The pain was worse. Finally, she gave up, leaned back and tears came to her eyes.

"I do not know what to do, Dieter. Crying like this you never do, so you must hurt very much." She wiped my face with a towel. "There is an infection somewhere. What are we going to do with you? No ear doctors are around anymore!"

By early morning I still had not slept at all and was worn out from crying. Frau Ludwig, Mutti, Ruth, Wolfgang—all took turns sitting by me. Even Helga held my hand a few times and talked to me, but nothing took away the piercing pain inside my head. *Please, God. I promise I will never touch her breasts again. Don't punish me this way.*

By mid-morning I was worse. Frau Ludwig told my mother of an ear specialist whose clinic had been near the S-Bahn station by the Zoo Garten. At least it had been there before the war. "A friend of ours, from Switzerland, he was. I'll try to find out if he's still there." Frau Ludwig rushed up the stairs again.

Someone is carrying me; Mutti sings as she rocks me back and forth; we're riding in a car. Flashes of sky and ruins and burning buildings. The pain! I scream and try to get away. I try to hit my head and stop the pain. Mutti holds my arms down. Someone carries me. Up stairs. A man's voice. A woman's. Who are they? A mask covers my face. A voice through the tunnel. "Breathe deep and count backward from ten, Dieter."

Slowly, very slowly, I try to focus on the huge spider on the ceiling. *Is it real? I reach for it. I'm paralyzed! My arms. My legs. I can't move.*

"Dieter. It is Mutti. You're safe. Can you hear me, Dieter?"

I looked hard toward the voice and blinked. "Mutti? Mutti, I can't move. Are we dead? Are we in heaven?"

"Nein, Dieter. We are in the hospital." She patted my cheek. "Do you feel better?"

"Ja! The pain is gone!" I looked back up at the spider. It was a large hole, with wide cracks zig-zagging toward the walls. "The spider is a hole?"

My mother laughed, and it sounded like a bomb exploding. I tried to put my hands over my ears.

"Untie me! Let me go!"

"Sh-h-h, Dieter, calm down."

"You're yelling again! It hurts when you talk."

"All right, I will whisper. You're tied down so you won't hurt youself. You've been thrashing around. Do you understand?" I nodded with the least amount of movement I could muster.

"The nurse here will take those straps off as soon as you are completely awake."

"How long have I been this way? Is the war over?" The nurse behind Mutti laughed. "Why did I have that awful pain?"

"A very lucky young man you are," said a doctor who came in and stood by the bed. "You are extremely lucky! You had advanced middle-ear infections in both ears. Your facial muscles were already affected, and one eyelid you couldn't even close." I nodded. "And I bet you couldn't whistle, could you?"

"I didn't try. There is nothing to whistle about."

He laughed and looked at the nurse. "You can take the straps off now. He's awake. He even has a sense of humor." He made some notes on the clipboard he carried. "Your mother got you here just in time. The corner of your mouth was pulled down like this," his finger traced a line on his own face. "And that one eyelid was stretched upward and to the middle. You did not look very good. We didn't even have time to take off your coat."

"Do I still look—"

"Nein, you look better. But it will take a few days before all those muscles return to normal. Don't be impatient.

215

Next time you come to see me you will be your good-look-ing self again."

A week later I was ready to go home. The Swiss doctor gave Mutti eardrops and other medicine. He led the way upstairs to the basement door. "I am very sorry, but there is no taxi this time. Viel Glück!"

There was nothing running in the inner city and we walked slowly through the narrow pathways between the mountains of smoldering bricks and blackened walls toward home. I held onto Mutti and felt at times as if I would faint. We walked twenty-five kilometers to reach Babelsberg-Ufastadt.

We were just two in a long line of people trudging in the same direction. Some pulled small wagons loaded with clothes and household things. We came up to one wagon, pulled slowly by an old white-haired woman. In it lay an even older-looking man, whose head hung backward, his mouth and eyes wide open. His arms dangled over the sides.

"He looks dead," I whispered to Mutti. "If he is, why is she carrying him around?"

"Maybe to find a place to bury him, Dieter."

As we passed her, I looked at her face. One eye was covered with a dirty patch.

Soon after that an old man offered us a ride in his wagon, and I fell asleep for the few minutes we rode along. Eventually, we reached Steglitz, which had not suffered so much. The streets looked like streets again.

Just before we reached our neighborhood, Mutti stopped.

"What's wrong, Mutti? We're almost home."

"Here, Dieter, let's sit on this wall. I have to tell you something." I sat but wanted to lie down and sleep.

"I didn't want to tell you this while you were in the clinic because I didn't want to upset you while you were sick. You needed to get well first."

I jumped off the wall, no longer sleepy. "What, Mutti? What happened?"

"Last week we heard on the radio that Würzburg was firebombed the day after you had left, but—"

"What about Peter and—"

"They are all right. That is all we know. Maybe Ruth heard more. I just wanted you to know before we got to the house."

"Those dirty Americans! Why would they bomb a city like that? Opa said it was an Open City."

"They are all right, Dieter. That's the important thing." She smiled. "And we were lucky today, too. All the way out here from the city without a raid."

Ruth leaned against the wall next to the basement door. "Willkommen, Dieter. You look a lot better. Can you whistle again?"

I tried to smile but couldn't. "I just want to lie down, please?"

My mother led the way to Ludwigs' house. "Surely another attack will come soon, so we might as well go to the bunker now."

"A letter came from Oma, Lis." Ruth handed it to Mutti.

"Würzburg was fire bombed the night after you left, Dieter. They say that more than four thousand people died in the fires and that most of the old part of the city was destroyed."

Mutti unfolded the small paper and read it to us.

"Liebe Familie. Two nights ago we were bombed. The three of us are fine. Our building was hit by a phosphorous bomb, and it burned down very fast. So quick the bombers came we did not have time to get to the shelter, but we soaked blankets in the pond of the park across the street and covered ourselves from the sparks. Someone came and rescued us. Peter started to stutter, but we hope it will go away.

217

They told us we would be sent to a farm away from the city.
When we know our address, I will send it to you.
Love, Your Emma. "

"Well, at least they did not get hurt. What a relief! But
my poor baby—he stutters . . . "

Mutti was right. The sirens blew soon afterwards. We
sat on our cots. Now the Ludwigs and Helga were there as
well. I asked Mutti for Oma's letter, and I read it again.

"It's my fault," I said to Mutti. "I shouldn't have taken
him to Würzburg, Mutti. See, our house is still standing. He
would have been safe right here."

"It is nobody's fault. We did what we thought was best
for him." Don't blame yourself for this." Her voice grew
louder. "It is the damned war's fault. It is Hitler's fault!"

"Sh-h-h, Frau Drescher!" Frau Ludwig pressed a finger
to her lips. "You can get us all in trouble if someone hears
you."

The long handle of the bunker door turned, and Herr
Ludwig stepped into the bunker. Behind him was a
Wehrmacht officer. *A general with an Iron Cross on his chest!*
Did he hear Mutti yelling about Hitler? Mutti looked at
the floor.

Herr Ludwig walked up to his wife. "The General wants
to talk about . . . well, you know what he wants to tell us."
He turned toward Mutti. "It looks like this raid is over, Frau
Drescher. I think you can go back to your house now."

Before we reached the door to our basement, I whispered to Mutti, "You think the Ludwigs have a secret?"

She didn't answer.

218

31

"Mutti, see that smoke over there? That's where Horst lives. I'm going to see if he's all right."

I ran fast toward the columns of smoke, through the nursery, across the tracks, and into the woods, into the heavy smell of explosives, around new bomb craters and over fallen trees, to a clearing where I stumbled onto a street. The ground was covered by a gray-white powder. *This is Horst's street. Where is his house?*

Smoking piles of bricks and wood. A few walls. *This is all?* Ahead of me stood a dust-covered woman. In her bloody hand was a small torn doll.

"Frau. Can you tell me which house is Horst Pagel's?"

She stood like a statue, staring straight ahead. Her lips moved but without any sound.

"Help us!" a scared voice yelled from a pile of rubble. "Here! Help!" I climbed over chunks of concrete and someone threw me a pair of heavy gloves.

"Use them. We have to get to the basement. People are in there!" The gloves were too big. I left them and scrambled on.

Several women, two old men, a boy about six, and I dug in the rubble to get close to the basement. A small tractor with a shovel attached pushed and pulled the big pieces of concrete and the bricks out. "Schnell! We have to get to them." Finally, we saw the top of a door. One of the old men hacked at it with an axe. A corner of the tractor's shovel hooked inside the opening and pulled, making a hole large enough to get through.

A man climbed in. A woman tied a wet rag over my nose and mouth and gave me a large flashlight, and I followed. I crawled into the black hole, into choking dust and total silence. In the beam of the flashlight I saw we were in a small basement room. Two little girls, little like Peter, lay on wooden bunks along the back wall, looking at me. "Keine Angst! Ich bin hier!" I ran and put my hand out. "Nein," the man hollered and stepped in front of me. Then I saw the blood. *But they're looking at me.*

He shined the light to our left. Four women sat in green chairs along the wall like they had just started their morning Kaffee-Klatsch. One of them held knitting needles in her fingers, the yarn still wrapped around them. An almost-finished mitten was in her lap. *She's looking at me, too!* I crawled back out and vomited on a heap of rubble.

I walked home slowly, back through the woods, paying no attention to where I was going. *Why were their eyes open? Why did they look at me? Are your eyes open when—*

"Dieter!" Mutti stood on top of the S-Bahn tracks, yelling. She saw me and came running.

"Um Gottes Willen! What happened to you? Your hands, they're all bloody!"

"Horst must be dead! I couldn't even find his house, and . . . " I started to sob. "They're dead. All dead over there. Little girls, like Peter—."

She grabbed my hands, but not before someone's blood covered my face.

32

I couldn't find Horst Pagel or any of his family. I went back over there a few days after I helped dig into their basement. This time I was sure I found the spot where his house once stood, but there was nothing left but a bathtub, sitting at a crazy angle and surrounded by mounds of bricks. The birch trees and pines we used to play hide-and-seek under were blackened and shredded stumps.

It was hard to believe this was where we had played. The yard was a crater, and the sidewalk where we had raced our bicycles was gone.

I heard a rattling noise behind me. A woman carefully zig-zagged her way around chunks of concrete, pushing a baby carriage toward me. When she got closer, I saw there were some pieces of splintered wood in the carriage. She grinned.

"I could be warm tonight if I had a stove."

"You don't have one?"

"Nein. I have nothing. I was bombed out last week." She pointed at the carriage in front of her. "This is what is left. My daughter is dead. The baby, too." She looked at the rubble. "You bombed too, ja?"

I shook my head. "It was my friend. I was looking for him."

"Nein, mein Junge. He is dead. They are all dead." She looked at the bathtub. "If I only I had water . . ." She slumped against the carriage handle. "It would be nice to bathe again."

She walked on past, pushing her baby carriage and sticks of wood. I turned toward home. *I hope Horst wasn't scared. That it didn't hurt too much.* I remembered out-running the bombs on the back of Major Graubert's motorcycle. *I bet you die in slow motion.*

The rumble of flak in the distance reminded me to start running again.

33

"It snowed last night, boys. Get up and find some wood."
Mutti pulled the blanket from over me. I tugged to pull it
back. "Nein, you lazy boy. Schnell! We're all cold."

I shivered as I dressed. *I hate the cold!* "I'm not going
alone. Dicker's got to go, too."

"Do you see him complaining?" Mutti nodded toward
Wolfgang. He was already up and pulling on his gloves. "He
knows it's your job to get the wood. Why can't you be more
like him? He makes a game of it."

Sure he does. He's a baby. Everything he does is a game.
I put on my coat and wrapped a scarf around my neck.
"C'mon, I'm ready.

We went outside and looked around. We had already
brought home everything we could find—pieces of wood,
dead branches, small twigs, anything that could burn in our
kitchen stove. The yard was picked clean.

"Maybe we can cut down some more bushes, Dieter."

"Don't be dumb. Do you see any dead ones left?"

"Wolfgang shook his head. "Then what can we do?"

"I have to think. Don't bother me for a minute." I sat
down on the steps and tried to remember where I'd seen
some wood.

Wolfgang came back in in a minute. "Do you know what we can do yet?"

"Nein. I'm still thinking." I waved him away. "Go play."

I just started thinking good when he was back. "What about now? You got an idea, Dieter?"

"I've just been thinking for a minute, Zwerg." I hollered. "Don't talk to me!" I reached over to swat him.

He ducked around the stoop and looked over the step. "I'm telling Mutti you called me a Zwerg. And you hit me. She'll be mad at you."

"Sure. You're so perfect she thinks you never do anything to deserve it. You're spoiled."

"I am not spoiled. You're mean."

"You're a Zwerg!"

"You're a Dummkopf then." He smacked my arm and started running. "Dummer Dieter, dummer Dieter."

I jumped up to catch him. "You wait, Zwerg," I yelled, running after him. "You'll be sorry."

"Dieter!" Mutti's voice stopped me short. I turned around.

"This is fetching wood for the family?"

I walked back to her. Wolfgang came around the corner of the house and stopped a few feet away.

"Come here, Wolfgang. Your brother is not going to hurt you. Are you, Dieter?"

"Nein, Mutti."

She grabbed my chin. "You look at me when you speak!"

I looked up at her. "Nein, Mutter."

"The man of the family, Dieter. That's who you are. Like Vati was. Can you imagine Vati treating you the way you treat Wolfgang?"

"But he gets on my nerves. Sometimes I just want to think." I glared at Wolfgang as he moved closer to Mutti and put his arms around her waist. "He keeps asking questions when I don't have answers."

Mutti's face softened, and she put her arms around me. "Ja, Dieter. I know. Answers, like everything else, are in short supply." Her hands covered my ears as she looked into my eyes. "A hard enough time I have finding answers. You can't be expected to know what I don't." She kissed my forehead. "Maybe this question of his I can answer. What does he ask?"

"Where to find more wood."

"Hah! That is what the fight is about? In a time of war you argue over something none of us have an answer to? Mein Gott!" She laughed. "The answer is not sitting here. Or chasing each other. The answer is down the street. Around the corner. By the tracks. In the park. Go!" She smacked my rear. "You, too, Wolfgang."

Wolfgang and I looked at each other sheepishly. I reached down and took his hand, and we walked out on the street. He carried a sack, and I had my handsaw.

"Look Mutti! Dicker found a fence post, and I got all of it out of the ground." I displayed a wonderful piece of wood, good for several fires.

Wolfgang tugged at Mutti's sleeve. "I found it Mutti. By myself."

She rumpled his hair. "See. I knew you'd have success if you went about your chores instead of fighting." She measured the wood with her hand. "Ja, this is a beautiful piece of wood." She leaned down and kissed Wolfgang. "Such a big boy you are." She turned to me. "Cut it small, about this long," she said, holding her hands about six inches apart. "An hour for each piece. And one piece a day." She smacked her hands together. "At least a week we'll have."

That evening we burned the first piece of the fence post.

"Stand here," Ruth said, arranging us around the stove. "A treat we have tonight." We stood as close to the stove as possible, holding our hands around a big pot of water. After

225

a while Ruth tested the water with her hand. "It's warm enough, Wolfgang, let me help you wash." She dipped the corner of a washrag in the pot, and wiped his face and hands. "There. Now, Dieter. Your turn. Hurry, before the fire dies." I took the washrag from her and cleaned my hands and face. Now I felt colder than when I was dirty, and I moved closer to the stove. I handed the washrag to Mutti.

She shook her head. "Nein, Ruth first. I go last."

After Ruth, Mutti cleaned her face and hands. "And the water is almost hot," she said. She put a funnel in the big empty wine bottle on the table. "Now, Dieter." I picked up the pot and filled the bottle. Mutti wrapped a towel around it. "Quick now. While we're all warm, let's get to the bunker." She handed the towel-wrapped bottle to Wolfgang. "You found the fence post. Would you like to carry the hot water it heated?"

"Ja, Mutti. I can do that." Wolfgang took the bottle and hugged it to his chest. "It warms my blanket first?"

"Ja, Wolfgang. If Dieter says so. He cut up the wood for us." Mutti looked at me.

"If you warm my blanket second," I said.

Wolfgang smiled, and we paraded out of the house to the bunker to begin our night.

"Another one, Mutti. That's three I've seen this week." I watched from the window as a soldier opened the back door of a staff car and an officer got out. "A general this time, Mutti. In the Wehrmacht."

"Not so nosy, Dieter," she called from the bedroom. "You know Herr Ludwig is important. Perhaps they are friends."

He's more important than that. "Oh, Mutter. Every day it's another staff car. They drive up, and a soldier jumps out and opens the door. Then an officer gets out and looks around, like he's being watched or something. And then he goes in the house. See. That's what this one is doing. Just like all the others." I left the window and walked to the bedroom door. "I think they're going to move, Mutti. They've got all those crates over there."

"I think Frau Ludwig appreciates that we don't ask."

I walked in and sat on the bed. "I don't see why they'd want to move," I said to Mutti's back as she rearranged the bureau drawers. "It's such a nice house. Unless Herr Ludwig is a spy or something, and he has to get out of Deutschland."

Mutti glanced over her shoulder at me. "Don't you be foolish, Herr Steiner. Your head works too much sometimes." She shut the top drawer and ran her hands over the front of the chest before she came over and sat on the bed beside me. "Berliners they're not," she said, "so a nice house wouldn't be enough to keep them in the city."

"If I was Herr Ludwig, a nice house would keep me here."

"Ja, Dieter. You're young. You dream." She reached over and patted my hand. "Before Vati died, we dreamed. We had plans to someday move into a house like that. Big trees would be around it. And a big yard, bigger than this one, for Vati's roses. A tall iron fence . . . And each of you boys would have your own room. And Vati's study would have bookcases on all four walls. The dining room would have built-in shelves . . . with indirect lighting . . ." She laughed. "Karl said for all my champagne glasses . . ." She sighed and bowed her head and her hands clasped over her mouth. "Now . . ."

"It doesn't matter. I like our apartment. This is a wonderful apartment. And we don't need all those bedrooms."

She turned away from me, but I knew she was crying. I reached into my pocket and gave her my handkerchief.

"Danke." She smiled as she wiped her eyes. "Sometimes I miss Vati so much I can't help but cry. Another Christmas without him . . . It's hard this time of year." She smoothed my hair back over my forehead. "He's proud of you, I know — the way you help me and your brothers."

"Ja, I know." I got up quickly and left and went out into the yard and stood for a moment. I looked at the snowman Wolfgang had built, then beyond it to the little cross sticking out of the snow next to the large birch tree.

I miss Putzi. And Horst. And I miss Vati.

I remembered the snowball fights Wolfgang and I had with Vati. *Right here. In this back yard. We laughed so hard when one of us hit him. Dicker had to run right up beside him . . . Vati pretending he was trying to get away . . . But he always let Dicker get him. "Enough, Jungs, enough!" And we'd stop so he could wipe the snow off his glasses . . . He always laughed with us . . . I can hear him now, just like he's still here.*

"Dieter!" Mutti touched my arm. "I've been calling you. What are you staring at?"

34

"It doesn't matter if it's only a pine branch, Dieter. It's the spirit. This is for Wolfgang. As long as it's green, he will remember it is Christmas." Mutti held out her hands, and I gave her the branch when I whacked it from the bottom of the tall pine. We turned and walked back toward the house.

"For children it's important to keep the traditions. You're older, Dieter. You could do without, like I could. Or Ruth. But Wolfgang . . . He needs to see something he thinks is Christmas."

We crossed over the railroad tracks and walked through the yard and into the house from the back door so Wolfgang wouldn't see.

Mutti sneaked the branch into the living room while I found a big jug in the closet. I filled it with water and took it to the living room.

I closed the door behind me. "Where do you want me to put this?"

"In the usual place." She pointed to the corner by the window. "Where always we have the tree." I put the jug down, and she stuck the branch in it. "Now, in the cellar is a box of balls. At least one or two must be there. On the shelf they should be. The one in the corner. On the bottom."

I came back with what was left of our old decorations. Mutti opened one box. The balls were in pieces. She opened another and lifted out a silver ball.

"Look!" She smiled. "This has a few that aren't broken. We'll use what we can. For Wolfgang this is important. He'll like these." She hung the silver balls on the pine branch. "Now in the bottom: hand me that sack of icicles. They always make a tree—" she laughed "—or *a branch*, look pretty."

"We have candles, Mutti." I showed her the box in my hand. "We've got six."

"One or two is all, and only for a short while. Then they go back. For later."

Mutti brought her favorite picture of Vati up from the basement and leaned it against the jug. It was his last picture, standing behind the fence of the barracks, smiling. Next to it she put a little picture of Peter. Then she put two small packages under the tree, one for me and one for Wolfgang. I knew they were mittens she and Ruth had knitted for us.

At six o'clock, after I made sure all the windows were covered with cardboard, I lit the two candles. Mutti opened the door. "Merry Christmas, Ruth and Wolfgang! Now you can come in."

Wolfgang's mouth dropped open. "That's not a Christmas tree!" He stomped his foot and scowled at Mutti. "You said we were going to have a Christmas tree." He stomped again and shook his arms. "That's not a tree!"

Mutti laughed a funny little laugh. "You're right, mein Sohn. It's a Christmas branch. Only the most fashionable families in Berlin can have one of these for the holidays." She walked behind it, her arms spread out, showing it off. "The Führer says only *special* people, like the widow and sons of Karl Drescher, are allowed to spend Christmas Eve in a cold house in front of something as wonderful and special as a Christmas branch." She beckoned to Wolfgang.

"Come see this wonderful branch. Pretend, as I have to, that everything is right."

Wolfgang walked up closer and looked at it. Still scowling, he crossed his arms. "I'd rather have a tree."

Mutti sank into a chair. Tears ran down her face as she looked at us. "My babies. My precious family. I would rather have your father."

35

"This is totally insane!" Mutti's hand slammed down on the kitchen table so hard, her coffee cup and saucer fell off and broke. The shattering noise brought Ruth running.

"Was ist—? Why all this—"

"Look at this, Ruth!" Mutti handed her the notice. "Just look at it. I don't believe it."

Ruth shook her head and put the paper back on the table. I took the dustpan and swept up pieces of the cup and saucer. I reached for the paper and re-read it.

You are ordered to report to the Volksturm barracks at Potsdam on Friday, February 16, 1945, at nine o'clock in the morning. Failure to do so will result in your arrest and immediate prosecution.

Wolfgang came to the kitchen door. He stopped when he saw Mutti's face.

She stared at the table for a long time, taking deep breaths, like she was going to explode. Finally, she looked up. "We should hide you. Up by the chimney in Ludwigs' attic."

"But the Gestapo . . . Besides, Rolf at school said that they'll just train us to fight fires."

"The Gestapo? Don't be stupid. The Gestapo has other

things to do than to hunt for a thirteen-year-old. Become a firefighter? I do not believe that."

I could fight fires, maybe save people. Important things instead of sitting in the bunker waiting for a bomb to bury us. "You've seen the pictures, Mutti. The HJ fight the fires. That's probably all I have to do."

"I do not like it. I do not trust them anymore. You know that." Mutti had calmed down, much to my relief, because I heard Frau Witte's voice. Ruth went to the door and let her in.

"Look at this, Frau Witte. I have to report on Friday." Mutti glared at me.

"You will do fine, Dieter. You are strong enough. I am proud of you. And that is a good way to help our Führer." She looked toward Mutti. "And you, Frau Drescher. You are proud?"

Mutti stared at her. "Nein. I do not wish him to go. I have lost one man from this family."

Ruth quickly changed the subject. "We had mail from Würzburg. It came a couple of days ago, and Peter is fine. But he still stutters badly."

Frau Witte smiled. "That is a small price to pay for the Führer. Mutti started to get up, and I patted her arm. She sat back down. "I am busy," she said. "You must be, too, Frau Witte."

"Ja. I am taking things to the basement. Those bomber Schweine will come again today."

"Then we both have things to do." Mutti walked her to the door.

Two days to go. Our mood matched the weather: low-hanging, dirty gray clouds, a biting wind from the east carrying the stench of cold, wet ashes and smoke from never-ending fires in the city.

I stood on the veranda and looked at the muddy brown patches of grass, the dead and frozen rose bushes along the front fence. I thought of my father buried deep in the ground somewhere thousands of kilometers away. I thought of Vati teaching me to prune the roses, comforting me when the sharp thorns drew blood from my fingers. I smiled when I remembered those times, and for an instant, I was happy.

I heard Mutti scold Wolfgang over something he did. From the apartment house next to us came the short laugh of a woman, and the never-ending march music thumped from Frau Witte's apartment. It all sounded so normal, so routine, as if nothing unusual was happening to us. But I looked at the bare trees across the street, the house next to the nursery with boarded-up windows and the gaping holes in its roof where bombs had blown away the red tile shingles, and at the steady trickle of refugees on the street—women and children and old men slowly trudging past our house like silent shadows, all heading west toward Potsdam— and I thought about what was to come. All of a sudden, I felt utterly alone. I wanted to cry, but tears didn't come easy anymore.

"Inside, Dieter, before you get sick."

Mutti's barked order brought me back from my thoughts. As I walked past her at the door, I stopped, turned around, and hugged her hard for a long moment.

"We will make it through all this. Don't give up your hopes," she whispered. "It is getting dark. We better get over to the bunker for the night."

"No, you are not going to school today. You keep Wolfgang busy while Ruth and I try to get some food this morning, verstanden?"

She buttoned up her old coat and pulled a scarf over her head to keep her ears warm. "And listen to the radio for warnings."

Soon after Mutti left, Wolfgang called from the living

room. "Listen, Dieter! Quick! They're bombing Dresden. It's on the radio!" *Mutti's sister! Tante Liselotte is there.*

The radio reported that large numbers of bombers had attacked Dresden during the past night, were still bombing the city this morning, and that thousands of women and children had been killed.

Why are they killing children? Why? I looked at Wolfgang. *He's not even eight. He's never done anything to deserve being killed. What's wrong with them? Maybe Frau Witte is right after all, and Joseph Göbbels. Hitler?* The memory of Weinberg's smashed store came back, and of people walking around with yellow stars on their coats, Sollie and his family disappearing, the message of the prisoner working in the yard down the street from us. *I don't understand anything.*

"You aren't listening, Dieter!" Wolfgang shook my shoulder. "What's wrong with you?"

"Nothing is wrong, Dicker. I was just thinking how lucky we are that we can live in this bunker. I wonder how the Ludwigs are doing and where they live now."

Wolfgang didn't hear me. "So many are dead in Dresden that they have to burn them in big stacks on the streets! Will you have to fight fires in Dresden when you go in the Army?"

He shuddered and wrapped his arms around himself. "I'm cold, Dieter. Aren't you scared? You will have to put out fires like that, won't you? You think Berlin will be bombed like in Dresden? We'll be safe in this bunker, won't we? But you won't be here with us, will you? Aren't you scared, Dieter?"

"Ja, ja, Wolfgang. Don't worry, we'll be safe." *I'll be stopping fires. All over Berlin.* "You will be safe. I will make sure."

He looked at the door. "What's taking Mutti so long? I hope she'll find something for us to eat."

"I do, too, Dicker." *Why am I still calling him that?*

He's not fat anymore. He's skinny, and his face looks so old. I put my arm around his shoulder.

"Soon they will be home."

Mutti emptied her shopping bag: one piece of the same stinky margarine, two eggs, and a small paper bag of gray flour.

If Mutti was worried about her sister in Dresden, she didn't show it. Didn't even talk about it until I finally asked her.

"You think Tante Liselotte is safe?"

"Ja, she is. I have to believe that. She said she wanted to move to the outskirts of the city some time ago. I am going to believe she did that, and she is alive."

"What if she didn't move? Maybe she's in the city still."

"No more do I want to talk about it, Dieter. She is safe."

Panic gripped Berliners. Surely, our city would be next. Even Josef Göbbels urged that as many women and children as possible should seek refuge anywhere in the countryside outside Berlin. Wolfgang heard the warnings on the radio and came running.

"Mutti, we have to leave! They're telling us to go!"

"Calm down. Remember what I told you? That is only for the people who live in the city, where all the houses are close together. Out here we don't have to worry about fire-storms. No more screams, please."

"But you're screaming yourself!"

For a moment, Mutti smiled. She pulled Wolfgang to her side and hugged him. "I am sorry. I guess I did scream. I won't do it again." She looked at me and held out her arms. "You come here and I hug you, too. Tomorrow you have to leave us. It is a sad time for me."

I hugged her back. "I will only be fighting fires, Mutti. I know how to do that. You don't have to worry."

"Ja. Karl told me that, too."

Early in the morning, Mutti and Ruth and Wolfgang walked with me for several blocks on my way to Potsdam. Mutti had found only my HJ cap. It felt strange to wear it without the rest of my uniform.

"You don't have to go with me all the way. I can find the barracks by myself. I'll probably be back before dark."

One hour later I reported at the Volksturm barracks with a knot in my stomach and sore feet.

The barracks consisted of three huts made of corrugated metal sheets in front of a burned-out building. Several boys huddled close together and stretched their hands toward the flames in a large metal drum. I spotted Helmut and Manfred, and we slapped each others' shoulders and shook hands.

I looked around. "Where's Rolf? I don't see him."

Manfred stretched his arm in salute. "He probably saluted so much he threw his shoulder out of the socket." We all laughed but stopped when a big boy in a HJ uniform took a step toward us and glared. He nodded toward the buildings. We turned in time to see a soldier headed our way.

"Achtung! Form three lines here in front of me. Schnell!"

We lined up. There were twenty-four of us, and I was somewhere in the middle. I still didn't see Rolf. A steady and cold drizzle, mixed with a few heavy snowflakes, soaked into my jacket, and my feet felt like clumps of ice. The soldier read from the paper in his hand.

"You are ordered to train here on rifle and Panzerfaust, then wait for new orders. How many have had training on these weapons before?"

I can take a rifle apart, but I've never fired real ammunition. Once I held a Panzerfaust at a meeting. I didn't raise my hand. I looked around. Ten hands the soldier counted.

"You stay here. The rest follow me."

We trotted along behind him. "What are they going to do with us?" I whispered to Helmut. "What about fighting fires?" Helmut shrugged.

We walked through water puddles and mud, around and to the back of the burned building. There, with the motor running, stood a gray Army truck. *Nein! They're taking us away!*

"Get in the truck and sit down," the soldier bellowed.

As we climbed over the tailgate, another soldier handed each one of us a steel helmet. I looked at mine and noticed a sharp dent, like a heavy scratch, along the side of it. *It belonged to someone! Is he dead?* I looked inside. *Is this blood on the strap?* I ran my finger over it. *What if it's blood? What if some—*

"Adjust your headstrap so it fits tight and does not slide around your head!" The soldier walked away as the truck moved ahead, leaving thick, smelly blue smoke behind us.

We rode about twenty minutes, through streets filled with rubble and holes, a few times close to bomb craters and walls of buildings ready to collapse. I looked at the others around me, all staring at their feet or watching the rows of burned-down buildings. *Why didn't I listen to Mutti? I could have hid in Ludwigs' attic.*

Finally, the truck stopped on a gravel road along a field, bordered at the far end by thick woods.

"Out! Schnell!"

I caught my pants leg on the edge of the truck. "Schneller!" the soldier screamed. *I hate that word.*

We formed a line behind a wooden podium where a rifle rested. One by one, we fired several rounds of ammunition into the woods. My shoulder ached when I finished.

I moved to a different line. A soldier told us how to use a Panzerfaust. *My shoulder! I can't put anything by my shoulder. How can I get out of it?* But he didn't make us fire it. *Gott Sie Dank!*

Two hours later we climbed back in the truck. We were freezing cold. I sat with Manfred and Helmut.

"Think we can go home tonight?" They looked at me but didn't answer. The silence made me nervous. "Maybe the telephone lines will work and they'll let us call?" Still no answer. "They won't keep us overnight will they?" They turned their heads away from me. After a long while, the truck stopped at the metal huts.

An older man in civilian clothes, a rifle slung over his shoulder, hollered as we climbed out.

"You will stay here tonight." He pointed toward the huts, "New orders come tomorrow. In that line over there is hot soup."

Stay here? All night? I couldn't move. I looked around. *Maybe I can run away after dark. I'll be a deserter—*

Someone shoved me from behind toward the soup line. I turned around. It was Manfred. "At least let's get something warm in our stomachs," he said, pushing me. "Come on! Aren't you hungry?"

The soup was watery but hot. It even calmed me down somewhat, although I was still scared. And it was warmer inside the hut than outside. No one talked, and the only sound was the spoons clanking against tin cups.

The civilian with the rifle came in. I was surprised how old he looked. He was an old man.

"When can I go home?" "Why are we using guns?" "I thought we were going to fight fires." "Are we going to be real soldiers?"

"Nein!" he hollered. "I do not know what kind of orders you will get in the morning. All I know is, you are to stay here tonight."

The questions began again. "I need to call." "Where is a telephone?" "I have to tell my—"

"Nein!" he hollered again. He held up his hand. "There

is no phone. All the lines are dead. Ja, we will let your parents know where you are."

"How?" I was shocked to hear my voice so loud.

"When the phone lines are repaired. That is how."

"But you don't know our numbers! How can—"

"Verdammt! We will ask you the numbers! Genug! Get some sleep. You will need it." He opened the door but stopped and turned around.

"There are Army guards around here. If anyone has a flashlight, do not use it!" He turned out the light and left. He locked the door from the outside.

I stared into blackness. I moved and pain shot through my right shoulder and I moaned.

"You have to hold the rifle tight, Dieter. Push it into your shoulder when you fire. Then the recoil isn't so hard."

"Danke, Manfred." I lay back and pulled the thin blanket up around my chin. *This smells awful.* But I was too tired to care much. I put the blanket under my chin so I wouldn't smell it as much and used my arm for a pillow. An eerie, blue-grey light came through the only window at the far end of the hut. Now and then, I saw the red flicker of an explosion or fire.

"Schnell! Raus!" *Is it already tomorrow?* In total darkness, we stumbled out of cots and into each other. I groped for my HJ cap and found it inside the steel helmet.

Overnight, frost had hardened the mud between the huts. We stood in formation, shivering.

"Slap your arms, Dieter. It will get the circulation going."

"Danke, Manfred."

I slapped and waited in silence. The sky toward Berlin glowed in a deep red.

"Did you hear any bombers last night, Helmut?"

"I didn't hear anything, Dieter. But your snoring woke me up once. I kicked your cot, but you were dead. I almost got mad at you." He smiled. His teeth chattered. In the cold we all looked like we were smoking.

"Remember when we pretended this was smoking?" I blew out and held an imaginary cigarette to my mouth.

"Ja. When we were little."

"Ja. When we were little." I swung my arms some more. "Things were different then. I never thought I'd be doing this."

"You always said you wanted to be a soldier."

"Ja, I did. I didn't think I'd have to be so cold."

"Ja. You were stupid." Helmut laughed.

I smacked his shoulder and he hit me back and I swiped at him again.

A car drove up and stopped in front of us. The driver was in uniform, but the man who came with him wore civilian clothes with an armband on his left sleeve.

For a few moments he looked us over.

"Listen carefully," he said. "A truck will be here shortly to take you to be fed. From there you will be taken to the east of Berlin." He held up his hand. "That is all I know, so do not ask any questions."

He climbed back into the car and drove off. Two soldiers with rifles walked toward us from between the huts.

"Get back inside until we call you."

An hour later, the truck arrived and we climbed in. We sat as close together as we could so we warmed each other. I sat between Helmut and Manfred again.

Slowly, the truck rumbled along, and I recognized some of the houses. *We are going through Babelsberg.* I jumped up and stumbled toward the tailgate. *If we continue on this road, we'll go right by the house.*

We passed the S-Bahn station Babelsberg-Ufastadt. Several of us leaned far out of the back, screaming and waving.

"Slow down, please!" someone yelled. "Let us off!" "I need to tell my mother!"

In another minute we went by our house. "I'm out here," I yelled. "I'm going to the east." But I didn't see Mutti or Wolfgang or Ruth. I sat on the floor of the truck and beat the wooden planks with my fists.

As we crossed the bridge over the Teltow Canal, I looked back. *This is the last time I will be this close to home.*

The truck came to a halt at the S-Bahn station Sundgauer Strasse, and we were allowed to get off.

"Why didn't he stop, or at least slow down when we yelled? He drove right by our houses!" Helmut was crying and shaking his fist at the driver.

An old man came up and gave us bread and sausage. A soldier stood nearby, but he didn't say anything. Several women walked closer. One of the them handed me a cup. "You must be thirsty."

"Ja. Danke!" She watched me as I gulped the water.

"How old are you?"

"Thirteen-and-a-half."

"Such a child! Such a shame it is. What are you doing on this truck? Where are you going?"

"We don't know. They only told us that we're going to the east of Berlin, somewhere."

She shook my hand. "Viel Glück, mein Sohn," she said and turned away.

"Frau! Please wait. Do you have something to write with? I have a piece of paper. My mother doesn't know where I am."

She searched in her handbag and handed me a pencil.

"Our address this is." I gave her the piece of paper and returned her pencil. "Can you read it?"

She nodded.

"Please, then, let her know that you saw me here? Please?"

She nodded and hurried away. The soldier who had been watching us ordered us back on the truck.

Street signs, where they were still standing, told us that we were going around the southern parts of Berlin, heading east.

"We're not going to fight fires," I said. "They're sending us against the Russians."

I said it with a dull voice, to no one in particular, and nobody answered. We all knew it.

Hours passed. Finally, the truck slowed to a crawl and pulled into what looked like an old warehouse, its roof gone but blackened walls still standing. Several other trucks were parked ahead of us. Groups of men and boys huddled nearby. The soldier who had been riding with us yelled his orders: "One weapon for each of us. Ammunition is over there, on Table C. Line up over there, then back here!"

He counted us as we jumped out of the truck.

I was given a rifle and several clips of ammunition. Behind me, Manfred received a Panzerfaust but no shell. Walking back to the truck, I looked at the groups around us. *They don't even look like soldiers.* Most of them had steel helmets, but the rest of their clothes were ordinary civilian clothes. Trousers of every color. Long coats. Short coats. Jackets. A few of the older men did have uniforms, but they weren't complete.

Someone shoved me hard from behind. "Get on the damned truck!"

Quickly, I turned, ready to shove back. But it was a soldier, this one with a machine pistol over his shoulder. A sergeant.

"Jawohl, Herr Feldwebel."

I sat up at the front, behind the cab, next to Manfred. When we were all in, the sergeant pulled down the canvas to cover the back. The truck moved out of the building and rumbled into the street. The slit in the canvas at the tailgate showed the sky getting dark. *My second night away from home.*

243

36

"Günter, watch for a sign." I yelled toward the back of the truck. "We want to know where we're going,"
"The backs of signs have nothing to read."
"Then stick your head out, and read the fronts. Idiot!"
As the truck drove in and out of the potholes in the road, twenty-four bodies bounced in unison. Every few minutes Günter stuck his head out and looked. We had driven several kilometers when he shouted, "Sign coming."
"Fürstenwalde two kilometers, Frankfurt/Oder fifty-three kilometers," he shouted a few minutes later.
Nein. Not the Eastern front. Not the Russians. My fingers were stiff from holding the cold steel rifle barrel, and my toes were numb in my soaking wet boots. *I don't want to fight the Russians. What if I'm captured? They'll cut my arms off. And dig out my eyes.* I looked at the back of the truck. *I'll jump off. I'll hide in the woods. But what if I break my leg when I jump? I'll get run over by another truck!*
Manfred slumped next to me, his chin resting on his chest. His rifle leaned between his legs, and he looked like a little round dwarf.
"You all right, Manfred?"

He shook his head slowly. "I'm scared," he whispered. "But don't tell anyone I said that. You won't, will you."

"Nein," I whispered. "I'm scared, too."

"You are? I didn't think you'd be."

"Ja, I'm afraid. I don't want to die. I've seen too many dead people. I don't want to look like they do."

The truck hit a big hole, and Manfred lurched forward. His rifle fell in front of him. I held his arm, and he steadied himself. He grabbed his gun and straightened up, resting the gun butt on the floor and holding it tightly between his knees. "See, my hands are so stiff I can't hold my rifle anymore. We're going to get killed, you know."

I didn't answer.

"I know I'm right, Dieter. I can feel it."

"Look, let's stick together. We'll protect each other. You'll see. We'll make it!"

I wish I could believe that myself.

The truck turned off the paved road and rumbled onto a narrow path through thick brush and pine trees. After a few minutes it stopped. The driver turned the engine off, and the sound of gunfire paralyzed me.

"Raus! Raus! Schnell!" an officer in a mud-spattered uniform bellowed. "Over there, behind the bushes." He pointed to a long hedgerow. "Line up over there. Schnell!"

I was the last one out of the truck. I joined the others hovering in a group. I watched the truck drive between the trees and out of sight. *We're alone. Completely alone out here.* At first the only sounds came from a light wind making a soft, swishing noise in the pines and from bursts of machine gun and rifle fire.

"All right, two squads." The officer's voice sounded tired and worn-out. We milled about as we tried to divide. *"You go there"—"I want to go with Wilhelm"—"You've got more than we have."* The officer walked between the two lines

245

and evened out the groups. I was the last one in our squad, behind Manfred. Helmut was in the other line. The officer walked to the front and turned around. "Our orders are to hold the Russians along the railroad tracks over there." He pointed to a railroad embankment.

"Your squads will be at least a hundred meters apart. I will be with one group, and you will not fire until I give the command. Some of you have the Panzerfaust. Good! You will aim them only at tanks when they are close enough and you can see them, not just hear them. Verstanden?"

"Jawohl." Our answer was barely audible. Manfred's whole body shook. "Don't be so scared," I whispered.

"We're going to die," he said over his shoulder. "And I don't want to."

I reached up to tighten the chin strap on my helmet, but my own hands shook so hard I couldn't do it. *I'm as scared as he is.*

"That way you go," the officer told us. "Wait at the tracks for my orders. No firing of weapons until I say so. You others come with me."

Single file, we trudged through bushes and mud in the direction the officer pointed. Minutes later we reached the bottom of the railroad embankment with the tracks a couple of meters above us. From the other side came the rumble of a tank crashing through the woods. We spread out along the embankment, three or four meters between each of us, and flattened ourselves to the ground. I was at the end, partially covered by a small cluster of bushes. Next to me, a few meters to my right, Manfred buried his head under his arms.

Hiding from the enemy. Just like Würzburg and the fighter plane with the smiling pilot. Now I wear a steel helmet and look like a Deutscher soldier, and Russians in a tank certainly won't smile.

The only noise was the tank as it snapped through the trees toward us. *Why didn't they give us a PanzerFaust instead of rifles?* I pressed the side of my face against the dirt. "Bitte, bitte!" I pleaded. "Don't let me die."

Suddenly, the long, thin barrel of the tank's cannon appeared above the track, maybe ten meters away to my left. *He's crossing over to our side!* I froze. My stomach hurt. My head pounded. Only my fingers moved, and I scraped the ground as if to dig a hole. I turned my head toward Manfred. "Don't move! Play dead!" I called in a hoarse whisper. I turned my head back and peeked out from under my left arm just in time to see the tank reach the top of the embankment and stop, its treads crossways on the tracks. *Make him move. Make him move. Make him move.*

My heart beat wildly as the turret circled toward us and stopped. The barrel of a machine gun slid out its side. Numbness swallowed me whole and I felt suspended, as if I was floating just above the ground. The machine gun cracked and as the first burst of yellow flashed from its barrel, I squeezed my eyes shut and pressed my floating body into the dirt.

Manfred screamed. A rain of bullets hit the gravel between the tracks above and ricocheted off the trees in ear-piercing screeches. Others down the line shrieked as they were hit. I waited for the end, but suddenly there was only quiet.

I was afraid the tank could see the movement of my eyes if I opened them. I remained motionless, thoughtless, too terrified to move my eyelids. Manfred moaned, then choked. He made a soft, gurgling sound and was quiet. I didn't move.

Neither did the tank. It's motor droned. I waited, frozen. *Like the mouse Putzi caught and held under her paw. He'd stared at her, waiting. She'd stared back, sweeping the floor with her tail. I'd thought it was funny. He'll decide when, just like Putzi did. I can't take this!* I wanted to jump up and wave my arms at him. *Shoot me, you Schweine. Shoot me.*

I opened my eyes a little. *Where is he? I can't see him.* The motor droned on. *He's watching me from inside.* I stared and it stared back. *Get it over with!* The tank jerked forward and I jumped. *Mein Gott! Did he see?* I held my breath and hugged the ground. The tank tipped and rolled down onto our side of the embankment and stopped. *He saw me. He's taking a closer look.* It turned away and rumbled off. *Away!* I breathed again. *Are more coming? Or soldiers? Is anyone alive?* I still didn't dare move. Now that the tank was gone, I heard the sounds of guns in the distance. *Where's the other squad? What time is it? I'm so tired.* It feels so good to be alive and close my eyes . . .

The guns were farther away. I opened my eyes. *It's almost dark. I've been asleep.* I shivered as I sat up. My clothes were damp and my hands and feet completely numb. Except for the gunfire in the distance, there was no other noise. Manfred lay on his back. "Manfred? Are you alive, Manfred?" I crawled over to him. He looked awake, but he didn't move. I shook him. "Can you hear me?" *He's not going to answer.* I felt for his heart anyway. "Is anyone alive?" I called. "Anyone there?"

Can I be the only one? Did the others already go? I didn't dare stand up. *Someone could be waiting. Get away from here. Find a place to hide.*

There was almost no light now. I crawled away from the embankment, toward the thick brush leading into the pine trees, being careful not to make noise as I went. When I reached the pines, I stood up and stretched. I was alive. And I was all right.

But I was scared. *How can I find a way out of here when I don't even know where I am?* I had to move in the opposite direction of the gunfire. *What if that's toward the east?* I stopped and leaned against a tree. *The tank came from the other side of the tracks, so Berlin must be this way.* In the distance a fearsome, reddish glow lit up the sky. It had to be a burning house or a fire in a village. I walked toward it with confidence. *I can get help or directions.*

I stopped again. *What if the Russians are still there? I'll be shot.* I threw my steel helmet as far as I could into the woods. I took off my uniform jacket and buried it under a pile of snow and leaves. *At least my sweater is not Army. I won't look a soldier.* I walked on, colder now without the jacket but feeling safer from the Russians. *But how can I explain to our soldiers what I'm doing out here alone in the middle of the night?* Again I stopped.

Think, Dieter. Think. "Walk at night, hide during the day," I said aloud. *Ja, if I walk fast enough, I'll make it back before the Russians get there.*

Slow though I was, I walked through the fields toward the fire. I heard trucks in the distance, but in the dark I couldn't tell exactly where they were. *Are they going to the front or going back? I can't stand here all night. I need to know where I'm going.* I felt the cold suddenly and jumped up and down to warm up. *Stupid idiot! Why did I throw the jacket away? I could have waited.* I hugged myself to keep warm, but it didn't work. *I have to keep moving.* I walked on, still toward the fire glow. *If they were Russians, there would be more of them. Ja, there would be more.* I walked a little faster, feeling that home was beyond the glow.

Daybreak proved my direction right. The sun was behind me. I was walking west. I didn't recognize anything from our trip yesterday, and I saw no road signs. I had to find something fast, before the sun rose and I was a target. I started running, looking from side to side and occasionally behind me. *A shack. A farm building. Get out of sight.* Even as I ran, I shivered in the cold morning air.

In the distance I spotted a cluster of haystacks. I ran across the field. There was no one in sight, man or animal. I knelt at the first stack I came to and burrowed inside. The hay was old and moldy. I started to sneeze and held my nose. *If I start I can't stop. Not in a haystack.* When it passed, I made a little tunnel for air and arranged myself so I could breathe. *It feels so good to lie down.* I closed my eyes. *Just a little nap. Just a little sleep.*

The faint sound of motors startled me awake. It sounded like trucks again. *Ours or Russian?* They'd be too far away to see, even if I stood up. *It doesn't matter. I'm not too far from a road.* I took my knife from my pocket and laid it on the ground, pointing it in the direction of the trucks. I settled back to wait. I know west and now I'll find a road. Happily, I waited for complete darkness.

Later I reached a paved and deserted road, flanked by tall trees on both sides. A pale moon gave enough light for me to see overturned wagons, suitcases, and clothes thrown along the ditch. The stink of rotting flesh hung in the air, becoming stronger as I walked on. I held my nose and breathed through my mouth. Just a few meters ahead I saw the bloated body of a horse with its legs sticking straight up. I hurried around it, then slowed down. *What if I step on a human body?*

Although I seemed to be the only living thing in this ghostly landscape, I was not scared anymore. Way ahead I saw burning buildings. *There has to be someone alive.*

Thoughts came to me, thoughts about Mutti and Wolfgang, Ruth and Peter. *Is our house still standing . . .* I walked faster toward a farmhouse along the road. Flames had consumed most of it already, illuminating the street with a flickering, eerie, orange glow. Following a cloud of sparks, I looked up. What I saw made my blood turn ice cold: On a bent light pole across the road from the burning house hung the body of a man, a rope twisted around his neck. In passing, I noticed a piece of paper stuck to his chest. On it was printed I DESERTED MY FATHERLAND. I glanced at his face. It was not the face of a man but that of a boy no older than me! He wore the jacket of an Army uniform, white socks on feet without shoes, which probably had been taken off by someone who passed here before me. Quickly, I glanced around me, shuddered, and moved on. I had to get closer to Berlin before daybreak.

37

I wanted to crawl in a ditch and sleep. I wanted to get off my feet, to rest, to close my eyes, to eat something, but the constant rumble of artillery fire pushed me on. *A few hours of night, that's all. Keep moving.*

One foot after the other. *Links, rechts, links, rechts. Hier komm' ich, Mutti. Hier komm' ich, Mutti . . .* As I marched toward Berlin, I thought about how good my own cot will feel. *Mutti's soup. Wolfgang. Hier komm' ich, Mutti.* Even the cellar seemed like a welcome place. *Maybe Mutti will have potatoes. If I get to a farm . . . I can buy a potato . . .* I stopped. *I've got no money!* I felt in my pockets. *Where's my Ausweis? Without my papers . . .* Suddenly, money was not important. I saw myself hanging from a lamp post. *Nein! Not after all this.* I looked behind me. I was still alone. Nothing had changed. I searched my clothes but found no identification card. *It was in my jacket! I threw it away! Dummkopf. Or in the haystack? Yesterday? Or the day before?*

I can't stand here and wonder. Move. I looked toward the red sky in the west. The fear of having no identification made getting home my only goal. Food and sleep could come later. There was nothing I could do but get there—fast. I trotted now in spite of my aching feet, pushed more by the lack of an Ausweis in my pocket than by the gunfire at my back.

At the first sign of daylight I looked for a hideout. I spotted the outline of a shack, maybe fifty meters away, and staying close to the ground, ran toward it.

I crept inside the shed and sank to the floor, catching my breath and feeling safe. *There must be a house around here. When's the last time I ate?* Something rustled beside me. Too tired to jump, I shied away. "A rat!" I said aloud.

I held my breath. *Did anyone hear me?* I was so tired I didn't care. The ground I sat on was damp, and soon I was cold. I wanted to sleep, but I stood up and ran in place to warm myself. I stopped to catch my breath. Staying away from the door, I looked outside through the cracks in the walls. I looked in all directions, hoping to spot something I could sleep in that might be dry.

Gradually, the red glow in the sky toward Berlin changed to a cold gray. In a corner I found a piece of wood and placed it on the ground, pointing toward Berlin.

Suddenly, I heard voices far away. I froze. A car started — *or is it a truck? Who? Russians? Deutsche?* Trembling, I dashed from side to side, peeking through cracks. *There!* A hundred meters to the north soldiers walked behind a slow-moving small truck. *They're headed east. Deutsche.* I counted twenty-two. My eyes strained to see if there were any more. *That's all of them.* I breathed easier now. I looked again to the west at some buildings I'd noticed. Surrounded by high pine trees, a house and barn were no more than two hundred meters away. Smoke rose from a chimney. *Someone is there. I can crawl along that row of bushes.* I looked at the rising sun. *Is it too light? Do I dare?* Hunger and cold made up my mind. I started running for the bush row.

Staying as low as I could, I reached a nearly collapsed barn next to a small house. I crouched behind a pile of boards and watched the house for several minutes. Aside from the smoking chimney, I saw no sign of anyone, so I stood up.

"Halt. Wer ist da?"

My arms shot into the air.

"Ich bin Deutsch. Don't shoot," I said, afraid to turn around.

"Komm' hier, schnell."

I turned and ran for the door. It stood open just enough for me to slip inside. I faced an old man with snow-white hair, leaning heavily on crutches that looked like thick tree branches. For a moment he eyed me suspiciously.

"From where did you come? Nobody lives here anymore."

"Berlin. My family lives in Berlin. I want to get back, but I've lost my papers."

"What do you want from me?"

"To hide, ja? Until dark?"

The old man looked at me in silence, then his eyes softened. "Without your papers they will hang you."

"I know. I've seen them."

He turned around and walked ahead of me into a small room, empty except for a dirty mattress along one wall and a small iron stove beside it. Through another door I saw a kitchen.

He pointed to the stove. "Warm yourself. You are hungry?"

"Ja, I am very hungry."

He went to the kitchen, and when he came back, hobbling on only one crutch, he offered me a small plate with a piece of ham and two slices of bread.

"Soldiers stayed here last night. They left this for me."

I stuffed a slice of bread in my mouth and took a bite of the ham. "I saw them a while ago," I mumbled with a full mouth.

He returned to the kitchen and brought me back a cup of water. I drained the cup. "Danke. More, please?" He went back and filled the cup again. He watched in silence as I took another bite of bread, a bite of ham, and a swallow of water.

"Why are you still here?" I asked between mouthfuls. "You are not afraid of the Russians?"

He waved his hand. "Too old I am to be afraid." He leaned his crutch against the wall and slid into a chair. "All my life this is my home. Too many memories to leave now. My daughter-in-law—" He pointed to a picture of a man and woman on the wall above the mattress. "She took the boys and left a long time ago. My son . . . at Stalingrad." He paused a moment. "My son, he was killed at Stalingrad."

"Also my father."

"At Stalingrad?"

"Ja. He's buried at Krasnodom."

I swallowed the last bite of ham and wiped my mouth with the sleeve of my sweater. "Danke, lieber Herr."

"So many at Stalingrad. You have good fortune to know where he lies." He looked away, as if remembering something. "I will find him sometime. When I am dead, I will find him." After a moment, he looked up and smiled. "You were hungry, ja?"

I nodded. "Very hungry. Where did she go?" I nodded toward the picture. "Your daughter-in-law. Did she go far?"

He shook his head. "I don't know. At least they got away, Gott Sei Dank. I pray they are safe." His voice was sad. "Only the young are left. What terrible things he does, this Hitler." He reached for his crutch and stood up. He motioned to a straight chair against the wall. "By the window you should sit. Watch the road." He came over and picked up the empty plate. "I will watch out the other side. We see somebody come, you hide in the cellar." He pointed to a door in the kitchen. "Down there, behind the shelves."

"Is it far to Berlin?"

"If you walk fast, one night you will be there." *He's like Opa.* "You can't watch now, can you? Tired, ja?

"Ja. I'm very tired. I've walked all night."

"Maybe you sleep first. I will watch the road."

"Time you leave, Junger Mann." I jumped awake. "How long—"

"All day you slept." He handed me a cup. I sat up and drank the water.

"Take this." He handed me a jacket. "My son's," he said. "You need to be warm."

I stood up and put it on. The sleeves hung down below my hands but it was warm. "Danke. I was very cold last night. Danke."

"Schnell." He shoved me toward the door. "It is dark enough now. Don't waste time." He patted my head. "God speed."

I turned to thank him, but the door was shut. Chilled awake by the evening air, I was thankful for the warmth of the jacket. I buried my hands deep inside the pockets and stumbled up to the road. My hand closed over a piece of paper in my right pocket. *My papers? Of course not, Dummkopf. This isn't your jacket.*

The rumbling booms of artillery fire convinced me I had no time to waste, and I headed toward the red sky over Berlin.

The longer I walked the more my left foot hurt. *I wish I had his crutch.* I limped along for hours when suddenly, out of the darkness, I spotted shadows ahead of me on the road. Voices, too. *People!* I slowed. *Who are they?* As I walked on, the outlines of buildings appeared from the dark along one side of the road. Soon they were on both sides. The sky became a brighter red, bright enough to see that the shadows ahead of me were small groups of women and children. *Refugees. All going to Berlin.*

I caught up with the nearest group—two women, one

very old, the young one pulling a cart. In it was a small child, wrapped in a blanket and lying on boxes.

"Is this a Berlin suburb, liebe Frau?" I asked.

"Probably." She didn't look at me.

"Where are you from?"

"Frankfurt."

"That's more than fifty kilometers. All this way you walked?"

She didn't answer. I walked on, passing more people. The stream of people walked out around the bloated, stinking body of a horse, its ropes still tied to an overturned wagon. Broken suitcases, clothing spilling from them, were strewn about the pavement. Like everyone ahead of me, I stepped over a rolled-up mattress and the shattered pieces of a lamp. I was glad to be a part of the flow of refugees. *I'm almost home. If they just don't ask me . . .* I avoided looking at the occasional gendarmes and soldiers standing alongside the street. For the first time in my life, I wished I was shorter and looked younger. *I won't have a chance if I'm stopped with no Ausweis.*

But I felt the best I'd felt since I had left home. I was getting closer. Swallowed up in the stream of refugees, I moved along as if I belonged to them.

Dawn brought another gray, overcast morning, damp and cold. I walked slower now, limping badly, but at least keeping pace with others. With each step a sharp pain shot through my left heel. I glanced around. Many of the old men and women limped. They walked slowly, with their heads down. Some of them looked like every step hurt, and they moaned as they walked along. I fit in perfectly.

A few meters ahead, at the next corner, stood two men in civilian clothes with black-lettered armbands. *Polizei!* They watched the refugees pass. My heart pounded. I felt the paper in my pocket and wished it was my identification papers. I dragged my left foot even slower. *Don't look at them.*

Keep your head down. I passed by, feeling their eyes in my back.

"Junge!"

I kept walking.

"Junge!" he shouted, louder this time. "Halt!"

I turned around and pointed to myself.

"Ja, Du." He motioned for me to come back.

Don't show how scared you are. Walk slow. Look normal, you're almost home. I limped back and faced them.

"Ja? You want me?"

"A Krüppel?"

"Jawohl, Herr Polizei Mann. Since I was born." I patted my right thigh. "This leg is shorter."

"Where do you live?"

"In Babelsberg."

"This is East Berlin. Why are you here?"

"I was with my aunt in Fürstenwalde, but I want to get back to my mother and brother. My father died at Stalingrad."

He studied me with a cold stare. "Wait here."

He walked into the crowd of refugees and stopped the next wooden cart, pulled by a woman. He pointed at me as he talked to her. She shook her head and he let her pass. He stopped another cart and spoke to the old man who pulled it. Again he pointed at me. The old man looked and then poked through his cart. He brought out a stick. *A walking stick.* The Polizei Mann shook his hand and came back to me.

"Take this," he said, handing me the stick.

"Danke."

He patted my shoulder. "You have a long way to go. Most of the S-Bahn is bombed out."

The other man had disappeared inside the door of the house behind him. Now he came back out, carrying a tin cup, which he handed me. "You look thirsty."

I drank in big gulps and handed the cup back. "Danke."

"Now go. Heil Hitler." Both raised their arms. Leaning

258

on my new stick, I weakly returned their salute, turned and hobbled away.

My hand closed over the paper in my pocket again. Now that it was light, I could see what it was. I pulled it out. *Two Marks. The old man gave me money. I didn't even ask his name.* I searched for an S-Bahn station. When I reached it, I looked at the map by the ticket counter that showed the bombed-out tracks. A woman sat behind the window reading a book.

"Can you tell me if the U-Bahn has more lines—"

"I don't know," she said without looking up. "Go to the U-Bahn, and find out for yourself."

"Damn it, you work for both don't you? You stupid—"

Her icy glare stopped me. I walked away quickly, cursing under my breath. *I'm the idiot to get myself in trouble now.*

The cane made walking easier. My foot hurt so much there was no need to fake my limp anymore. The streets began to look familiar, even though only burned-out shells and mountains of bricks lined both sides. Shrapnel holes in a large street sign left enough letters for me to know that I was on the Schloss Strasse in Steglitz. A small crowd stood next to a bus stop sign. *I'm in luck.*

"The buses still run that way?" I asked a woman, pointing to the west.

"Ja, sometimes. If we can get on it." She looked down at my leg and the cane. "Bist Du ein Soldat?"

Before I could make up my mind about how to answer, she grabbed my hand and pulled me to the head of the line. "Let him on first. He was a soldier."

She walked back to her spot. When the bus finally came, only a few of us could get on. The woman smiled and waved as I climbed the steps. I paid for my ticket and thought about the old man on the farm. *If it wasn't for him . . . And I don't even know his name.*

259

The bus stayed packed all the way to the Wannsee S-Bahn station. I held on to the bar above my head and fell asleep once or twice, waking up quickly when my knees buckled. But the bus was so crowded, I couldn't fall.

After a long ride, the driver stopped and opened the doors. "I go no further. Everyone off. There is no S-Bahn to Babelsberg and Potsdam today."

I made it. Three or four kilometers but close enough. It was almost dark, so I decided to take the shortest way, following the S-Bahn tracks through the woods and brush. It would go right up to our house. *They won't be guarding the tracks.*

Did we get hit? Nein. We've been safe. Ja, they could have hit it. What day is it? I've been gone . . . A week? Two? Did Mutti get my message? If she didn't . . . What if she left? Nein, she wouldn't without me. Would she? She might. Nein, she wouldn't do that! I stopped and sat down on the side of the tracks. *What am I going to do?*

"You! Over there! Why are you sitting? You do not hear the bombers?"

The blisters didn't matter anymore. I ran as well as I could. The S-Bahn bridge over the Teltow Canal was heavily damaged, but the road bridge next to it was open. *Ten minutes and I'll be home.* I ran across the bridge and down the street. *Hier komm' ich, Mutti. Hier komm' ich.*

There it was—our house. Standing. Ludwigs' and the apartment building. All three standing. I ran toward Ludwigs' door. I pushed but it wouldn't open. It was barricaded from the inside. The cane served its last useful purpose. Repeatedly, and with newfound strength, I smashed it against the door. "Open up. It's me. Dieter," I yelled. "Mutti, are you there? Anybody?"

I turned and looked at our house. *They can't be over there.* Again I smacked the cane against the door.

"Wer ist Da? What do you want." It was Wolfgang.

"Dicker. It's me. Dieter. Open the door."

"Mutti, komm' schnell," he yelled. "Dieter is back."

I heard him move whatever was against the door. I pushed it open. Wolfgang jumped at me, and I fell backward, catching myself against the banister of the porch. He wrapped his arms around my waist. "You're home. I love you, Dieter."

My mother stood in the doorway, staring like she didn't know me.

"It's me, Mutti. Dieter." I looked at her, but she didn't seem to see me. "I wasn't gone that long." Wolfgang pulled my hand, trying to get me inside. Ruth stood behind my mother, smiling.

"What's wrong with Mutti?" I asked. "Is she all right?" *Did she go crazy? Or lose her voice?* As if Ruth could read my thoughts, she shook her head, still smiling.

Wolfgang pushed me into Mutti. I reached to touch her, but with one swift motion her arms closed around me and crushed me against her.

"My Dieter. My own Dieter." She rocked me from side to side and cried. "We thought we would never see you again, lieber Dieter." She stepped back and looked into my face. "What did they do to my boy? Where were you? Who took you? Everyone we asked. We went to your school. All they said was you went to a camp."

"Ja. A camp outside Potsdam. We were in a truck, and right by here we rode. But the driver, he wouldn't stop or slow down. We yelled. Didn't you hear us?"

She shook her head. "Nein. I did not know where you were." She kissed my cheek again.

"And I gave a woman at Sundgauer Strasse our name and address. And a message for you. You didn't get it?"

"Nein. But now it does not matter, ja? You are home." She hugged me again, and we rocked back and forth.

"Mutti, bitte. Can't I lie down? I walked for days, and my feet are full of blisters."

I moaned as I took off my shoes. The sock on my left foot was caked to the skin with dried blood.

"Mein Gott, Dieter." Mutti kissed me again. "My baby. Ruth, bring some water. This has to be soaked. Hurry, please."

I talked while my feet were soaking, and every few minutes she tugged gently on the bloody sock to loosen it.

"And Manfred? And Helmut? They were missing, too. You were with them?"

"Ja. We rode together."

"They are safe? They came home with you?"

"I don't know, Mutti. We were on our own after that tank rolled away from us."

"A tank? Nein, Dieter. I do not want to hear."

In silence she worked on my foot in the now-reddened water.

It felt so good to lie back and be with my family. I thought about the old farmer. *In his memory, I should save at least one Mark of his money.*

"You stay in bed down here for a while, Dieter. I don't even want you upstairs, verstanden? If you had listened to me in the first place, they would not have sent you to the Front."

I nodded.

"The stories we hear from refugees are terrible. One told us the officers watch for the older boys. When they see one, he is taken away from his family. Sent immediately to the Front."

"I think Vati saved me one time."

She smoothed the blanket around me. "Ja? How was that?"

"Two policemen stopped me. I told them that Vati died

at Stalingrad. And that I was a Krüppel. They gave me that cane over there. And then a cup of water."

A proud smile crossed her face. "You take care of yourself good." She patted my cheek. "But too fast you grow up."

"Remember? Vati said I was the man in the house. I'm supposed to be grown up. How's Peter doing with Oma and Opa? Are they getting bombed like us?"

"Nein. They are still in that small village, east of Würzburg. I wish it was west since the Americans are close to the Rhine. That's west of Würzburg."

"The Americans? Ja? Maybe they will get here first."

Wolfgang came into the bunker, followed by Ruth who shut the door with a loud bang. "Here they come again," she said, "right on time for the morning bombs."

We listened to the radio day after day, waiting for announcements, and followed the reports of how far the Americans had pushed into the western parts of Germany.

Soon, another rumor spread. The Americans would not, or could not, reach Berlin ahead of the Soviets. The rumors were heard so often we began to believe them more than the official reports on State Radio.

Day and night, the flow of refugees was endless. I wanted to talk to them, but Mutti threatened to lock me into the bunker.

"I am not going to lose you again, mein Herr. You stay out of sight." Her look scared me into silence.

I went up to the second floor and looked out a front window at the people who trudged past. From up there, they looked like a slow-moving river. The small carts they pulled were piled high with suitcases and boxes. They rattled over the cobblestones with a noise I'd gotten so used to, I didn't hear it unless I stopped to listen. Some people carried babies or other bundles. Little children walked alongside many of them. *Where do they go when the bombers come?*

263

Looking at them, I was glad I was safe inside Ludwigs' house with the bunker. *What is it like to hide under a cart?* The front door slammed, and I looked down at the yard. It was Mutti. She walked through the yard and out the gate to a woman sitting on the sidewalk. The woman looked up at her and they talked a moment. Mutti helped her up. Together they came slowly back to the house, Mutti's arm around the woman's shoulder.

By the time I got downstairs Mutti had pulled chairs close to the stove in the kitchen. Ruth and Wolfgang sat beside them.

The woman was old, her face as gray as the hair hanging out from under a dirty black scarf. Her mud-splattered shoes were held together by thick strings. Her hands shook as she held them above the stove.

"This is Frau Schultze," Mutti said. "She used to live in Danzig."

"Danzig? In Prussia? That's farther than—"

"Ja, Dieter. We know in Ost-Preussen it is."

I looked at the woman. "You walked over four hundred kilometers?"

She shook her head weakly. "Nein, nein," she muttered "Sometimes . . ."

Mutti put her hand on my shoulder. "Don't tire her with questions, Dieter. Let her rest. She didn't always walk. Sometimes there were rides. A train. A few times, buses. Once a cart."

"They are awful . . . Murder Schweine . . . daughter tried . . . " Frau Schultze mumbled in a low voice, difficult to hear.

Mutti stroked the woman's head. "You do not have to talk. Get some—"

"I warn you, all of you." Her hands were folded in her lap now, and she twisted her wedding ring as she spoke. "My daughter and her two children lived close by. The Russians came. Our soldiers pushed them back." Tears filled the wrinkles around her eyes. "I went to their apartment. I found them." Her eyes widened. "I found them."

Mutti reached down and held the woman's hands. "Frau Schultze. Do not talk about it."

"My grandchildren. Mein Gott! My babies." She wiped the tears away with a grubby hand. "All dead. All gone. I cannot stay here now." She pushed herself out of the chair and shuffled to her feet. At the door, she turned around. "Leave. Do not stay here," she said. "Bitte, Frau. Save your family."

She left us in stunned silence. Wolfgang stood close to Mutti. "Are they going to shoot us, Mutti? Do Russians really shoot civilians?"

"Nein. We cannot believe they are savages. We will not be shot."

"Where's she's going to go?" I asked.

"Wherever she has to," Mutti answered. "Komm' now. Schnell. Soon the bombers will come again."

For most of the rest of March, I stayed out of sight in our neighborhood, venturing outside only after dark. By the beginning of April, the aerial bombing had come to an omnious halt. Several days and nights we nervously anticipated the final blast of thousands of tons of explosives raining onto the city, but the time passed without the wailing of a single siren. Then the lack of bombs made us even more afraid.

Several days in a row we left the bunker and actually enjoyed the outside. We went to our house and examined the damage. Mutti and Ruth swept the plaster dust from the floors, laughing at their feeble attempt at spring cleaning. Mutti even gave in to Wolfgang's pleadings, and one night she let us all go to sleep in our own beds.

In one swift motion I sat up, instantly wide awake. The cardboard in our window shook, and from the living room I heard our last remaining glass window rattle. I jumped out of bed and ran into the hall. Mutti was there, the flashlight in her hand.

"What is this noise? It is different than bomb attacks. Did you hear any bombers or sirens?"

"Nein, I didn't hear anything. But I know what makes this noise. It is artillery fire but still far away."

She brushed by me into the kitchen and stood at the stove, trying to start a fire.

"Go wake up Ruth and your brother. We better get back into the bunker. If I can get a fire going, we will warm up before we go."

It wasn't yet light when we walked over to Ludwigs,' but flashes of white, yellow, orange and red covered the sky to the east.

Ruth locked the bunker door behind us.

"Now we wait," Mutti said.

For a long time we sat on our cots, silent, staring at each other and the floor and the walls. I lay down, but I wasn't tired, so I stood up and walked around. Then I was bored, so I sat down again. Finally, Mutti walked over to Wolfgang and put her arm around his shoulder.

"Why is your hand shaking, Mutti?" he asked.

She didn't answer but moved her arm away and turned the radio on. Nothing, not even static. The lightbulb flickered once, then again. Mutti looked at me, alarmed.

"Do you remember what Herr Ludwig showed you on that motor out there, the generator?"

"Ja, I think so. I smell something—like oil burning. I'll look at it."

Outside, I put my hand on the metal housing of the generator. It was hot and made a strange noise. I hurried back inside.

"It's been running too long. Maybe we should shut it off for a while. Should I?"

Mutti nodded.

"Then we can leave the door open for fresh air. Maybe even the emergency door. Is that all right?"

Mutti nodded.

"I think he is right, Lis." Ruth stood up. "Why don't we go back upstairs. It is too depressing in here. I feel like I'm choking." We followed her out the front door and sat on the steps.

It felt good to be outside again, but still nobody said anything. The only sounds came from the street, the crunching of wooden wheels of overloaded wagons on the cobblestones, a baby crying.

Wolfgang snuggled up to Mutti and put his arms around her neck. "What is going to happen to us, Mutti?"

"I don't know. We will wait and see."

"Can't you go out to the street and ask people?"

Mutti looked at him with a thin smile that looked like she was in pain. "Not now, Wolfgang. Maybe later."

"Can I go with you when you go?"

"Nein. But you and your big brother can collect more wood for our stove. That's an important job. As much as you can carry, bitte?" She looked at the sky. "We do not have to worry about bombers now, so go."

We walked across the street, through the stream of refugees, through the nursery, and into the woods behind it.

38

For a few days we stayed in our house, slept in our beds, ate
in our kitchen—if my mother and Ruth were able to scrounge
up something from a store in Babelsberg.

The rumbling from the east kept getting louder, like a
thunderstorm soon to be overhead, and the flow of refugees
slowed to a trickle. Rumors spread that the Red Army was
closing in on Berlin from all sides, even from the west, and
that the rest of the Russians were smashing their way toward the Elbe River. No one doubted the stories of burning
and looting, rape and murder.

One day, about midmorning, Mutti, Ruth, and I leaned
on our elbows on the wall along the front of the veranda,
letting the sun warm us. Bright green leaves sprouted from
tree branches. Spring was finally here. Below us, Wolfgang
sat on the bottom step, drawing lines in the sand with a
stick. Footsteps in the hallway broke our silence, and we
turned around.

"Guten Morgen, Frau Drescher."

I stared at the woman standing at the door. She smiled
nervously, and for a moment I thought she looked like the
girl from the apartment building next door. But she had missing teeth, and there were dark lines on her forehead and in
the corners of her eyes. She looked like a freak.

My mother's eyes widened. "Is that you, Frau Schneider? Mein Gott, what happened to you?"

"Ja, Frau Drescher, it's me. I made myself look as old as I could. Don't you know what the Russians do to Deutsche women? Even young girls?"

"Please, do not speak so loud. Wolfgang is sitting down here. He can hear you," Mutti whispered. "Come inside."

In the living room Ruth kept staring at Frau Schneider. "How did you do all that? You look like you're seventy."

Frau Schneider laughed, exposing her blackened teeth. "It was not difficult, Ruth. Flour I used on my hair and face, my eyebrow pencil for the wrinkles, and black tape on my teeth. The people in our house told me I should have left a long time ago." Her voice trailed off. "I don't know why I didn't."

For a few minutes nobody spoke. Then, with a long sigh, Frau Schneider added, "I was born here in Berlin. I love this city, and I want to stay. My friends are here, and this is where I belong."

She pulled a handkerchief from her pocket and dabbed at her eyes. "I cannot cry or the flour, it will wash off."

My mother looked at Ruth.

"We better think about doing something like Frau Schneider. That artillery fire is getting louder—and closer. Perhaps we should move back to the bunker." Mutti stared straight ahead as she spoke. Her voice was flat. "Anything else have you heard about the Russians, Frau Schneider?"

Frau Schneider glanced quickly at the veranda. "Ja," she answered. "The Americans have told the Red Army they have complete freedom to do anything they want to Deutsche. They can do to us like our soldiers did to the Russians." She shuddered.

"Do what to us? What did our soldiers do to the Russians?"

"Can I speak in front of Dieter?"

"He is old enough. Go on, bitte."

"They look for women and young girls. They rape them first, sometimes they nail their hands to fences or walls afterward and shoot them with their machine guns. A boy from Gorlitz told me a soldier slit his mother's belly open because she screamed she was pregnant. Another was—"

"Genug!" Mutti's hand slammed the table. "No more! I do not believe our soldiers did that to Russian women. My Karl would never do that. Never!"

"I am very sorry, Frau Drescher." Frau Schneider patted Mutti's arm. "But these are not rumors anymore. There's proof that—

"Nein! I do not believe it." Mutti kept shaking her head. "My Karl, he would not do things like that."

Frau Schneider stood up. "I have to go. Be safe."

When she reached the door, Wolfgang walked in from the veranda and stared at us.

"What happened? I heard Mutti yell. What's wrong?"

Mutti got up and walked over to him. "Nothing, Wolfgang. Frau Schneider told us something that scared me for a moment. That's all." She put her arm around his shoulder and gently pushed him back out onto the veranda.

A moment later, the noise of a truck engine sputtered closer and stopped. "Komm' schnell, Dieter," Wolfgang shouted. "An Army truck with soldiers."

"Mein Gott! The Russians?" Mutti yelled as she and Ruth jumped up, and I bolted for the door.

"Nein, nein, nein," Wolfgang said with disgust. "They are *good* soldiers. They are *our* soldiers."

We stood at the top of the stairs, watching several men climb off the truck with picks and shovels in their hands, rifles slung over their shoulders.

On the other side of our street, two of them immediately started to smash their picks into the sidewalk. As soon as they had loosened the small, square stones, two other soldiers dug a foxhole about one-and-a-half meters long, and deep enough for them to stand in with only their heads and shoulders above ground level.

"What are they doing, Dieter? Why are they digging holes into the sidewalk?"

"They're making foxholes, can't you figure that out?" I didn't want to let the sudden rush of fear in my stomach come out of my mouth. "Want to go over and watch how they do it?"

They worked feverishly, not even noticing us. Closer and closer we inched, trying to see as much as we could. Suddenly, one stopped shoveling. "What are you dumme Kinder doing out here?" he yelled. "Get back into your house! Can't you hear the gunfire? Go! Now!"

We turned and started running toward the house. Behind me, another voice yelled.

"Hey, you! The big boy!" My heart pounded in my ears. Without stopping, I turned my head and looked back over my shoulder.

"How old are you?"

"Nine." I ran across the street, Wolfgang behind me. I opened the basement door and pulled him inside, ice-cold fear in my stomach. My chest heaved as I tried to catch my breath.

"They're coming down the stairs, Dieter!" He clung to me, his arms wrapped around my waist.

Mein Gott! They're coming for me!

"Dieter! Wolfgang! What happened?" Mutti knelt in front of me. "Why are you hiding? We saw from the veranda. What did they say?"

"One told us to get back in the house," I whispered. "And another one asked how old I was."

Mutti pushed us ahead of her. "Get to Ludwigs' bunker. Stay low so they won't see you from the street." Before she shut the door, she called to Ruth. "Stay upstairs by the door and watch."

I shut the bunker door and locked it. For endless minutes, we sat still and quiet. The faint noise of artillery fire seeped into the bunker. The only other sound was the wild beating of my heart.

Finally, we heard the knock on the door. One long, three short, then one more long. *Ruth.* Mutti opened the door, and she came in.

"They got on the truck and left. Nobody is out there now, just the holes." Her mouth laughed, but her eyes didn't.

"We will all stay down here now. Ruth and I will check occasionally, but you, Dieter, you stay down here until I tell you it is safe." Mutti shook her finger at me. "That, Herr Steiner, is an order."

During the night we took turns staying awake, like sentries, for short periods. Ludwigs' outside door could not be locked anymore, and even with the heavy chair leaning against it from the inside, anyone could get it open who really tried.

The next day I was bored, tired of looking at the gray cement walls of the bunker, listening to artillery fire getting closer.

"Mutti, can't I at least look out the window upstairs?"

"All right, but don't let anybody see you from the street. Is that clear?"

"Jawohl, meine Mutter!" I hurried up the stairs, eager to see daylight.

Cardboard covered all but one of the windows in the Ludwigs' front bedroom. Staying well back in the middle of the room, I could see a small portion of the street between the trees. I knelt so I could see the foxholes. *Soldiers are in them!*

I almost fell getting down the stairs.

"Mutti, Ruth! There are soldiers in the foxholes! They're facing west. And their rifles point that way, too!"

Ruth jumped up and clapped. "Gut!" she said, dancing around. "The Americans! They will not be as bad as the Russians. They won't kill us." She grabbed my mother. "Lis, we don't have to be afraid."

Mutti smiled. "At least we can maybe get some sleep. And relax." She put her head back and closed her eyes. Her whole body went limp. Then she bolted up. "But the American—they have been at the Elbe for a week. Why are they not here?"

"Who cares?" Ruth reached over and pulled Mutti to her feet. "Just so they are the ones when the time comes." They jumped around, hugging each other, and then they grabbed me. "And I won't have to wear this," Ruth said, pulling the tape off her teeth.

I felt good that my announcement had changed the mood of the family. I felt safer now and walked toward the front door and out into the yard. Through the fence I saw a small stake truck stopped near the two foxholes, its motor running, an infantry soldier leaning against its open door. A couple of women, whose backs were turned to me, and four or five children looked interested in whatever was loaded in the back of the truck. I turned to see if Mutti was watching. She wasn't. I ran toward the truck.

A large pile of weapons filled the truckbed: Panzerfausts, hand grenades, rifles, machine pistols, small handguns, boxes upon boxes of ammunition, even bayonets for the rifles!

"So you have finally decided to defend our Führer!"

Startled, I turned around. Frau Witte! I hadn't seen her in weeks. Her face was gray, and strands of black hair hung around her eyes like a witch. Her bony finger poked hard into my shoulder.

"After all, the HJ taught you how to fire rifles and the Panzerfausts, ja?"

I was scared. With a quick glance at the soldier, I could only nod. *Did he hear? He must have.* But he continued to stare at a piece of paper in his hand, still leaning against the truck's door. Then he looked up.

"Schnell! Take what you want! I have to get across the Canal before . . . " He stopped abruptly and climbed into the driver's seat.

Before what? I reached for a handgun, a box of ammunition, and turned to get back to the house. Frau Witte, still behind me, blocked my way.

"A Luger? What are you going to do with a Luger? Stop a tank? You really think—"

"Ja. I think." I pushed past her, ran into Ludwigs' yard and stopped near the front door of the house.

"Can we see the gun? Bitte?" Behind me were the little kids. "How does it fire?" one asked. "Are you going to kill a Russian?" another wanted to know. "Can I hold it?" said another. "Can you really shoot someone?"

"Well, ja. I guess so. If I have to, I will. I was in the Hitler Youth. And I've been at the Front. I know how to handle weapons." I stood very straight, heads taller than any of them. I held the gun in my right hand. "Now you see, first, you have to put a bullet in it. It won't fire without a bullet." I opened the ammunition box and took out a bullet. "See, this is how to slide a bullet into the—they call it the chamber, or the magazine."

"Then can you shoot it?"

I laughed. "Nein. The safety switch here must always be on, so it can't fire by accident." I pushed the safety, holding the gun in my right hand with its barrel, pointing downward, resting between thumb and forefinger of my left hand.

"Watch. It can't fire now." I squeezed the trigger.

A deafening crack and a sharp stinging pain in my left hand. For a moment, sheer terror gripped me. Blood was on my left hand. *I've blown off my fingers!* No, I could move them. They were all there.

"Dieter, who did that? Did you?" Mutti rushed up to me

274

and shook me by the shoulders. "What did you do?" She kept shaking me."Tell me right now. What happened?"

"I . . . I don't know. I thought the safety was on, and—"

She pointed to the children and started yelling. "Do you realize what you just did? You idiot! You could have killed one of them! You could have killed us. Where did you get that gun?" She raised her arm as if to hit me. The children scrambled away.

"A soldier handed them out on the street. Frau Witte was there and she—"

"Nein! I do not want to hear that. Do you know that bullet came through the kitchen window and hit the ceiling? It could have hit Ruth—or me. How much war do you need? Get rid of the gun now." I backed away as she raised her arm again.

"I'm sorry, Mutti. Really. I thought the safety was on."

"I said get rid of it now! Then let me see your hand."

"It's nothing, Mutti. It must have been the recoil."

I looked around for a hiding place. *Even if Mutti's mad, I may need to use it to save her and Wolfgang.* On wobbly legs, I walked toward a large evergreen bush in the front yard where we used to play hide-and-seek. *I hope that old birdnest is still there. It's a perfect place to hide the gun.* I poked through the branches. *There it is!* After covering the gun and the box of bullets with another branch, I circled the bush. You couldn't see anything inside it.

Now I want to see the hole in the ceiling.

Even Ruth gave me an icy glare when I went in. I looked at the small black hole above the table while Mutti bandaged my hand. She was still breathing hard when she put her hands on my shoulders. She stared into my eyes. "Promise you will never pick up another weapon again."

"Ja. I'm sorry."

Her hands stayed on my shoulders. "Promise me, Dieter!"

"Ja, I promise."

275

"Can Wolfgang go with me for a few minutes to the canal? We'll be right back."

"Ja, go. He needs some exercise."

I wanted to run all the way, make a race with Wolfgang. But my legs didn't hold up for more than fifty meters. I was panting, my knees were rubber. When we reached the bridge over the Teltow Canal, a soldier stopped us.

"Halt! You cannot cross here anymore. Go back!"

"Why not, Herr Soldat?" Wolfgang asked.

"Back to your mother. Why are you running around here, anyway? This is not a playground anymore. Go!" He waved his rifle at us.

I spotted soldiers holding packets of something and climbing through the underside of the S-Bahn bridge. Watching for a moment, I tried to see what they had. *Dynamite!* I pulled Wolfgang by his arm. "Schnell, Dicker! Run!"

Gasping for breath, we reached the house quickly and ran into the kitchen.

"Mutti, they're getting ready to blow up all the bridges!"

"I knew that would happen. They're destroying everything. Sit down and eat some Mehlsuppe. That is all we have to today."

"But they're going to blow up the bridges!"

"And how does that affect us, Herr Steiner? Not at all. Sit down."

I sat. The thin flour and water mixture didn't even look like soup. I wasn't hungry enough to want any right then, so I rested my elbows on the table and sat with my chin on my hands.

"This dinner not special enough for you, Dieter?" Mutti pushed the soup bowl closer to me. "Beggars are not choosers, junger mann. This may not taste good, but it will keep you alive. Eat."

The earth shook violently with the first explosion at the exact moment I lifted the spoon to my mouth. Wolfgang screamed. The table lifted off the floor, soup splattered onto my face, and the chair slid out from under me. Wolfgang's screams came through the ear-splitting thunder of the next explosion, the next one, and another, and more.

I was on the floor, my chair toppled behind me. Ruth and Mutti were under the table and Wolfgang under them. Just as suddenly, the floor stood still again. Pieces of plaster from the ceiling covered the floor around us, and a fine white dust floated in the air like fog. We all started coughing.

Mutti was the first one up. "There went all the bridges," she said. "The Americans must be closer than we think."

We went outside and brushed the dust off each other. Then we broke into laughs—we all had white hair.

39

If I'd been at a festival and these were fireworks, I probably would have loved it. But the rifle and machine gun fire, exploding mortar shells, and the swishing of artillery grenades promised pain, or worse, death. But I was used to it. I just hunched my shoulders higher and crouched low to the ground when I ran between our house and Ludwigs'. It was routine now.

I sat on the toilet barrel, trying to hurry. A stray bullet ripped through the trees, and I ducked. *I don't want to be killed sitting on the toilet!*

A horrible scream rose above the gunfire. *Who did they hit?* The noise came in waves from somewhere nearby. I jumped off the barrel and pulled up my pants. *Where does it come from?* I ran through the front yard toward the street, fastening my pants and slipping the suspenders over my shoulders as I went.

A horse! It lay on its side on the cobblestones in front of Frau Kundert's building, its head arched back, its legs pawing the air. It was still harnessed to a small wooden Army supply wagon. I ran up closer. *It won't stop screaming!* I covered my ears. *Die! Die! Please die!* I moved toward it. The pool of blood by its front legs grew as I watched. *Nein! Please die! Stop!*

I ran to Frau Kundert's. She came to the door. "A horse, Frau Kundert," I yelled, pointing to the street. "It's been shot. Or hit by shrapnel. You have to do something."

She hurried inside and came back with her coat on. She passed me without saying a word. She had a long-bladed knife in her hand.

"Danke, Frau Kundert! You can do something!"

Without answering, she walked toward the screaming horse. Then I saw in her other hand a gray metal bucket. She sank to her knees along the back of the horse and the knife disappeared.

"What are you *doing?* Nein, Frau Kundert, nein. Bitte."

The horse's legs kicked violently.

I tried to scream louder than the horse. "Bitte, Frau Kundert. It's not even dead!"

She stood up, her hands and the front of her coat glistening with blood. A hunk of meat filled her bucket. She shuffled back toward her building without looking at me.

I took the three steps to the door in one leap. Down the hall and into the kitchen I ran, crashing into Mutti. Ruth stopped her from falling, and both of them stared at me, eyes wide open with fear.

"What is it, Dieter?" Mutti asked, holding me by the shoulders. "Such horrible noise! And you are crying?"

"Frau Kundert . . . " I stopped to catch my breath. "On the street . . . "

"Frau Kundert? She is hurt?" Mutti shook me. "Tell us!"

"Nein, it's a horse. It's been hit. And Frau Kundert—she cut—"

"A horse?" Mutti looked surprised. "Schnell, Ruth. A dying horse!"

Ruth snatched open a drawer and pulled out a large knife while my mother grabbed a small bucket from the pantry.

"Nein, Mutti, it's alive," I cried as they rushed past me. "Nein, nein, nein!"

40

Throughout the night explosions came closer and louder. Toward morning the bulb flickered two, three times, then total darkness. The generator sputtered and went quiet.

"Get the candles, Dieter. We put the last battery into the flashlight, and that's for an emergency."

I groped around in the corner, feeling for the candle box.

"What do you call this, Mutti? Not an emerg—"

"Just bring the candle! How many are left in the box?"

I struck a match. "Here, Wolfgang, you count them."

"Four, Mutti. And the one on the table."

Ruth watched me as I lit the candle in front of her.

"It is safe in here, Dieter. You don't have to be afraid."

"I'm not!"

"Then why does your hand shake so bad?"

"Isn't yours? I haven't slept all night and my stomach hurts." I rubbed my ice-cold hands together, then stuck them in my armpits. "Maybe it's already light enough outside. I want to go upstairs and look around."

Mutti pointed her finger at me. "You stay away from the windows and come right back!"

"Jawohl, liebe Mutter. Stop worrying. I'm old enough to know better now. I've learned."

Outside the bunker, artillery explosions sounded closer than yesterday. I took two steps at a time up to the second floor. It was barely light enough to spot the foxholes, and in each of them I saw the outline of two steel helmets. Relieved, my breathing slowed, and I headed back down the stairs to the bunker.

"Good news—we're still Deutsch," I announced, shutting the door behind me and sitting down on my cot.

"Maybe by tomorrow we will be part of America," Mutti mumbled.

All of a sudden, I remembered that there was something different about the foxholes. I jumped up.

"Was ist los, Dieter?"

"I don't know for sure, Mutti. Something's different. I better go back and look again."

"I am going with you this time."

Mutti edged closer to the window. "Mein Gott! They are facing east now!" She raised her hands to her mouth and stared speechlessly at the street.

"That means it's the Russians, ja?"

She didn't answer. She grabbed my arm hard and pulled me toward the stairs.

"Ruth! Ruth! Are you down there?" she yelled from the top of the basement stairs.

"In the kitchen I am."

Mutti rushed ahead of me down the hall. "Ruth, we have to do something. It is the Russians. They are almost here." She pushed Ruth into a chair. "Sit down," she said and started to sit herself. She jumped back up and pulled on Ruth's arm. "Nein, let's go back in the bunker." Wolfgang and I followed them.

"Why does Mutti look so scared, Dieter?" he whispered. I didn't know how to answer.

"We have to find a place for Ruth to hide." Mutti looked at each of us. "Any ideas?"

I raised my hand. "The crawl space up in the attic, next to the chimney. We'll hide the ladder and nobody can get up there."

Mutti stared at me for a moment, then started to smile. "You know, a pretty good idea that is. It may just work. Let's go and look at it, Ruth."

We trooped to the attic where Ruth climbed the ladder and disappeared in the dark at the top. Her face peered down at us. "I'd have enough room to lie down all right."

Mutti followed her while I held the ladder steady. "Should I get the flashlight?"

"No. It is light enough. We can see." After some mumbled and whispered words, both came back down brushing cobwebs out of their hair.

"That is a good place, Dieter. But what are we going to do with the ladder? How can we hide it so no one will be suspicious?"

I looked around the attic. *There's no place to hide a ladder this long. If the Russians see it they'll know it goes someplace up here.* I thought for a moment. "What if Ruth pulls it up behind her? Maybe it will fit behind the chimney?"

Mutti patted my back. "You are smart, Dieter. Go back up, Ruth, and try it." We pushed the ladder, while Ruth pulled. Only one rung stuck out when she called down to us.

"The space is no more. It won't go any further."

"Wolfgang. Bring me the saw from the basement."

"Jawohl, mein Bruder."

Ruth had climbed down by the time he came back with the handsaw. "It's tight up there," she said. "I cannot stand up, but right behind the chimney there's enough space to lie down. It will be safe there."

I sawed at least thirty centimeters off one end of the

ladder. Ruth climbed back up and pulled the ladder up behind her. This time it disappeared out of sight completely.

"Simple, isn't it, Mutti?" I smiled at her when she shook my hand.

"Now, Dieter, we get a mattress and a blanket and pillow. And we will find some food, something that does not spoil too fast."

"You should go up there, too, Mutti."

She smiled. "No, Dieter. I will not leave my boys." She pulled Wolfgang and me to her and hugged us.

"Lis, you are sure? Even if it is tight there we could make it. I think you ought to come up there with me."

"Nein, Ruth. I promised Karl. I told him I would take care of the boys no matter what. I will do that."

"But, you know what—"

"Nein, nein, nein." Mutti held up her hand. "We do not discuss such possibilities, ja?"

"You don't have to worry about Dicker and me, Mutti. We can take care of ourselves. We know how to, don't we, Dicker?"

"Ja, Mutti. Dieter and I, we can do everything. You can hide if you want to."

Mutti kissed us. "Mein Gott! You would think I am an old woman who has to be fussed over. I can stand up to anything the Russians do. We have gone through this war together, and we will end it together. For Ruth it is important to be hidden. She is young."

Sleeping was impossible that night. By morning I was so awake I stood up, thinking I might walk around the bunker and tire myself enough to finally fall asleep, but the walls seemed to spin. I felt lightheaded and quickly sat down and closed my eyes. I wanted to throw up, but only managed to gag.

"I have to get some fresh air, Mutti."

Outside, I heard the artillery fire. A second later the swoosh of the grenade went overhead, followed immediately by the unnerving crash of the explosion. There was another sound—the tac-tac-tac of machine guns between volleys of rifle shots.

A touch on my shoulder made me jump. I hadn't heard Mutti come up behind me. For a long while, we stood there without saying a word. I tried to figure out from what direction the gunfire came, but it was useless. It came from everywhere. For a few minutes it faded, then flared up—louder and more intense than before—then subsided again.

I looked at my mother, her face drawn tight and her eyes staring straight ahead, eyes that didn't even blink when an explosion shook the ground. *What's happened to us? Have we lost all feeling?*

"Are you scared, Mutti? Scared of what's going to happen?"

She pulled me closer to her.

"Not really, Dieter. Maybe it scares me that I am not scared."

"You mean because we're so used to this?"

She nodded, then smiled. "Remember how you used to jump when we set off fireworks on New Year's Eve? Those big rockets Vati shot into the sky? They really scared you, ja?"

"Ja." We fell into silence again. I looked over at our house, and our back yard with the mound of sand over my bunker, remembering when I sat in it and watched bombers fly through the fireworks of the flak, and the searchlights . . . I felt safe in my bunker then, and I thought it was exciting.

In the distance, rifle and machine gunfire sounded like breaking, dry tree branches in the woods. But there was a new sound in the air this morning, a sound that sent cold chills down my back—a short, terrifying *swishh-h-h-h!*

Mutti grabbed my arm. "What was that?" Her eyes searched the sky directly above us.

"I don't know. Maybe the soldiers can tell us."

We rushed out to the foxholes and found two men in one of them. Although they looked too old to be soldiers, they wore helmets with their civilian winter coats. One of them was missing an arm. The machine gun was gone and the other foxhole was empty. Mutti walked up to the men.

"You're with the Volksturm, ja?"

"Jawohl. Why do you ask, Frau?"

"There is a new sound. Is it a new weapon?"

"You mean the rockets? We heard them east of Berlin. They come in clusters and very fast. We named them Stalin Organs because their sound alone can kill you." The men laughed.

"Where are your comrades?" she asked, pointing at the empty foxhole. "Awhile ago they were there."

"They were ordered back behind the canal," said the one-armed soldier. "You and your young one should get back into your basement, Frau. The Russians fire mortar grenades everywhere." He took his helmet off. His hair was snow white.

"Danke," Mutti said. "We will go home." She took my arm and we went back to the house.

"Did you see that, Mutti? A soldier with only one arm?" I shuddered. Mutti didn't say anything. "Can I take the bike and see what the bridges look like?"

"With such fighting so close you want to see the bridges?" I nodded. She shrugged. "Don't stay long."

The bridges were heaps of twisted steel, half-submerged in the middle of the canal. The wall of the house closest to the bridge on our side of the canal had caved in. On the other side I saw soldiers digging more foxholes.

My stomach churned. *What if the Russians attack right*

now? Five minutes to home. I started to sweat and my hands were clammy. *How stupid to come here.*

The sudden roar of a plane made me scramble to find cover. Lying flat on my stomach, I looked up just in time to see the small red star on its side—a Russian fighter plane with one engine, flying so low and incredibly slow that my first thought was it would crash. But it didn't. *How can it stay in the air, flying that slow?* I heard machine guns fire, and in another minute the plane was gone. At breakneck speed I was gone as well and home in minutes. Mutti was sitting peacefully in a chair, her hands folded in her lap.

"The bridges are gone, Mutti. All five of them."

"That's all right, Dieter. We are not going anywhere."

"Did you hear that Russian plane?"

"Ja. I heard.

In recent days, I noticed drastic changes in my mother. Most of the time, she was quiet, staring at the walls or out the window. Occasionally, she and Ruth exchanged a few words, small and unimportant words.

"What's wrong with Mutti?" Wolfgang asked. "She always looks sad. Did we do something wrong?"

"Nein, of course not. She'll get better when all this shooting ends. It worries her. And we haven't heard from Peter in weeks . . . . Ach, Scheisse! Let's go and see what our Buddel Kiste looks like."

We went over to our back yard. One wall in my bunker had collapsed, and weeds grew out of the sand. I looked at where the empty rabbit cages had been before we burned the wood and the tar paper from my secret hiding place. I stood there, staring, thinking, remembering. *Helga's giggle . . .*

The short burst of a machine gun sounded close.

"Wolfgang, where are you?" I yelled and ducked closer to the ground.

"Right here."

Wolfgang sat in front of the little cross on Putzi's grave, brushing the leaves away. Loud voices and another burst of fire made us both jump up and run, just as a line of soldiers appeared from the front of our house. A dozen of them, carrying Panzerfaust and rifles, were led by an officer. He stopped in front of us.

"Is this your house?"

"Jawohl, Herr Lieutenant!"

A brief smile crossed his face. "Russian tanks and infantry are in Drewitz and Potsdam. We have to stay in your house." Turning to his men, he yelled, "You four take your positions upstairs. The rest follow me."

They quickly disappeared into our basement. Wolfgang and I ran toward Ludwigs' house just as the roar of another plane came near.

Inside the bunker, Mutti was knitting. "I have to do something. I am sick of sitting around. Where were you two?"

"In our yard. Mutti, soldiers are in our house."

"So? The front line will soon be right around us. Let's hope they leave before the Russians get here, or we will all be—"

"Be what?"

"Did you get rid of that pistol?"

"Ja. I put it way up in that big bush in the front yard."

"Go look and make sure."

The nest is gone! The gun, too. Frantic, I crawled underneath and all around the bush, clawing at the branches, bending them. *Nothing. It's gone. Somebody found it—or saw me hide it.*

My mother stood at the door, watching. "Well?"

"It's not here."

She turned and went inside. I followed, though afraid of what would follow.

Mutti stood in the kitchen, arms folded, glaring at me. "Do you see now how stupid it was to take that gun?"

"Ja."

"If the Russians find it anywhere in the yard, we are all dead. Do you realize that?"

I looked at the floor, grinding my teeth, and did not answer.

She looked at Ruth. "I hope it is not someplace else in this yard. If the stories are true, we don't stand a chance."

"Did you hear any more?" I almost whispered.

"Dieter, we have to get rid of anything that shows a Swastika, or a picture of Hitler, or Göring, or Göbbels. Let's go home and search everywhere. You clean out the drawers in your dresser, look for pictures—anything that shows Deutsche soldiers—and your Hitler Youth things. We do it now. Later will be too late. Ruth, find that metal yard basket, and we'll burn everything in it."

"What other stories did you hear?"

"Later, I tell. Now go and find those things."

We rushed over to our house, ducking low when the swoosh of a grenade or mortar round came close.

"Can I keep my HJ belt buckle, Mutti? It won't burn."

"Idiot! See this Swastika in the middle? Bury it in the back yard, between the bushes. Deep!"

She put pictures of Vati and Uncle Willie in their Army uniforms into a small round tin can with a pretty Christmas scene on the lid.

"Dig another deep hole for this, over there where the rabbit cages used to be. Hurry!"

I dug as quickly as I could. In the distance the rumble of artillery sounded like a thousand drums all playing at once. Another Russian plane flew nearby. I heard its machine guns and flattened myself on the ground until it had lumbered past. I still wondered why it didn't fall out of the sky. Looking up, I saw Frau Witte's face staring from her kitchen window. *What's she doing up there?*

As I ran back toward Ludwigs' house, a sudden outburst of loud voices came from the front of our house. I changed my direction. Staying close to the walls, I turned the corner at full speed—and stopped as if my shoes were nailed to the ground.

Several screaming women stood at the foot of the stairs to our veranda. They shook their fists at Frau Witte on her balcony. Frau Schneider was there, and so was Frau Kundert.

A huge Swastika flag hung from Frau Witte's balcony, so large that its bottom dragged the middle steps of the stairway to our veranda. It was an incredibly large flag, the type used around the Olympic Stadium or along parade routes in the city.

"Take it down! Now!" "We will come up and tear it down for you!" "You crazy idiot!" "You will have us all killed!"

I spotted Ruth, and then Mutti, running toward me. I pointed to the problem..

Frau Witte leaned forward. "You are all traitors to the Führer, you Schweine! I'll have you arrested if you even touch my flag! You should be killed!"

Mutti gasped and hugged Ruth

I pointed across the street. "No big trees there. Russian planes can see this flag for kilometers." Then I saw the foxholes. "Look, Mutti! The foxholes are empty! The Volksturm are gone!"

"Mein Gott! Now we are nothing!"

"What do you mean?"

"I mean we are nothing. Not Deutsche, not Russian, not anything."

My mother lowered her head, tears in her eyes. I felt that every hair on my head stood straight up.

Several women ran up the steps to our veranda, grabbed the bottom of the flag and pulled. Frau Witte screamed hysterically, holding on to the flag with both hands, but she was no match for the women. It fluttered down, draping itself over a bush. In a blur of movements, someone bundled it and ran into the backyard.

I wanted to follow, but Mutti held me back.

"There are enough of them, Dieter. Let's get back to the bunker."

As we filed back into Ludwigs' front door, I saw the crumpled flag in the metal basket, already in flames.

The weather had been unusually dry for late April. It felt more like June, even July on some days. It was hot. But downstairs, the bunker was comfortably cool.

Wolfgang could not sit still. He scratched his legs and his arms and rubbed his back against the door jamb as if he were a dog. "I itch all over, Mutti. Maybe the water isn't so cold anymore in the canal, or the Griebnitz See. We could take a bath there, couldn't we? I'm itching all over."

"I know you do, Wolfgang. We all itch. But going to the canal or the lake is out of the question right now. You know what is going on outside, ja?"

"How about those garden spots between the railroad tracks?" I suggested.

Mutti looked surprised. "Have you gone crazy? What are you talking about?"

"The garden spots, the land between the tracks before you get to the Teltow Canal where people used to grow vegetables. Sometimes we played there, and I remember seeing people pump water. Should I go and find out? It's only a few minutes."

"But those few minutes could cost your life."

"Mutter, I know how to run, and I know how to hide. I'll be careful, I promise."

Wolfgang started jumping. "I want to go, too!"

"Nein! You stay." Mutti grabbed him by his arm and hugged him to her. "You go, Dieter, but hurry."

Armed with two tin buckets, I was on my way. I hurried along the side of the road, ready to duck under the large trees lining both sides. Above me, I heard those slow Russian fighter planes, but they were not near enough that I was afraid.

I stopped and dropped flat on the ground when I reached the first gardens, a whole lot that was wide open. Close to my left, along the S-Bahn tracks, the ditch was fairly deep. There were no big trees to hide under, but enough bushes and a few small wooden shacks where I might run. *The pump should be somewhere in the middle of the lot. Should I run for it? Or crawl?* I waited for the planes to go away. I took one more look at the sky, saw no planes, and took off running inside the ditch.

There's the pump! I flattened myself on the ground and listened, scanning the sky and the land around me. Nothing. No movement, no sound of shooting close by. The pump was maybe ten meters away. I crawled over to it and pumped the handle furiously. I pressed my ear against the cold steel and listened . . . *Ja, there's water!* The pump handle flew, my heart pounded.

A minute later I was back in the ditch, stumbling with the two buckets, their handles slippery with my sweat. I walked as slowly as I could. After all of this, I didn't want to spill a drop.

When I reached the street, I sat and leaned against the trunk of one of the big trees to catch my breath. *I made it. The buckets are still full. We have water!*

I got back to the bunker and Mutti bundled me into blankets. "You rest," she said. "Sweating that much could chill you, and we don't need our oldest man to become sick." She hugged me, and smiled, and I felt good about myself.

We carried most of what little food was left up to Ruth's hiding place behind the chimney, together with an old wine bottle filled with water. Afterwards, we all went down to the bunker for the night.

None of us could sleep, except for little naps. Every few hours, Mutti lit the candle and gave us each a stale cookie and a small tin cup of water. We ate in silence. Then the candle was blown out. Until daylight we sat in darkness and waited. The door of the bunker was shut and locked tight, but sounds of the fighting outside filtered through the escape tunnel. Louder, and so much closer. I couldn't stop shivering. Mutti, sitting across from me, held Wolfgang tight to her side. Much more often now the floor vibrated.

From somewhere in the dark came Ruth's shaky voice. "You think this bunker will hold up if the house gets hit and collapses on top of us, Lis?"

"Herr Ludwig told us it would. A meter of concrete is over our heads."

I pulled up both legs and pressed my arms around my knees to keep from shaking. *What if we suffocate?* I held my breath and slowly counted. Heartbeat pounding in my ears, I gave up at twenty. *That won't hurt too much.*

When I heard the faint sound of voices through the escape tunnel, I thought my heart would stop.

Mutti put a finger to her mouth. "Sh-h-h-h-h-h!"

I pressed my ear to the tunnel door, straining to hear better.

"That's Deutsch. We're still Deutsch! I'm going up to see who it is."

I peeked around the corner of the front door. Four soldiers were standing by the basement door of our house. Frau Witte was handing something to them that looked like bread or cookies. *Where did she get them?* I watched until she disappeared inside the basement. Then I quickly walked toward the soldiers. I recognized the officer from the group that occupied our house yesterday.

"Herr Lieutenant," I said. "Where are all your other men?"

He glanced down at me for a second, but his red-rimmed eyes looked right through me. He was cleaning his handgun with an oily rag. He wiped it off, then pointed it toward the sky and squinted through the barrel.

"Russians we found on the other side of the tracks. They killed my men. The four of us got away." His voice was so coarse and rasping that I had a hard time understanding him.

He shoved his gun at me and pulled out the magazine.

"See these three bullets in here? We will go back, and I can kill two more Russians. The last bullet will be for me." He motioned to his men to follow. "Come on, we will show the Bolshevik Schweine! We will do it for the boy here."

A few minutes later gunshots cracked close by, then short bursts of a machine gun. I ducked into the basement hallway just as something shoved me hard in my back.

"What are you doing out here! Can't you tell the shooting is getting too close?" Mutti yelled right into my ear. More gun shots outside, then screams. For a split second, we froze. The words were foreign!

"Come! We make a run for the bunker." Mutti pulled on my arm.

Just as we got to the top step, one of the soldiers ran toward us, his right arm dangling and bloody. With his other hand, he tried desperately to pull off his uniform jacket.

"The Russians are just over the tracks. I'm getting out of here! Burn my—"

"You get out of here *with* your jacket! Go now, go!" Mutti, her face distorted, shoved the man as hard as she could. "Don't leave anything here! They will kill us all!"

"Where's your officer?" I yelled.

The soldier held his finger to his forehead like a gun. He ran across our Buddel Kiste and Mutti and I ran to Ludwigs' house.

"Ruth! Ruth, where are you!" Mutti yelled as soon as we were inside the door.

The answer came from the basement. *"Ich komm'. Was ist denn los!"*

"Get your things, Ruth. Get to the attic and stay there. Dieter will take your blanket and pillow up there."

We stood at the bottom of the ladder. Mutti hugged Ruth. "Now, Ruth," she said. "You listen carefully all the time. And do not make a sound. When it is safe, Dieter will come and tell you. The flour for your hair?" Ruth nodded. "The tape?"

"Ja, Lis."

"A cover for your pot?"

"Ja, Lis."

They smiled at each other, and Ruth gave us each a quick hug. She climbed upstairs and pulled the ladder up behind her.

41

What's it feel like when you die? Does it hurt? Does it take a long time? I remember, in church, the minister talking about how peaceful heaven is. How does he know that? Now I don't know who to ask. Even if there is a God, he won't answer my questions. "Vati's lucky."

"What did you just say, Dieter?" Mutti stared at me.

"Nothing."

"Ja, you did. You just mumbled something about Vati was lucky. What kind of talk is that?"

I got up and walked over to her. "I didn't mean it that way, Mutti. I was only thinking that he doesn't have to live like we do. Nobody's shooting at him."

She looked down, then back at me. "I've thought that, too, Dieter. Ja, our Vati is in a good place now." She nodded toward Wolfgang on his cot. "Anything is better than this."

Wolfgang came over to us. "Can a dead person feel anything?"

"Of course not, Dicker. They can't—"

"Sh-h-h, Dieter. Nein, Wolfgang. There is no more pain."

"What about cold? You think Vati is cold, since he's buried in Russia?"

Mutti smiled. "Nein. Do not worry."

"Will he ever come back here? He'd like to be buried here, in Deutschland, ja?"

"Oh, Wolfgang. The dead don't care. They're spirits now. With God." She smiled a little smile. "Cold won't mean a thing to Vati. He did not like the cold, but now he won't need a coat." She laughed but looked embarrassed. "That's the first time I've laughed in awhile. Your father would have laughed, too." She held out her arms to Wolfgang, and he sat down at her feet and put his head in her lap. "You know, boys, questions like that concern us, because we're still alive. We don't understand. And we can't imagine the way of life in heaven. We just have to trust that God knows best for all of us."

Wolfgang looked up at her. "Even for the Allies? Does God like the Allies?"

"Dumb Dicker! He may not like Deutsche, but he certainly can't like the Allies. They bombed hospitals. And killed Vati. And—"

"Don't tell him that, Dieter. God is the god of all of us."

I looked at her. "I don't even think there is a God."

Wolfgang stood up. "I don't either, Mutti. If there was, how can he let them kill us? He can't be a very good God if—"

"Sh-h-h, boys. I don't know why God lets terrible things happen. He lets us kill them, too. We shoot them down and—"

"But they came over here," I shouted. "They fly over Berlin, Mutti, just to kill us!"

Mutti grabbed my hands and pulled me closer. "Dieter, understand, so Wolfgang does not get confused. Even Vati, if he had a chance, would have killed the Russian before he was killed. He may have killed Russians. We don't know."

"But that's different. Vati would have done it to save himself. He would have been protecting himself."

"Oh, mein Sohn. Vati went to Russia. He was on *their*

land. He was taking *their* homes away from *them.*" She pressed her head against me and held me tight. "I don't know why I'm trying to get you to understand something I don't understand myself. We try to trust, Dieter. That's all. Try to trust." She wiped her eyes and pushed me away. "Now go and think on things for yourselves. I've talked enough about this. I don't even know why I just said the things I did. I have to think, myself."

I went over and sat near the corner and Wolfgang got back on his cot and stared at the ceiling. The muffled sounds of rifle shots, and the slow tat-tat-tat of Russian machine-pistols filtered in through the escape tunnel. Every now and then someone screamed. *Someone's in pain, maybe dying.*

"I don't hear the machine guns anymore. Or the artillery. The mortars have stopped! Is it the end? Mutti, is it?"

Mutti's face looked like a mask in the flickering light. She sat down next to Wolfgang. "Is this our last candle?" she asked quietly.

"Ja, I guess so."

"We have to wait." She stared straight ahead. She looked like a painting I'd seen once. She didn't move at all.

"Mutti, you think Ruth is safe up there? What if bullets hit the roof? Maybe I should run up and see?"

"Nein, you don't! Right here we stay, together, until . . . until something happens, whatever it might be. Come over here and sit next to me, bitte?"

Her arm went around my shoulder. Outside, the gunfire had slowed to a few shots. The floor had stopped vibrating. In a tight huddle, we sat in the far corner of the bunker, right next to the escape tunnel, silent, watching the candle wax melt, listening.

"Can you hear my heart beat, Mutti?" I whispered. "It's loud enough in my ears."

"What did you boys do with your bikes? Where are they?"

"Don't you remember? We put them next to the fireplace upstairs. And I let the air out of the tires."

She patted my back. "Good boy. Maybe they won't steal them now."

We sat for a long time in absolute silence, Mutti holding on to us. She turned and kissed Wolfgang and then me.

"Both of you have been good boys to me," she said, "especially since Vati died. The way it sounds out there tells me that we do not have much time left, so listen carefully. More so now than ever before, we will have to look out for ourselves. Nobody will do it for us. You know what we heard about the Russians. How much is true, we don't know. What they are going to do to us . . . " She shuddered. "I am cold, that's all. Now, there are things we can do to make it easier. Maybe." She hugged us closer. "When you see the first Russians, be polite and friendly—"

"Even if they look like they're going to shoot us?"

"Sei mutig, Dieter. Both of you."

I pulled away from her. "Be brave? I'm scared, Mutti. I don't want to be shot."

"I don't want to be shot!" Wolfgang climbed over on Mutti's lap. "Don't let them shoot me, Mutti."

Mutti hugged him. "I won't let anyone shoot my boy. Don't you worry. I will be with you all the time." She put her finger to her mouth and shook her head at me. "Dieter was just talking. They're not going to shoot you." "Now listen. And do not interrupt, Dieter. Don't look like you're afraid of them. If the Mongolians come, remember they look different—"

"Mongolians? What are Mongolians?" Wolfgang's eyes widened.

"They look like the Chinese—with slanted eyes. Some of the refugees told me that they fight with the Russians. They're Russian soldiers."

Wolfgang pulled up the corners of his eyes. "They look like this, like in Vati's books?"

Mutti laughed. "Ja, like the Chinese."

"What if they want to kill us?"

Mutti sat up straight and put her shoulders back. "Then we will show them we are strong. And brave." A sad smile crossed Mutti's face. "Like your father was." She gave us each a quick hug.

We waited again, and waited, and waited more, in the awful quiet. When I closed my eyes, I imagined Mongolians coming at me with swords. I imagined them cutting off my head, and slicing Wolfgang in half, and throwing grenades on us. I had to keep my eyes open and focus on the candle flame. *I can't be brave. I'm too afraid.*

"How long have we been sitting here, Mutti? "Can't we at least open the door? I don't hear any guns."

"Nein, not yet!"

Wolfgang walked back and forth from wall to wall, muttering to himself.

"Wolfgang, sit down! You are making us crazy!"

"I don't want to, Mutti. I want to get out of here."

Mutti hit the cot with her fist. "I said, 'Sit down here.' Now."

"Maybe I should take a look outside," I said. "It must be daylight, and it's been quiet for a long time. And maybe Ruth can—"

Mutti put her hand over my mouth. "Sh-h-h! Listen!" We stood like statues. She glared at Wolfgang, finally pulled her hand away from my face, and pressed her finger against her lips. Her hand shook. "Listen," she whispered.

Then I heard them. *Not Deutsche voices. They must be Russian.* A loud laugh, and another. Much closer, like directly in front of the outside door of the escape tunnel. *What if they throw a grenade down here?* A giant knot squeezed and crushed my stomach. I wanted to say something, but I didn't dare make a noise. We held tight to Mutti and pressed ourselves against the wall.

The voices faded. There was a sudden crash of splintering wood from upstairs.

"The door's coming down. Let's go up, Mutti! They'll shoot us if they find us down here!"

From the top step I had a clear view of the front door. A rifle butt was smashing a hole into it.

"Hello, stop! I will open. Don't hit it anymore!"

On wobbly legs, I stepped closer to the door and started to move the heavy chair. The rifle butt disappeared and was instantly replaced by a bearded face with glaring eyes, yelling words I didn't understand.

"Ich verstehe Sie nicht," I pleaded with the face while I forced a friendly smile onto my own. I shoved the chair away from the door.

With a loud crash the door flew open, knocking me against the wall behind it. When I looked up, I stared into the small black hole at the end of a gun barrel. I froze, then slowly raised my arms. Mutti stood at the door to the basement. She held Wolfgang behind her. Her other hand covered her mouth. I had never seen her eyes so wide open. Remembering her words, I tried to look strong.

"Ich bin kein Deutscher Soldat," *please believe me.* "Ich bin nix Soldat." I nodded toward Mutti. "Meine Mutter und mein Bruder."

The Russian did not move or look in their direction. He stared at me. *He hates me.* I stared back and didn't blink. *That red star is so shiny. His eyes shine, too. I am going to die. Look at the hair in his nose, how long it is. I am going to die.* For endless minutes, we faced each other. Slowly, my eyes wandered down to the gun in his hand—his finger was curled around the trigger. *I am going to die. Now. Here.*

*I am going to wet my pants. Ach, Scheisse. I don't want to
pee my pants when I die.*
The tank in the woods—the turret lifting—the gun shots.
The Russian slowly raised his gun toward my head. *Now I
will find out how it feels.*
*Shoot, you bastard! Get it over with, Russian Schwein!
Before I pee. Don't pee while you die, Dieter. Sei mutig!
Sei mutig!*
He shifted his eyes and suddenly focused behind me.
His mouth opened into a wide grin and he looked like a
monster in Grimms' fairy tales, with black holes of missing
teeth. He shoved the gun's muzzle into my chest and slammed
me backward. I fell and he stepped over me, yelling something. Another soldier came in. They looked at the bikes
and laughed. They strapped their guns over their shoulders
and climbed onto the bikes, talking loudly to each other.

It didn't matter to them that our bikes were small and
the tires flat. Laughing and giggling, they pedaled past me
through the hallway and straight down the concrete stairs,
the metal rims whacking each step. Weaving crazily through
the front yard, they barely missed crashing into the brick
posts of the front gate and disappeared.

Mutti rushed over to me and hugged me so hard that I
squeaked in pain and pointed at my chest.

"Watch it, Mutti, that's where his gun hit me."

"Dieter, those bikes saved your life. Maybe ours." Tears
rolled down her cheeks. "Here, let me see your chest."

"It's nothing, Mutti." My hands shook so bad I couldn't
unbutton my shirt.

Hers shook almost as much, but she managed to unbutton the top two and pulled my shirt down. "Ach! It is already black and blue." I winced when she touched the bruise.
"If he had fired his gun, Dieter . . . " She shuddered.

Wolfgang pulled Mutti's hand. "I want to go outside. I
want to see our house."

301

"Nein. We wait here. There will be more. We will watch and see what happens."

The three of us sat on the top step, breathing fresh air for the first time in days. The yard was littered with tree branches and pieces of roof tile, and the top of the tall pine tree in the middle of the front yard was gone.

"Look, Mutti—see the bullet holes over there, next to our bedroom window? And look higher—Frau Witte's window is gone completely! A grenade hit it. We should go over and see what's left."

"Later. Lots of time we have for that. All the time in the world."

"But . . . how about the Wittes? Shouldn't we—"

"To her, whatever happened—I do not care. She deserved it."

The sun tried to break through low-hanging clouds, and the drifting smoke from fires looked like early morning fog. Without gunfire and artillery shells all was so quiet that we could actually hear voices from some distance. They were Russian voices, and I was scared. Mutti, too. Her hands still shook.

We looked toward the front when the gate squeaked. Old Herr Hankele came into the yard, walking very fast, with milk bottles in each hand.

Nearly out of breath, he stopped in front of us.

"Russian soldiers at the Red Cross warehouse," he said, wheezing. "Ja! They gave me these bottles of milk, real milk! And they give bread and butter to women. Before it is gone, you should hurry and get some."

"It's a trap," I warned. "Why should they give us anything?"

"Who knows? But see." He held up the bottles. "They were not mean to me." He shrugged. "Perhaps because I am old."

Wolfgang pulled on my arm. "Maybe they aren't bad soldiers. Something you could get us, Dieter, bitte?" He looked at me with pleading eyes.

"What if I get shot? They're the ones with the guns and the bayonets."

Herr Hankele hurried toward the gate. "Dieter," he called over his shoulder, "They were friendly. I saw it myself."

Do I worry about bayonets, or get something to eat? Milk. And bread. "All right, I'll go. It's a long walk, but I will go. I hope I make it back. If I'm killed, Wolfgang, it's your fault."

Two Russian soldiers, machine pistols slung over their shoulders and long-handled knives stuck in their belts, leaned against the wall of the Red Cross building while they smoked long black cigars. Next to them was one of the large, steel roll-up gates, blown open by a grenade. *Look at those boxes and crates! So many! It must be the food!* Crowds of women and children swarmed everywhere. I was tired from the long walk and wanted to sit down and rest, but I knew that wasn't smart. I stopped in front of the two soldiers and wiped the sweat off my face with my sleeve.

Behind them, another soldier bent over a small stack of bottles and packages. He stood up when he saw me. His grimy face was covered with as much sweat as mine and streaked with dirt. *He looks tired, Or mad. Maybe both.* A machine pistol was on the ground in front of him, but I stared at the long bayonet lying there next to it.

He held out a bottle. "Da?" he said.

Da? Does he mean I can take it? I was too scared to move.

"Da?" His mouth turned down under a long mustache.

Should I run away? Take the bottle and then run? Sie mutig. They don't like cowards. I can't go back without something. I forced myself to face the soldier.

Now he hesitated, and glared at me. *Like that other Russian! What if he can see how scared I am? Maybe he thinks I'm the son of a soldier who killed his family* . . . I lowered my eyes and looked at the bayonet on the ground, holding my breath, and remembered Mutti's words. *Sie mutig!* I pulled my shoulders back and stood as straight as I could. I held out my hand. "Ja. Bitte," I said.

He kept his eyes on me and slowly handed me the bottle. He turned around, reached down, and brought up a package of margarine. And a small chunk of bacon! And then he said something in Russian and smiled.

"Danke," I heard myself say with a shaking voice.

He smiled again and waved me on. I moved away from the three soldiers and started toward home with my treasures.

They'll be proud of me. Suddenly, I didn't feel tired anymore. There was no pain in my legs, or in my stomach. I floated like a feather. I even whistled.

"Look at what I brought back, Mutti!" I yelled as I ran through the front gate. She and Wolfgang were still sitting on the same step, but they stood up fast when they spotted me.

Mutti took the bottles. "Look, Wolfgang. This is real milk. Remember what it is like to drink real milk? And . . . .this is butter? I do not believe."

She gave it back to me. "Take it to the basement, Dieter. Find the coolest spot, so the butter won't melt. One bottle we drink now."

I was still breathing hard from running from the corner. "The Russians; they're really not bad, Mutti. Honest. They even smiled. Maybe we don't have—"

"Calm down. You're all out of breath."

"But we don't have to be so afraid of them. Can Ruth come down from the attic? It must be awful hot up there!"

"Sh-h-h, Dieter!" She smacked the side of my head as

she looked around. "No one knows she is there," she whispered. "Don't turn foolish because you got some milk."

I felt sorry for Ruth, crouched into that small space. "You think she still has water, Mutti?"

"Dieter, be quiet! We don't talk about such things out here, do you hear?"

I nodded.

"All right," she said. "Now, I am sure she has water. We have to be patient. We can't rush things. Her life depends on our quiet. Take this bottle and the butter now. Come back, and we drink some real milk."

42

"We can't keep sitting down here, Mutti. The Russians were nice to me yesterday. Can't we go out now?"

"Ja, the Russians were nice to you in the afternoon. How were they yesterday morning?"

"They were different. But they probably won't be back. Can't we at least check on our toilet barrel? We could use that now instead of these buckets. The shooting has stopped. We don't have to be afraid."

Mutti sighed. "Ja, maybe," she said. "Those pots from the basement, you can empty into the barrel. Nein! Better you dig a hole between the bushes, deep enough. Ja. You can do that. I will stay by the door and keep watch. If I call, you come right back."

"Come with me, Wolfgang. You can help."

"Do I have to, Mutti? I don't like the stink."

"Help your brother." She gave him a push. "Your nose you can hold."

It felt good to do work outside, but I didn't like hearing all the voices talking Russian nearby. I glanced often at my mother, sitting by the door. We worked quickly. I had to admire Wolfgang. He hadn't complained, although several times he held his breath until the vein in his forehead bulged.

I handed the shovel to him. "Take this back. Look, Dicker. Someone's coming through the yard." Three men in long leather overcoats looked at us but walked toward Mutti. Wolfgang started to run, but I grabbed him. "Don't! They might shoot."

"They don't look like soldiers."

"I don't care. Walk slow."

By the time we reached Mutti, the men stood in front of her. Each of them carried a revolver in a holster around his waist and wore the same felt cap with earflaps and the red star that the soldiers had worn. But they weren't in uniform.

Slowly, Wolfgang and I edged ourselves close to Mutti. They looked at each of us; we looked back but didn't speak. Two of them had dark complexions and black, piercing eyes, while the third man looked completely different. His hair was light blond, and his eyes bright blue. He didn't look at all like a Russian. He looked friendly. As I stared at him, he started to talk.

"Wir sind Politische Kommissare, nicht Soldaten."

Er spricht Deutsch! Gutes Deutsch.

"Bitte keine Angst," he added, putting his hand toward my mother.

I held my breath while Mutti said nothing for a moment.

"Entschuldigung," she finally stuttered. "But you are what?"

The blond man smiled. "We are Political Commissars of the Red Army. We are officers, but we don't wear uniforms. We are not here to scare you or harm you."

Mutti's lips moved, but before she could say a word, he continued in perfect Deutsch. "We like your house. We want to live in it for a few days. Do you have rooms with beds? We will bring food."

Again, he held out his hand toward Mutti. This time, she took his hand and shook it.

"Ja! You can sleep here. Please feel welcome."

The blond turned toward the other men and spoke to them in Russian. Their expressions turned into smiles.

Mutti led them into the house. As they walked through the door, the officer stopped and pointed at the jagged hole.

"Who did that?"

Mutti hesitated.

"Russian soldiers," I blurted out. "This morning. They stole our bikes, and almost—"

"Halt Dein Mund, Dieter!"

The blond man spoke to his comrades for a minute, and they nodded.

"I need paper, Frau. One piece."

I ran to the kitchen, returned with a piece of cardboard, and handed it to him. He wrote on it, in big letters, then asked for a thumbtack or a nail. Quickly, I found him one and a hammer, and he nailed the cardboard to the door.

"What does it say, Herr Commissar?" I asked.

"Do not worry what it says. Nobody will bother you again."

"Dieter and I will show them where they can sleep," Mutti said to Wolfgang. "You stay down here."

We walked ahead of the three men, up the stairs, and showed them the bedrooms.

The officer looked surprised. "Where are the others?"

"Other what?"

"Other people."

"There are no others," Mutti answered. "It is only myself and two boys."

"You live in this big house alone? Nein, there must be others."

"This is not ours," Mutti explained. "Our house is next door. When these people left, they told us we could use the house and the bunker in—"

Suddenly, he looked suspicious. "What bunker? Where?" His hand reached toward the gun on his belt.

Mutti's words came fast. "Nein! Nein! It is a bomb shelter, in the basement. No soldiers, go look."

He shoved Mutti. "Show it to us, schnell!" He followed her toward the stairs. The other two drew their guns and motioned for me to walk ahead. Wolfgang stood at the bottom of the staircase with a frightened look on his face as we rushed past him.

The blond Commissar stopped at the basement door and gave me a shove toward Mutti. The door to the bunker was wide open.

"You two. In first. I will be right behind you." We walked in, and as soon as he was inside, he held his nose. "Such a smell!"

We stopped in the middle of the bunker. I could hear Mutti's heavy breathing next to me in the dark, then the beam of a flashlight circled slowly around us along the walls, until it stopped at the escape door.

"What's that!"

"The emergency exit to the back yard." Mutti's voice was shaking. She grabbed my hand.

"Open it!" He turned and said something in Russian to the other officers who ran quickly upstairs. He stepped up close behind me and pushed me toward the door.

"Go in there and open the outside door. Now!"

I crawled fast, lifted the heavy steel bar, and pushed hard until the hatch swung open. Outside, the officers lowered their guns when they saw me and stuck them into their belts. Behind me, the steel door slammed shut again.

"You must understand that we have to be careful," the officer said when we were all together again. "I hope the guns didn't scare you." As he spoke, he smiled. "We don't hurt women and children, but you lost the war. Tell me, Frau, where is your husband?"

I saw Mutti's face and quickly answered for her. "Our father died a long time ago."

"Where?"

"In the hospital. He was very sick."

The blond one gave me a long, quizzical look and then spoke to the others. Before they all disappeared on the stairs, he stopped and pointed at us.

"You stay inside. You do not leave. You have food?"

Mutti shook her head.

"We sleep first, then we will get food for you."

Mutti and I looked at each other and smiled. *We've been so scared of them, and they're going to bring us food. I don't even care if it's Russian food.*

"What do you think they'll bring, Mutti?" Wolfgang asked after they went to bed. "I'm so hungry."

"We'll find out when it arrives." She shook her finger at us. "But we do not beg, verstanden?"

We didn't answer.

"Did you understand what I said? We do not beg!"

Her warning was clear, but we only nodded. We sat on the front steps again, silent, looking around aimlessly. I thought about food. About eating again. The sun was high and hot, and the birds in the trees made the only sound around us. I envied them.

"I wonder what it's like to eat worms . . . "

Wolfgang grimaced. My mother said nothing and looked as if she didn't even hear what I said.

"By the sun it must be almost noon," I said, trying to make conversation. "What time do you think it is, Mutti?"

Still no reaction, no answer.

A crashing sound from upstairs shattered our moment of peaceful silence. Instantly, we were on our feet, staring at each other. Inside my chest, a hammer beat against my ribs.

"It's the door again, Mutti," Wolfgang whispered.

"You stay down here," she whispered back. "We'll go."

From the sound of heavy footsteps on the floor above us, we knew they came from more than one person. Then we heard loud voices in Russian. Cautiously, we edged our way to the top of the basement stairs, then slowly toward the fireplace room. As I passed the front door, I saw the Commissar's note lying crumpled on the floor. Suddenly, the steps and voices ceased.

I turned the corner to the big room with the piano, and stared into the black hole of a machine pistol's barrel. My arms went up. The face at the other end of the weapon turned me into ice—the familiar cap with the red star, above two thin slits of eyes—*a Mongolian soldier!*

Without moving a muscle, but looking and pointing toward the ceiling, I heard myself stammer: "Commissars, upstairs. Friends!"

Another Mongolian came from the dark hallway to the kitchen, machine pistol pointed directly at my mother. With my arms still high, I took a careful step backward.

"Don't shoot. Commissar friends upstairs."

As I said it, the sounds of doors opening and slamming and running footsteps came from the top of the stairway. The two soldiers jumped backward into a crouching position on the floor by the piano and pointed their weapons toward the stairs.

As my mother pulled me into the hallway, a flood of yelling and screaming in Russian started. I peeked around the corner.

The three Commissars were in long gray underwear. They stood with their legs spread apart, each holding a pistol aimed straight at the two soldiers, who had dropped their weapons in front of them and raised their arms. The Commissars looked like they'd been asleep.

The Commissars yelled some more, and the two officers took the two soldiers and their weapons out the front door.

311

The blond Commissar turned and faced us. "I apologize for them. They're combat soldiers and don't know how to behave. They won't be back." He turned toward the stairs.

"Danke, Herr Commissar." Mutti's voice shook as she said it. She still held on to my hand in a tight grip, and her hand shook as well. We went back to the bunker where Wolfgang sat in a corner. His hands were pressed against his ears and his eyes squeezed shut.

Mutti sat down beside him and lifted him onto her lap. She rocked him gently. "Sh-h-h, Wolfgang, it's all right. Nothing happened."

It was very quiet for a long time. Then she looked over at me.

"Did you see if the note was back on the door?" Her voice was still shaky.

"Ja, Mutti. It was."

She sighed. "Maybe we didn't have to be so afraid." She put Wolfgang on the cot and lay down beside him. "Let's take a little nap," she said, and closed her eyes.

I didn't want to nap, but I knew better than to argue. I sat there and thought. I wondered about the house. And what I'd do if the Russians came after me again.

Wolfgang's impatient voice broke the silence. "Let's go to our house, Mutti, bitte? I can't even remember what our place looks like inside. And I have to go to the toilet real bad."

I looked at Mutti, waiting for an answer. She stood up from her cot, groaning, and held her back with both hands.

"You know you can't go in the house. You go to the barrel."

"I don't want to go alone! What if—"

"Dieter will go with you," she said quickly, then looked at me. "We have enough newspaper yet?"

"Ja. Didn't you see the stack upstairs, next to the fireplace? I saved a lot of them." I looked at Wolfgang and motioned toward the door. "All right. I'll go up with you and watch from there."

Before we stepped outside, I heard voices from the bedrooms upstairs. "The Commissars are awake, Mutti," I called down quietly. "We should be safe."

"I hear them. Let's hope they stay here for a long time." Wolfgang hurried toward our back yard and disappeared in the bushes.

Frau Witte and her husband stood outside the basement door, watching us. I didn't look at them as I slowly followed Wolfgang. She spoke, but I didn't answer.

It was already quite warm. Only once a rumbling sound from the east reminded me that somewhere in the city people were still killing one another. On the other side of our house, Frau Kundert and Frau Schneider were with a small group of women who stood by the back door of the apartment building.

I looked over to Ludwigs' front door and saw the three Commissars come out. They said something to Mutti, then left through the garden gate. Mutti walked slowly toward me.

"Are they coming back?" I asked.

"Ja. By the end of the day they'll be back, he said."

"Did you see Frau Witte over there?" I nodded toward our basement door. "She smiles all the time. Now she really looks like a witch." Mutti looked over there quickly and then turned back to me. "Get Wolfgang. I want to look at our house now."

We stood in the hallway, looking through the splintered double door into the living room. The draperies hung in shreds around the windows to the veranda. The floor and furniture were covered with dust and plaster, and glass crunched under our feet as we walked through the apartment. "It looks just like Kristallnacht, Mutti."

"Ja, and you remember what you did then?" she snapped.

313

"You brought home a knife from Herr Weinberg's. Don't talk to me about Kristallnacht. Men are animals!"

She pushed aside large pieces of plaster in the dining room. "Look at the buffet," she said. "What did they do?" Both doors were wide open and all the plates and glasses smashed.

"They used their guns," I said. "They ruined everything."

"Not my champagne glasses." Mutti smiled. "Remember how you've laughed at my hiding them? Now you see what would have happened."

"Go look at your bathroom." Frau Witte's voice startled us. She stood in the hallway at the door, unsmiling.

Mutti didn't say a word but left the room and went toward the bathroom. Something about the way Frau Witte looked made me feel sorry for her. She seemed to be so empty. Her eyes looked as if she was blind. Wolfgang and I followed Mutti.

She stumbled over the chunks of porcelain, and looked up. "Mein Gott! Look at this."

The water tank that had been high on the wall above the toilet bowl was in jagged chunks on the floor. There were bullet holes in the corner of the ceiling. The layer of straw poked through.

Frau Witte's monotonous voice sounded behind us again. "They did it in the apartment building, too."

Mutti turned and brushed past her, walking quickly outside. Wolfgang came running after us.

"There's blood on the veranda," he said. "It's all dried up, but it's blood. I know it is, because I had to chase the flies away.

"Halt Dein Mund! I don't care to hear this now." We followed her as she walked toward the women standing in the back yard. Wolfgang tugged at my arm and motioned to slow down.

314

He waited until Mutti was a ways ahead of us, then cupped his hand around his mouth. "There's blood in our room, too!" he whispered. "Real blood."

43

"Frau Drescher! You're all alive!" Frau Schneider hugged my mother, then each of us. "The war is over, ja? Someone came by here and said that the Führer was shot, or he killed himself." She smoothed her floured hair. "Maybe now I can wipe this stuff off my face."

Frau Kundert stood away, by herself, staring straight ahead, wearing the same coat with dried-up blood on its front. She was talking to herself, and I walked closer to hear.

"—killed the horse . . . poor animal . . . it is all my fault . . . "

Mutti and Frau Schneider came over and put their arms around her.

"Come with me, Dicker. They don't need us." We went around the side of the building toward the street. We saw what was left of the horse.

"Let's go back, Dieter. I don't like looking at dead horses."

"Ja, I agree."

When we got back, one of the women was talking to Mutti.

"—should have seen it! For a long time that Russian looked at the chain from the water tank. He yelled at me." She held out her hands and shrugged. "But could I understand? Nein. Then he pulled the chain, and when he heard the water gurgle, he shot at the tank!" She threw her head back and laughed. "And I ended up on the floor. It was not wise to laugh at him. Lucky I did not get hit by bullets."

They all laughed and started telling more stories. Frau Schneider took the black tape off her teeth. Only Frau Kundert didn't change her expression. She just stood there looking at the ground, mumbling and shaking her head.

I touched Mutti's arm. "Can I go and see if Ruth needs anything?" I whispered. "The Commissars are gone."

"Ja, I guess it is all right. But I do not think it's safe for her to come out. You tell her that. Take her a small piece of bacon and bread."

On my way back to Ludwigs' house I saw that Frau Witte was with the women now. I hurried by her, wondering why she'd become so friendly again.

Each bedroom door was shut. *What do the Russians have in there? Do I dare look? Nein!* I climbed the stairs to the attic, looking over my shoulder as I went, to see if someone was watching. It was like an oven up there, and I was sweaty by the time I stood under Ruth's hiding place.

"Ruth, you up there?" I said in a loud whisper. "It's me, Dieter."

There was a shuffling, moving noise above me. "Where else would I be, Herr Steiner? Of course, I'm here."

Her face appeared at the edge, her hair plastered down with sweat. "Did you bring anything to drink? I am out of water, and my buckets are full. Those men I hear downstairs, who are they?"

I explained as fast as I could. "And they won't be back until later. Get the ladder down. I'll take your pots and bring some more water. But it's rain water."

"I don't care, Dieter, just hurry. I want to see your mother and Wolfgang."

317

Ruth came down the ladder, carefully balancing a bucket. She gave me a quick hug. I shrank away. "You stink awful, Ruth!"

"Of course I do. It's hot up there all day, and then it gets cold at night." She wrinkled her nose. "You don't smell like roses, either, you know."

"Mutti and Wolfgang are at the apartment building, talking. She doesn't think it's safe yet. I'll hurry with the water."

Our supply of rain water was low. *Soon I will have to go back to the pump in the gardens.* When I gave Ruth the half-filled bottle, she was wiping the bacon grease from her mouth.

"The Commissars act friendly, but Mutti said for you to stay up here. I'll come back tomorrow if they leave again. Oh, and they said they'd bring us something to eat."

She carried the empty bucket and her drinking water upstairs. She smiled as she pulled the ladder back up, and I waited to make sure it couldn't be seen.

Just before dark, the Commissars came back, each carrying a large paper bag which they emptied on the dining room table. We stared at the huge, round loaves of bread, maybe a dozen long sausages, a large clump of butter, and four big bottles filled with a clear liquor. Wolfgang moved toward the table, but Mutti grabbed his arm.

"Remember what I told you? No begging!"

"But I'm hungry, Mutti."

"I know. We all are. You behave, and wait."

The blond officer smiled. "We brought this for you to share. Sit down and eat. You must be hungry. You like vodka?"

Mutti laughed briefly. "Nein, Danke. But ja, we are hungry."

She brought two more chairs from the kitchen, some plates, forks, and knives. The Commissars were already sitting. The officer shook his head and waved away the silverware and plates. "We don't need them."

They had already broken off large chunks of bread, and they held them with one hand while they gripped whole sausages with their other. They took big bites of sausage and big bites of bread.

One of them reached for a bottle, pulled the cork, and took a long gulp. He burped loudly and handed the bottle to the Commissar sitting next to him, who tipped it up and took several swallows. He handed the bottle to me.

"Nein, Danke, Herr Commissar. I am too young."

I gave the bottle to Mutti, who quickly passed it on to the officer sitting on the other side of Wolfgang.

The blond one grabbed the bottle from his comrade and thrust it back into Mutti's hand. "Nein! You must have a victory drink with us!"

She looked at me, and I thought she looked scared, but she raised the bottle to her mouth and took a little sip. She made a face as if she'd bitten into a lemon; then her smile came back and she handed the bottle to the third Commissar.

I breathed again and took another bite out of my piece of bread. Wolfgang was busy with a smaller piece of sausage. The bottle came around again, now half empty, and Mutti took another short sip as the Commissars applauded. The blond started singing in Russian, then stopped and looked at my mother.

"You play the piano?"

"Ja, a little."

"Then play for us!" he commanded. He burped again. The cork was taken from a second bottle. Twice around the table and the bottle was empty.

How can they drink so fast?

"Play, Frau," the blond one shouted. "Play more!"

Mutti played nervously, keeping her eyes on the piano keys.

One of the men stood up and started dancing, at times squatting on the floor and kicking his legs straight out in front of him. Wolfgang grinned. The other two clapped, and Wolfgang clapped along with them. Mutti looked nervous and kept hitting the wrong keys.

"I can't play in this rhythm," she said to me. *Don't cry, Mutti. Sie mutig.*

The other two Russians joined in the crazy dance. They jumped all over the room, knocking over two of the chairs, and an empty bottle fell off the table and shattered. Wolfgang stopped clapping. I was scared. We edged backward, closer to the hallway.

One of them stopped dancing, reached under the table and brought up another, smaller paper bag. He turned it upside down. A pile of watches fell on the table, at least two dozen. Wristwatches, pocket watches, even a small alarm clock.

Wolfgang poked me. "Look, Dieter, that one looks like Vati's!" he whispered.

"Lots of them look the same," I whispered back.

They stopped dancing and sat at the table again. "Frau, komm' hier!" the blond bellowed. Mutti walked over to the table. Wolfgang and I went over and stood on either side of her.

Each man pulled out a pocketknife and used it to take the backs off all the watches. The insides spilled on the table, screws, little wheels, springs. Some of them fell off the table and rolled over the carpet. The men laughed and yelled. They drank some more and pounded the table.

We just stood there, saying nothing. Their eyes were bloodshot, and I knew they were drunk. Mutti looked scared and pulled Wolfgang closer. The blond looked up at her and motioned to a chair.

"Sit down, Frau!" he shouted. Mutti sat down quickly.

Grinning, he pointed at the table. "You fix them. Put back together!"

"I-I-I cannot do that. I-I am not a—"

"Fix them. Now!" Suddenly, he looked mean.

The officer turned to the others and said something in Russian. They slapped the table. The screws and springs jumped in every direction. They laughed loudly and slapped it again. Mutti's mouth twitched.

Finally, they stopped laughing. The blond searched through the pile and picked out small watch, still in one piece. He handed it to Mutti.

"Here, you take this. It's yours." He laughed again. "We made a joke. We are happy that war is over for us. You are good Deutsche Frau."

He patted Mutti's arm and stood up, fell back into the chair, and stood up again. The others laughed, and he said something to them. Together they staggered toward the stairs and, still laughing loud and burping, pulled themselves up along the banister.

For a long time, we stared at the table. Chunks of bread, two empty bottles, pieces of sausage, watch bands, and screws—all in one messy pile.

"Get the broom, Dieter." Mutti pointed at the floor, littered with the broken glass. She shook her head. "How can they drink so much? And so fast?"

I swept the floor, but I didn't touch anything on the table.

"Can we take some of this food up to Ruth?" I whispered.

"After they leave tomorrow."

44

I had a nervous night in the bunker with little sleep. I tossed and turned. The scene of the drunken Commissars wouldn't leave my mind. It scared me to watch how fast their moods had changed, how they ate, and how quickly they destroyed all those watches. And then they were nice again and gave Mutti that expensive-looking one. I tried to make some sense out of it all, but the more I thought about it, the more confused I became.

As soon as the sun came up, we left the damp air of the bunker. From upstairs, I heard loud voices and laughing.

"They're up already, Mutti."

"Ja, I hear them. Let's go outside. They will leave soon."

Before we reached the door, Wolfgang slipped into the music room and came back. He held something behind his back and had a big grin on his face.

"Look what I got for us!" He held out a large chunk of bread and a piece of sausage.

"I told you not to—" For a moment, Mutti looked mad, but the frown on her face quickly changed. "Danke, Wolfgang. They won't miss it, and we need it."

Outside, she broke the bread into three pieces. We each had a mouthful of sausage, too. The bread was already dried out, but I didn't mind chewing harder. We finished just as the Commissars came out. We watched as they left, then Mutti led the way to the back yard where the same group of neighbors stood. Everyone seemed to enjoy getting together again, unafraid of air raids and gunshots.

"What's that smell, Mutti?" I asked.

"I don't know," she answered over her shoulder. "Maybe it's because none of us have had a bath. It doesn't matter. We are alive."

Frau Witte was nowhere in sight, but her husband sat on a wooden box next to the basement door of our house. I stopped beside him while Wolfgang and Mutti went on.

"Did you put flour into your hair, too, Herr Witte?"

He shook his head. "Nein. I have just got more white hairs. The war ages everyone."

"This awful stink! Do you know what it is?"

"Dead bodies. They smell when they rot, especially when it gets this warm. Humans and animal—when they're dead they all smell the same. They should be buried."

"Who should do it, the Russians?"

"They will probably make us do it. They're the victors."

He lowered his head and stared at the ground. "I smelled this all the time when I was in France, in the first war. You get used to it very easy."

I walked over toward Mutti and the women. *Picking up rotting bodies. Ugh-h-h.*

Mutti and the other women were talking, in low voices, and nobody smiled. This morning, four of them still had gray hair, and their faces were the color of paper. They looked like an assembly of ghosts, ready for the Fasching.

I glanced around, looking for Wolfgang, and spotted him standing at Putzi's grave. Frau Kundert was with him, her arm around his shoulder. I turned away from the women to go over there, but men's voices from beyond the back fence stopped me.

Two Russian soldiers staggered through the bushes along the fence, yelling and laughing. They waved machine pistols above their heads, and one held a large bottle in his other hand. I looked for Mutti and wanted Wolfgang to come with me, but I knew it wouldn't be smart to yell for him.

"Mutti, they're drunk!" I whispered.

She squeezed my hand hard. Everyone was quiet. The women stared at the soldiers as they stumbled closer and stopped in front of them, close enough that I could smell their breaths. They grinned, and poked each other, and laughed, and looked over each woman, walking around them, saying something in Russian, pointing to their breasts and hips. Mutti's hand had turned cold and sweaty. *Or is mine sweaty?*

One of the soldiers walked past us into the house. We heard him stumble up the stairs. The other one bent down and almost fell as he put the bottle on the ground in front of him. He turned quickly and aimed his machine pistol at us, screaming something at us. We stood frozen. Out of the corner of my eye, I saw Frau Kundert hiding behind the bushes with Wolfgang pressed tight against her back.

The soldier inside leaned out of a window on the second floor and motioned as if he wanted someone to come up.

"That's my apartment," whispered Frau Schneider. "What does he want? I better go."

"Nein! You stay!" Mutti said, barely moving her lips.

Frau Schneider took a short step backward. The soldier jumped toward her and gave her a hard push with the barrel of his gun. He waved the weapon in the direction of the window, shouting to his friend, then shoved her again. She stumbled into the stairway and disappeared. Then the soldier stepped closer to us, shouted something in Russian, and motioned with his arms. Quickly, we raised ours.

"I don't know! Bitte!" Frau Schneider's frightened screams were followed by a flood of Russian words. A

324

minute later she came down the stairs crying, her arms straight up. The Russian followed close behind, pushing her past us until they both stopped between us and the other soldier.

Frau Schneider's arms were still raised high, and her hands trembled. The soldier beside her held something in his hand and showed it to his comrade. It was a rifle bullet, still in its shell. *What are they going to do?* They shouted again—at each other and at Frau Schneider.

Prodding her with his gun, the soldier pushed Frau Schneider toward the building. She passed right in front of me. Her eyes were wide open, and her mouth trembled. "It does not belong to me," she said. "It is not mine." He shoved her against the wall next to the basement door and stepped back.

"It is not mine!" she whimpered, holding out her hands. "Bitte! I don't know—"

The force of the bullets slammed her against the wall. A moment later Frau Schneider lay on the ground, her head angled oddly against the base of the wall. It looked as if it didn't belong to her body anymore.

Long red smears of blood covered the wall where just a second ago she'd been standing. A large pool of blood spilled across her body and trickled down on the cement.

We stood rooted, barely breathing, afraid to look at the soldier in front of us. I couldn't stop looking at Frau Schneider. Her eyes and mouth were still wide open, like the little girls in that basement, and her fingers on one hand still moved and grasped.

Something whacked me in my side. I looked up. One of the Russians prodded me toward the basement door. Behind me, Mutti and another woman cried. My legs were numb, and my arms—still straight up—were going to sleep. *I don't want to die like Frau Schneider.*

The soldiers shoved us into a room with several mattresses on the floor. Wooden beams reinforced the ceiling, sandbags were in the window well, and the only light came from the hallway. Suddenly, Wolfgang stood next to me, with his arms up.

"How did you—" A hard jab with something sharp stopped me.

The soldier glared at the middle of my chest. In his right hand he held a long sword. The other Russian yelled something, then he pushed Wolfgang out into the hallway. Now Mutti stood next to me. I didn't know the other woman, a much older woman with very white hair. Our hands still reached for the ceiling.

The soldier in front of me shouted something, and droplets of liquor-smelling spit hit my face. He jabbed his finger into my chest, then pointed to my Lederhosen.

"Hitler! Hitler!" he screamed and grabbed the suspenders with his left hand. I prayed. *Don't use the sword, please!*

He pulled the suspender strap away from me so hard that I lost my balance. One vicious yank by his hand straightened me again. I saw the sword coming toward me.

The blade went upright between the strap and my body. I forced my head to the right, with my arms still straight up, and watched as the blade went up and down, a centimeter from the left side of my face. "Hitler!" he bellowed. "Hitler." The point of the sword looked razor-sharp, but he used the dull edge! *That will never cut it, you stupid idiot! Why are you so mad at me?* Suddenly, I knew!

There was an ivory pin sewn onto the horizontal strap between the suspenders. On it was a carving of a deer. Occasionally, Hitler and Göring wore the same type of Lederhosen. *He's seen pictures of them. He thinks I'm Hitler's son.*

The Russian spit and screamed into my face. The sword fell to the floor. He pulled the strap, this time with such force that he ripped the suspenders completely off. He pushed me onto the floor. I caught myself and crouched there, waiting for his next move. I'd forgotten about the other soldier until I felt his kick in my side, then in my back. He shoved me with his boot and kicked me toward the door, then into the hall. Wolfgang was out there. I turned around. The Russian pulled his gun up to fire.

"Schnell, Wolfgang," I cried, grabbing his arm. I heard them laugh behind us and my mother scream, "Nein, nein! Bitte, nein!"

Her cries echoed in my ears as I ran around the corner of the house and toward the street, clinging to the sides of the Lederhosen to keep them up.

"Hilfe!" I yelled as loud as I could. "Hilfe!"

Tears streamed down Wolfgang's cheeks. "Do something, Dieter," he cried. "Schnell! They're hurting our Mutter!"

I looked up and down the sidewalk and spotted two men in leather coats walking toward us—the Commissars who had moved into Ludwigs' house. One was the blond! They laughed and pointed when they saw me struggling to hold up my Lederhosen with one hand, while gesturing wildly toward the house with the other.

We ran to them. "Komm' schnell!" Wolfgang pulled on the Commissar's sleeve. "Russische Soldaten," I hollered, pointing toward the house and yanking on the other's arm. Both broke into a run and followed us.

The other women had disappeared from the back door of the apartment building. From the bottom of the basement stairs, I heard the soldiers shouting and laughing.

What's happened to Mutti? I don't hear Mutti.

The Commissars glanced at Frau Schneider's body. They drew their guns, pushed me out of the way, and rushed down the steps. Wolfgang and I held on to each other outside near the door.

"Did they shoot Mutti?"

"Nein, Dicker. They couldn't shoot Mutti." *They have. I know they have. She's dead!*

The two soldiers stumbled up the stairs, pushed along by the guns of the Commissars at their backs. *You killed my mother. Bastards! Bastards! Bastards!* The soldiers were yelling and trying to turn around to talk to the Commissars, who poked them with their guns and pushed them forward. One fell against the wooden railing and it splintered under his weight. The blond Commissar kicked him to get him back up—*kick him in the head!*—all the while shouting an endless stream of words. He marched the two soldiers ahead of him until they were in the middle of the backyard. They stopped and turned around to face him. They weaved drunkenly from side to side as the Commissar yelled at them again. When he finished, they turned their backs to him—*kill them, Commissar . . . kill them.* He raised his gun behind their heads and, in quick succession, fired it twice. *Ja! Ja! Ja!*

I shoved Wolfgang ahead of me and toward the stairs to the basement. In our hurry, we nearly fell down the steps. *First door to the right.* We stepped inside and my eyes slowly adjusted to the dark.

"Mutti?" A long, muffled moan made my heart jump. "Mutti! Is that you?"

She moaned again, then started sobbing.

"Mutti, you're alive! Wolfgang, run and get Ruth! Schnell! Tell her Mutti is hurt! Hurry!"

I knelt and groped for Mutti's hand. It felt wet and sticky. From behind me came the sudden beam of a flashlight and the voice of the blond Commissar. A pool of blood soaked the mattress around my mother's legs. *It's her blood on my hand!* Holding her hand tightly in mine again, I stifled the urge to cry.

"Sh-h-h, Mutti, you'll be all right. The soldiers are gone. Our Commissar here shot them." I glanced at him, standing silently behind me, and nodding his head. He turned and walked away.

"Ruth is coming, Mutti. Then we'll get help for you. Just don't move. Please, lie still."

She hadn't moved at all, but I wanted her to hear me talk. I was so scared that she didn't move, not even her fingers. *If you're out there somewhere, God, please don't let her die! We need her for a long time!* For a moment, I thought her fingers moved.

Another woman knelt beside me, and a minute later Ruth came rushing through the door.

"We have to get her out of here fast! Let's carry her on the mattress. Wolfgang, go and get the wagon from behind Ludwigs' house, and blankets from the bunker. Schnell!"

The three of us tried to lift the mattress, slowly and carefully.

"We need another person. It's too heavy. I'll go find somebody." The woman scrambled up the stairs. I stood up and looked around the room.

"Ruth, there was another woman in here. I don't know who she is, but she's older. They took her down here, too."

I found her, lying flat on her back on the cement floor, her arms straight out like she was on a cross. She gave no sound or movement, and her glassy eyes stared straight up at the ceiling.

Two women came down. Again, we tried to lift the mattress. Mutti cried out when we bumped against the door frame, but we got her outside. Wolfgang was waiting with the wagon.

"Hurry, Wolfgang, spread the blankets so the bottom is padded. Save one to cover her." I looked into the back yard. "Where are the dead Russians?"

"Other soldiers came and carried them to a truck," someone said.

329

My mother's face looked puffy with red marks along one side of it. Blood trickled out of her nose, and a large swelling closed one of her eyes. She was limp and heavy as we tried to put her in the wagon. It was much too short, so she had to sit, leaning against the back. Every few seconds, she made a deep, gurgling moan. Someone gave me a pad of gauze and a damp rag. I wiped her face.

The two women hurried away. Wolfgang leaned over Mutti and gently pulled the blanket all the way up to her chin.

"What are we going to do?" he asked, looking at Ruth and me. "Where do we take her? Where's a doctor?"

Ruth started to pull the wagon. "We can't just stand here," she said. "Let's try the Red Cross building behind the S-Bahn station. I'll pull. Wolfgang, watch Mutti's face. Dieter, you push."

We reached the sidewalk, moving slowly and avoiding every little hole and rut. But the wagon had wooden wheels, and Mutti cried out at the slightest bump.

"Ruth, let's try to make it to the hospital in Babelsberg. She needs a doctor, not the Red Cross."

"You're right. But look at her. We have to move faster."

Small and large craters dotted the street and sidewalk between our S-Bahn station and Babelsberg. We could not avoid some of the smaller holes. Suddenly, the cries stopped.

"Wake up, Mutti!" Wolfgang shouted, shaking the wagon.

"Don't shake it, you idiot!" I yelled.

"Stop it, both of you. The pain was too much. She's unconscious. We have to hurry. Move it!"

We rolled up to a small door at the side of the building, the only part of the hospital not burned out.

"Stay here," Ruth said before she rushed inside.

It seemed like forever to me, but finally she came out

again, followed by a woman in a dirty dress but wearing a nurse's cap. She took one look at Mutti.

"No, don't move her!" she shouted. "Get the wagon inside, schnell!"

Mutti moaned when we lifted the wagon up three steps. "You wait out here," the nurse ordered. Then she and Ruth disappeared. A few minutes later, a man brought the wagon out, empty but for one blanket with a large red stain.

Wolfgang pulled at my sleeve. "What are they doing to her? Why is it taking so long? She's been in there a year it seems."

"I don't know. They'll tell us when they know more." I put my arm around his shoulder. "At least, we got her here."

There were no clocks anywhere around us, only burned-out buildings. Maybe three hours later, Ruth came out.

"She's still alive, boys. But the—"

"What's wrong with her?" Wolfgang interrupted.

"She was raped by the two soldiers and has some bad injuries."

"What's rape, Ruth?"

"Never mind, Wolfgang. We have to hurry home. The doctor asked if we had red wine at home and anything to eat. We must bring it to him as soon as we can. Quick now!"

We walked fast, the empty wagon clattering along behind us.

Wolfgang looked at Ruth. "Why do we have to take food to the doctor. Don't they have enough to eat?"

I poked him. "Don't be stupid, Dicker. It's for Mutti. Maybe the wine's for the doctor, but the food is for Mutti."

Ruth laughed. "Now who's being stupid? The wine's for your mother, Dieter. Not the doctor."

"Ha, ha, Dieter's being stupid," Wolfgang sang. "Dieter's being stupid."

"Well, it could have been for the doctor," I said. "I thought he might want to be paid with wine."

It was quiet in Ludwigs' house. Too quiet. I tiptoed up the stairs, looked into the first bedroom, and hurried back down.

"They're gone, Ruth!"

"The Commissars? They've left?"

"Ja. Their things aren't there."

"Maybe they left some food for us," Wolfgang yelled, running ahead of us into the kitchen.

Ruth stopped me. "To our house you go. Look in the basement. Look all over. Any place Herr Drescher's wine bottles might be." She gave me a push toward the door. "Find something."

In our house I rushed from room to room, trying to remember where I'd seen wine bottles the last time. *Boxes! Ja, he put them into a box.* Hurriedly, I ripped open the first box and found old clothes. Another box with more old clothes. I looked around the room and spotted the top of a green bottle behind some toys. It was wine, the cork still sealed!

"What if it's not red wine, Ruth?"

"Maybe it won't matter. Look. A box of eggs they left. We found them in the bedroom. Let's get back to the hospital."

45

Half an hour later we stood at the same door of the hospital. Ruth took the wine and eggs inside while we waited. A few minutes later she came back out.

"Can we see her?" we asked together.

"Nein. Your mother is very sick and in a lot of pain. The nurse told me we can come back tomorrow."

The walk back was slow and quiet. Just before we reached our S-Bahn station, Ruth stopped. She looked at us in silence.

"What's wrong?"

"Nothing is wrong. But the nurse urged me to take you to the Red Cross building over there." She pointed past the station. "She said there is a prison camp next to it."

"Why do we want to go to a prison camp?"

"Ja, Ruth. I don't want to go to prison." Wolfgang sounded scared, "I haven't done anything but try to sneak past the Russians and talk to the Americans."

Ruth smiled. "Nein, Wolfgang. It is not that kind of prison. It's a camp for American and English pilots who were shot down. The nurse said she heard that they protect women and children from the Russians. I think we should go there, and I will stay with you."

"What about our house?"

"Ja," Wolfgang said. "What about our house?"

"Never mind the house. Let's find out if we can stay at the Red Cross first."

Two men sat at a long table in front of a door. Wolfgang stopped when he saw them. He covered his mouth and whispered to me. "They look like Russians. I don't want to go there."

I pulled on his arm. "They're not Russians. Can't you tell their uniforms are different?"

"All right, boys. You wait here. I'll go and find out what I can."

Ruth walked to the table. The two men looked up at her and smiled. She spoke to them, then turned around and waved us over there.

"Spaces are hard to find, but if they can find room for us, we can stay here."

I looked up at the huge building with a mass of windows, four stories high, stretching for several hundred meters. Grenades had blasted holes in the walls, most of the tiles on its roof were gone, but a section of the painted red cross was still visible. Near every door, dozens of women and children huddled in groups with a few old men between them.

"Where's the prison camp?" I looked around.

"Right there, Dieter. Those two buildings."

They were strange looking, with rounded tops made of ribbed metal and a few windows along the sides covered with wooden planks. Both were surrounded by a two-meter high barbed wire fence, but the large gate was wide open. At the edge of woods behind the two huts loomed a high watchtower. A number of men in brown and blue uniforms stood in small groups inside and outside the fence—talking, smoking, and looking at us. Some were smiling, but most of them just stared with serious faces.

"Boys, we have to find a space." Ruth pushed us toward a door close to us. "The American said the basement is the safest."

We felt our way along dark corridors lined with people leaning against the walls. Here and there, a flickering candle provided enough light for us not to stumble and fall over someone on the floor. Except for a few mumbled words, it was quiet in this vast labyrinth of a basement.

"This place stinks, Ruth." Wolfgang held his nose. "Do we have to stay here? It smells like people don't use a toilet."

"Sh-h-h, Wolfgang. We are lucky to be here. At least it is safe."

"I'd rather be shot at."

"Listen to the brave one. If you'd gone to the front like I—"

"You weren't gone that long. I could have fought, too. I would have gone. I wasn't old enough."

"Stop it, you two. All we have to do is manage to get through this for a little while. Do it for your mother, ja?"

We followed Ruth in silence.

"This is the end of it," a man's voice in the darkness ahead stopped us. "You can't go any further. Around this corner is a small space."

"Are there any other doors?" Ruth asked.

"Nein."

"I am glad the bombing has stopped. This is a tomb."

"Ja, we know."

Around the corner was a space with even a small, ground-level window barricaded with sandbags. Quickly, I pulled the two bags down.

"We have two pillows, Ruth. And look at this." I showed her a small stack of folded burlap sacks inside an open cardboard box. "Now we have something to sleep on!"

Wolfgang was the first one to stretch out. In minutes, he was fast asleep.

"Ruth, you think Mutti will make it?" I whispered.

"Dieter, your mother is a very strong woman. I think she will make it all right."

"What's going to happen to our apartment? Or Ludwigs' house?"

"Let's not worry about that now. More important it is that we are safe, and this place looks safe to me. I like the Americans. They were so polite."

"Did they speak Deutsch?"

"One of them, but only a few words."

All at once, I thought of Herr Wise, and all those post-cards, and the flag, and wished I still had them. At least the flag.

A hand shook me awake. Ruth was kneeling next to me with something in her hand.

"Here, Dieter. While you were sleeping, I went over to the camp and a man gave this to me. I think he was American."

She handed me a small open box. In it were three gray-looking pieces of either bread or cookies. *Everything looks gray in this hole.*

"One for each of us?"

"Ja. We better wake Wolfgang if we want to go to the hospital. Maybe we can see Mutti. Put your shoes on and let's go."

At the hospital a man in white pants stopped us inside the door. "Nein, you cannot see Frau Drescher," he said. "We gave her something to help her sleep. Tomorrow you come back."

Ruth held his arm when he turned away. "Tell us, please. She is better?"

"Ja, better." He pulled away. "Now, go."

We walked back to the Red Cross building. Several Russian soldiers stood near tents between trees along the street.

"Don't look like you are scared," Ruth whispered. "Walk normal."

"Aren't you scared?" She didn't answer but gave a long sigh when we reached the camp. She pointed at a man standing by the gate.

"That's the one who gave me the cookies. Go and thank him."

She followed and stood behind us when we shook the man's hand. He said something I didn't understand, but he smiled.

Later, we stood with other women near one of the doors of the Red Cross building. Wolfgang looked up at Ruth.

"The Americans look no different from us. Do you like them?"

Ruth smiled briefly, looking a bit embarrassed.

"Ja, natürlich! Why should they look different?"

"They are bombers. But they don't look like they want to kill us now."

We slept three more nights in the basement of the Red Cross. Ruth went to the camp each day and brought back small boxes with strange-tasting things.

"Russians bring them this Army food every day until the Americans get here." She smiled. "And I am learning some English already!"

On the third day we were allowed to see Mutti.

Wolfgang and I stood on either side of her bed. *She's as white as her pillow. Her lips are gray.*"The Americans are coming to Berlin, Mutti," I told her. "And Ruth is learning English."

"And they are not mean, Mutti," Wolfgang said. "I talked to them. They gave Ruth food for us."

She smiled and patted our hands.

A doctor stopped at the foot of the bed. "Frau Drescher can go home with you tomorrow," he said to Ruth. "We need the space. Come at noon."

"Again we need the wagon?" Ruth asked.

"Ja, of course, with good padding. Frau Drescher, that bottle of wine and the eggs probably saved your life. You will make it now." He patted the mattress by her leg. He looked at Ruth. "She will need your help."

"Ja. Danke, Herr Doktor."

Mutti smiled. "Karl saved my life. Each day I have his wine with a raw egg stirred. This I have lived on." She looked at the ceiling. "Danke, my precious Karl."

"Let me pull this time, Ruth. You and Wolfgang push."

"Watch for the holes!"

With her eyes closed, my mother leaned against the back of the wagon. Only once did she cry out, when I couldn't avoid a deep rut.

I stopped at the S-Bahn station.

"Should we go on to—"

"Ja, we go home. That basement floor over there is not a place to put your mother."

"But the Americans can protect—"

"Move! Your mother needs something soft to lie on, and that is at home!"

Slowly and carefully, we rolled past the back door of the apartment building. Frau Kundert and another woman came up and stroked Mutti's hand without saying a word. Mutti opened her eyes and briefly smiled at them before we rolled toward our back yard. I glanced at the wall.

"What happened to Frau Schneider? I mean, her body. Did they—"

"Back there, along the fence," said Frau Kundert. "We buried her there.

Ruth waved us on. "Dieter, you and your brother start cleaning the big bedroom for your mother. Get all the glass off the mattress."

One day passed, then another. The silence made me nervous, and I jumped at the slightest noise. Sleep, which came in spurts, was filled with nightmares so real that after I woke up, it took me several minutes to realize I was only dreaming. The weather was warm and humid, and although all our windows were missing, the night air did nothing to cool us off. In the morning, as soon as it was light enough to see, we started our clean-up work. We gave up three or four hours later, beaten down by the sun. Ruth had a difficult time keeping Mutti from doing too much too soon. Still weak, she tired quickly in the heat. Our old fan was useless without electricity. I made several trips to the pump with my two buckets, and by the time I made it back, I was out of breath and dizzy. I dragged the mattresses out, and Wolfgang beat the dust from them. I took down the window frames that weren't broken or splintered and chipped away the putty. We figured that sometime in the future glass would be available again. Food, too, we hoped. Ruth made daily trips to Babelsberg in search of some but came back empty-handed.

46

"Come out and look," Wolfgang yelled. "Schnell, Dieter! American soldiers on trucks are coming, lots of them. I saw the flag on the first truck." He ran back outside.

Mutti and Ruth followed me out onto the veranda as the first of a column of trucks passed by. They were long, open trucks, each with a large white star on its side, and two rows of soldiers sitting in the back.

We stood silently, watching as truck after truck slowly passed our house. A few of the soldiers waved at us, and when Ruth raised her arm and waved back with a big smile on her face, a lot of them whistled.

Someone shouted, and Wolfgang came running toward us through the front yard. "I wanted to shake hands with the Americans," he said, barely able to catch his breath, "but the Russians chased me away."

Mutti put her arms around him. "Probably because you are Deutsch. "That is the way with war."

"Where are they going?" I asked no one in particular. "The bridges over the canal are all blown up."

"We will know soon enough, Dieter." Mutti pushed me ahead of her, back into the living room.

Word spread that the Americans put up a tent city in an open area along our side of the canal, and Wolfgang and I went to see it. There was one tent with a large red cross on its top and one with long tables where we could see soldiers eating.

All around us, the smell of food hung in the air. Wolfgang pulled at my arm.

"Maybe they'll give us some, Dieter."

"See those Russians over there watching us? They won't let us near them, I'm sure."

Wolfgang's eyes filled with tears, and he walked away. "I'm going home. At least I won't have to smell the food there." I caught up with him, and we headed back to the house in silence.

Ruth was in the kitchen. On the table in front of her were five potatoes. Wolfgang grabbed one.

"Potatoes! For supper?"

"Nein, Wolfgang." Ruth took it back from him. "Your mother said we will plant these. You know how to do it, and you can help me."

"I'd rather eat them. Tonight."

"I know you would. But if we plant them, we'll have a lot more. See, we will let these sprout. Then we'll plant them, and each one will grow more potatoes."

Wolfgang's mouth turned down. "I probably won't live that long," he said, and stomped out of the kitchen.

Over the next few days, rumors and stories covered the neighborhood like a blanket. We heard the Russians were leaving and Americans would occupy Berlin. We heard the Americans would stay just a few more weeks, and the Russians would occupy us. Someone said the Mongolian troops were going to take over Berlin, and that scared everyone. We heard that more American and British troops had moved into Berlin. Even some French soldiers had been seen. So what was true?

"I do not believe a word of it, Dieter, and you shouldn't either," Mutti warned. "We have been told so many lies for so long that I have to see something happen before I'll believe it."

"We haven't heard anything from Peter for so long. You think he's all right? And Oma and Opa?"

She put her arm around me and pulled me close. "Ja, that is what we have to think. He is probably a lot taller now. Since he lives on a farm, at least he is getting food. So let's not think anything bad. I am sure he is better off than we are, much better."

When I went outside, Wolfgang was sitting at the foot of the stairs from the veranda. I went down the steps, sat next to him, and gave him a long hug.

"Don't! It's too hot." He pulled away. "And why are you hugging me?"

I laughed. "I guess it seems silly to you. I don't know. The war is over. I'm glad we're all alive. That's all."

"Vati's not alive."

"Ja, I know, Dicker. Uncle Willie's gone. And Horst. And my friends from school that the Russians killed. But I wasn't thinking of them so much. I was thinking of you. And Mutti and Ruth. And myself." I looked at him and smiled. "That's why I hugged you."

"Well, Don't do it again. It's too hot."

I left him sitting there and went out on the sidewalk. Minutes later, a military car, a white star on its hood, came down the street. A strange-looking car, short and stubby and without a top, it was driven by an American soldier. Next to him sat an officer. It stopped in front of me. The officer motioned to come over to him. I looked behind me, but I was the only one here. *What's he want from me?* I walked over to him.

Colonel Wise, U.S. Army
Retired 1947. Died in 1957

"Hello," he said. "Du sprechen English?"

"Nein." *Not enough to talk to you.*

He said something else in English. I shook my head. He smiled and handed me a piece of paper. ELISABETH DRESCHER was printed on it. I looked at the officer, then back at the paper. *Why do they want Mutti?* The officer patted my shoulder, pointed at our house and then at me.

"Dieter?" he said, pointing to the house again. *He knows my name!* "Ja, mein." *Who is he?* He said a few more words, which I still didn't understand.

"Karl? Elisabeth?" He pointed at the house again. *How does he know us? Who is he?* I turned and ran into the house.

"Mutti, there's an American officer out there with a piece of paper that has your name on it! He said my name, too. And Vati's. Komm' schnell!"

"Du bist verrückt, mein Junge. Why would an American officer have my—you talk crazy!" Suddenly, her eyes widened. She brushed past, almost knocking me down, and ran toward the gate. I followed, with Ruth and Wolfgang behind me, and froze to the spot when I reached the sidewalk.

The American was hugging her. He hugged her so hard he lifted her up. When he saw us standing there, he quickly put her down. Mutti turned around.

"Komm' hier, Dieter. You remember this man?" She had tears in her eyes, but she was laughing. I moved closer and stared at the officer's face.

I shook my head. "Nein."

She laughed. "Say hello to Herr Wise!"

Herr Wise? My postcards? And my American flag! I stared at him, unable to believe he was here.

"Dieter! Say hello!" Mutti grabbed my hand and pulled me closer. "Say hello."

I looked at him, and then at Mutti. "Herr Wise? From Zehlendorf?"

"Ja, Vati's friend from America! Now you remember? He didn't speak our language then, but he has learned a few words."

"Ja, Dieter, ich spreche Deutsch. Gut, ja?"

I nodded but still could only stare at him.

Herr Wise said something to the driver who turned off the engine. Mutti and Herr Wise walked slowly toward the house with us close behind.

We sat around the table in our living room. "Well, Dieter," Mutti said. "Your English you should try. You remember any?"

I shook my head. "I . . . I don't know."

Ruth leaned against the wall next to the door, her arms folded. Wolfgang stood beside her. They watched Herr Wise as he looked at Mutti and spoke a few words in German:

344

"I stay. Berlin. With Army." He pointed to the brass eagles on his shoulders and looked at me. *"Colonel."*

"Colonel?"

He smiled and nodded. "Ja, Colonel." He pulled from his pocket a small dictionary and paged through it. He pointed to Mutti and then at himself. *"Hausfrau."*

Mutti laughed. "Hausfrau? Ich?"

Herr Wise nodded and pointed to himself again. "Ja."

He wants Mutti to work for him.

"In Zehlendorf," he added.

She smiled, and nodded. "Ja. Dieter, tell him we are lucky he found us."

"Danke, Herr Wise. Mutter says . . . *lucky* . . . " I pointed at him . . . *stop* . . . here."

The Colonel stood up, but Mutti held on to his sleeve.

"Wait, Herr Wise. Dieter, ask him how he found us."

I pointed to him and then to us. *"Find us?"*

He laughed. "Wohnungsamt. Zehlendorf. He looked in his dictionary again. "Files." He smiled. "Deutsche records."

The Colonel stood up and extended his hand. "Dieter. Auf Wiedersehn."

He shook hands with us, and we followed him out the door and stood there while he climbed in his car. He waved goodbye as the driver turned it around right there in the street and drove back towards Zehlendorf.

Late one afternoon, a few days after the Colonel's visit, Ruth and I sat on the front steps. We looked forward to the sunset. Now the heat would let up enough to make it comfortable.

We heard someone coming through the brush along our back fence. Ruth grabbed my arm.

"Look," she whispered, pointing toward the fence. "Someone's there! A soldier."

The outline of the man came closer. Although it was dusk, I recognized the uniform. "It's not a Russian, Ruth. He looks like an American."

He came around in front of us, a smile on his face. He held out his hand.

"Hello, my name is Bill. Ich bin ein Freund, do not worry. My name is Bill." On his left sleeve I noticed a black armband with the letters **MP** in white.

I stood up on the third step. "What do you want?" I was taller than the American now and could look down on him.

He took off his shiny helmet and looked at Ruth. "I live in the tents," he said. "You waved at us when our truck drove by this house. I would like to visit with you, can I? Bitte?"

Ruth looked at me, surprised. "He speaks Deutsch much better than Herr Colonel. These Americans are all so polite. Go get your mother."

He was sitting next to Ruth by the time we came back out but stood up immediately when he saw us.

"This is my mother, Herr Bill."

"Sprechen sie Deutsch?" Mutti asked.

"Ja," he said, and smiled. He shook her hand. "My parents are from Wiesbaden. They went to the United States during the Depression. We speak Deutsch at home most of the time."

"Wilkommen, Bill," she said. "Please sit down and visit."

The four of us sat on the steps in the dark. I sat right in front of Bill.

"Please," I said in English. *"Thank you." "My name is Dieter." "How much is the train fare?"*

Mutti and Ruth laughed. "He is trying his English," Mutti said. "Gut, ja, Bill?"

Bill smiled and clapped me on my knee. "Ja, *kiddo.* Now say *I love America.* Can you do that?"

"I . . . love . . . Amer-i-ca.

"See, you speak English very well."

I smiled at Mutti and Ruth. "Someday I will go to America. Herr Wise invited me once. He is back here now and is a Colonel. When I speak English well, I will go."

"You can come see me, too. In New York."

"New York City? I had a postcard from there."

"Nein. In Buffalo. That is a long way from the city. Well, everyone, I had better be going."

I didn't want him to leave. "Why did you come through the back yards?" I asked. "Why didn't you walk around in front?"

"Russians. They don't allow us to talk to you. They won't talk to us themselves."

"They won't? But you fought together."

He shrugged. "Who knows? I am just a GI—a soldier —not a politician." He stood up.

"Wait," I said, pointing at his armband. "What does MP mean?"

"Military Polizei."

I shrank from him.

"Easy, *kid*, I am not the Gestapo." He glanced at his wristwatch. "I really have to go now." He smiled at Ruth, who looked back at him shyly. "Can I visit again?" he asked. "Maybe tomorrow? After dark?" He put his hand under her chin. "You are very pretty."

Ruth lowered her head and smiled. "Danke," she said.

"What do you say? Can I come back?"

"Ja," she answered softly. "After dark."

He started down the steps and I followed. "Why do you live in tents, Bill?"

"Rumor is we are waiting for some Allied conference. Then we will be told where to move." He messed up my hair. "This time I really go." He went down the steps and turned around. "Say it again, *kiddo. I love America.*"

"*I love America!*"

347

He winked, clenched his fist, and held up his thumb. "Good boy," he said, and disappeared into the dark.

"Shut up, Dieter. I can't sleep. What are you talking about? "I'm speaking English. You wouldn't understand. *I love America. I love America.* "Go back to sleep." "I can't. I'm going to tell Mutti you're making noise." "I'll stop, *kid-do.* In a minute."

The next morning a car with Russian markings stopped in front of the house and three officers got out. They saw us standing on the veranda and quickly came up the steps. Mutti inhaled sharply and stepped back, pulling Wolfgang with her. Unsmiling, and without a word, they brushed past us and into the living room. They looked around for a few minutes, then one of them pointed to Mutti.

"You move out," he said in Deutsch. He looked at his wristwatch. "In four hours." He pointed to himself. "I come back."

We looked at each other, saying nothing. Mutti's hands became fists, and she glared after the Russians.

"What is he saying, Mutti?" I whispered. "Get out in four hours? Where can we go? Back to the bunker?"

"Nein, Lis." Ruth shook her head. "They are moving in there. And in the apartments, too. I saw them."

"We will find someplace. We have not much time. Let's not think about where. We will manage."

Her shoulders sagged as she walked to the bedroom. "Dieter, borrow the wagon at Müllers'. Bring it to the stairs. We have little time."

We loaded pillows and blankets, a few clothes, pots and dishes, until the wagon was piled so high we had to tie everything down with rope.

"My champagne glasses, Dieter? Are they on here?"

"There's no room."

"Then we leave something else. Go, bring them up."

When I returned from the basement with the box of glasses, Mutti had rearranged the things in the wagon so there was space for her box. She carefully packed the clothes around it. "Now, tie everything down again." She looked quickly at the house. "Ruth, you stay here and watch. We'll be back."

Mutti pulled, we pushed.

"Now we are refugees, ja?" Wolfgang said. "Where are we going to live?"

Mutti didn't answer. We trudged toward Kohlhasen-brück, a small enclave on our side of the Teltow Canal, less than a half-kilometer from our house but inside the city limits of Berlin.

An old man sat on the front steps of the first house we reached. Across the railroad tracks directly behind it, I could see the gardens with the water pump. Mutti stopped and walked up to the man.

"Excuse me, but is there room for us in this house? The Russians forced us out of ours, and we don't have—"

The old man pointed up in the direction of the roof and nodded in silence.

"Are you the owner?" Mutti asked.

"Nein, they are gone," he mumbled, without looking at us. "You can have the room upstairs. Door is in the back."

At the top of a narrow stairway, so narrow that only one of us could go up or down at a time, were two doors. One led into a toilet, the other into a small attic room with one window. Off in one corner I saw a cooking stove. It was stifling hot under the roof, and sweat pasted my shirt to me as we emptied the wagon.

My mother handed me a pencil and a piece of paper.

"Write down this address. We will tape it to the fence at the house in case someone looks for us. Like Herr Wise."

When we went back, the Russian officer was there.

"Who else lived in this house?" he asked.

"Nobody else," Mutti answered. "Just us, and a man and woman upstairs."

"You lie! Too much room. I have Frau." He held up two fingers. "Two children. Live one room." He waved his arm at us. Go away!" he shouted. "Do not return."

I returned the wagon and joined Mutti and Ruth and Wolfgang. At the turn of the road, before our house disappeared from our view, Ruth stopped and looked back.

"Look at it," she said. "We stayed through all the bombing and fighting, and now we get thrown out."

I choked back the tears that wanted to come. Mutti's arms were on our shoulders, Wolfgang on one side and me on the other, as we walked slowly toward Kohlhasenbrück in silence. It wasn't very far, and there was no reason to hurry.

"Mutti," I said. "When that officer stopped us in the front yard, I saw a soldier carrying something into the cellar. What if it was food?"

"Ja," she answered. "It could be."

"I know how to get in from the side door," I reminded her.

She shook her head. "That is too dangerous, Dieter. They will have guards everywhere." We walked on a ways when she stopped and patted my shoulder. "But maybe you can walk by the house later and see. Ja, that is what you can do."

The next day, Wolfgang and I went back. We didn't stop but walked by slowly. I watched out of the corner of my eye and saw just one Russian sentry. He carried a machine pistol over his shoulder while he walked guard duty along the front of the apartment building, passing our house, and then Ludwigs'. He didn't appear to notice us.

Wolfgang stopped and stared. I yanked his arm.

"Don't stare at him, Dicker! Look down. Kick some

350

stones." I watched the guard disappear behind Ludwigs' house.

We walked another hundred meters or so, then turned and went back. The sentry came around the side of the apartment building. This time he looked over at us.

I shoved Wolfgang. "Pretend we're playing tag," I whispered and started to chase him until we were past our house and the guard. *Just like playing war games in the HJ again. But his gun was real.*

"Mutti, there's only one guard, and he walks around three houses. That's enough time for me to get into the cellar."

My mother stood at the small window. I waited for her answer. Outside it was already dark. "I promise I won't take any chances."

Mutti continued to look out the window. I walked up beside her. "I'll need some kind of a cloth bag, Mutti. Paper makes too much noise."

Finally, she turned around and faced me with a thin smile. "You think of everything, don't you?"

"Ja," I said proudly. "And I have to wear something dark. That's another thing I learned in the—"

The sharp movement of her finger jabbing in my direction got my attention. Her eyes narrowed. "Listen once and for all, Herr Steiner. I don't want to hear you talk about the HJ ever again, verstanden? Not ever!"

"What's wrong? You weren't in a bad mood before."

Wolfgang stood in the far corner with wide eyes. "I have to tell you something else," she said, looking toward Ruth. "Ruth cannot stay here with us. It is too small. We do not have enough room. Tomorrow she wants to try to find her friends in Moabit. She promises to let us know as soon as she knows where she is going to stay."

"Ja, I will. I promise."

351

Wolfgang ran over to Ruth and threw his arms around her. "But you'll come back, ja? Promise?"

Ruth stroked his head and nodded. In the dim light I could see she was crying. "Ja, I will try," she said. I turned away.

"I have to go, Mutti, it's almost dark."

"Bring back candles, if you find them." She handed me a small burlap sack and gave me a quick hug at the door. "And be careful, Dieter."

The outline of our house loomed ahead of me. I stared at a light in one window. *They have electricity? Those Schweine!* I wanted to throw a rock and smash the light. *Remember why you came here, Dieter. Stay calm. Be brave.*

Slowly, I moved closer. I stopped behind the last tree between me and the house and waited. Finally, I heard a cough and footsteps, then the shadow of the guard passed our house and faded into darkness at Ludwigs' house. I started counting and stopped when he came around again. I had a little more than five minutes to reach the cellar.

I took off as soon as he disappeared the next time along the far side of Ludwigs' house. I stayed low and was careful not to make any noise with my shoes on the pavement. I crouched at the bottom of the four steps to the cellar door and waited. When he came around again, I started counting.

Reaching for the hidden key above the door frame, I slid into the cellar on my stomach and carefully shut the door behind me. I didn't move, letting my eyes get used to the darkness. By the door I found a box of candles. *They're the ones from Christmas.* I stuffed them in the bag. Muffled voices came from upstairs, but they came from the front of the house, not right over me. I swallowed my fear, took off my shoes, and slowly stepped toward the narrow wooden stairway leading up to our kitchen. In the darkness I used my feet to probe my way. I reached the stairs.

Which of the steps creak? I can't remember! I waited for the voices to become louder, then tested the first step. *Safe!* I moved up one and tried the next. *Safe again!* Sweat rolled from my forehead and made my eyes burn. The voices faded. I waited. Again they talked, and I put my weight on the next step. *Damn! That's it.* I carefully stood on the step, held my breath, and listened. *They don't hear me.* The next two steps were safe. And the next one as well.

Blackness surrounded me on the small landing at the top of the stairs, just centimeters away from the door to our kitchen. The voice of a man came from somewhere in the front of the house, followed by the short laugh of a woman.

I felt around me with my hand and touched a sack of something soft. I unrolled the top and felt inside. *Flour!* I pulled out the candles and put the box in my pocket. Hurriedly, I filled the bag and felt my way back toward the stairs. *Someone's coming!* A thin beam of light appeared at the bottom of the door. A man and woman were there. They talked, dishes clanked, they laughed. I froze, my feet on separate steps. *What if they open the door—will I die for a little bag of flour?*

Just when my legs became tingly and numb, the voices faded to the front of the house. I sat down to let the feeling come back into my legs. Then, ever so slowly, I groped my way back down into the cellar. The step creaked again. I shook all over, and the burlap sack swung back and forth. I held it tighter. *I can't drop it now.* When I reached the door, I opened it slightly and gulped the night air. I shut it again and waited for the guard.

His footsteps came. When he was gone, I opened the door a thin slit and peeked out. He was standing no more than three meters away. The red glow of his cigarette momentarily lit up his face. *He's looking right at me. I can't shut the door, he'll see me for sure.* Suddenly, he moved and disappeared behind the apartment building.

With shoes in one hand, bag in the other, I didn't bother to shut the door. As if the devil's breath was behind me, I kept running until I reached the house in Kohlhasenbrück.

"Um Gottes Willen, Dieter." Mutti blew me a kiss with both hands. "We thought you were caught. You know you were gone almost three hours? What happened?"

I could only shake my head. My chest hurt every time I wanted to breathe. I handed Mutti the candle box and gave the bag to Ruth. I slid down along the wall next to the door and sat on the floor. Mutti lit a candle and held it on its side. When the wax dripped onto a saucer, she set the candle in it.

"I won't do it again, Mutti. The Russians came into the kitchen, and I was just outside the door to the cellar. I thought I'd be killed. I brought you flour, I think. Look in the bag."

Ruth brought it to my mother. She picked up the candle and held it to see in the sack. They both laughed, and Mutti closed the bag.

"It's gray flour, Dieter, filled with weevils."

"Weevils?"

"Ja. Like worms. I know what they are. We'll get them out, don't worry. It must be very old." She laughed. "We should have left it for the Russians."

"I am leaving these clothes, Lis. They are nothing but rags now. We should have left them at the house." Ruth laughed weakly. "Guess I will begin a whole new life." Mutti and Ruth stood arm in arm and talked quietly. Ruth cried and hugged my mother, then Wolfgang and me.

"You are like my own family," she said. "We've been through so much together." She blew her nose and wiped her eyes. "But this is best. I have to find my friends." We walked to the front gate and hugged and kissed again. Mutti's

354

eyes were shiny, and big tears rolled down Wolfgang's cheeks.

"Can I go with her, bitte?"

Mutti hugged him. "Nein, Wolfgang. You can't leave me. We'll see her again soon. She is only going to the city."

Ruth opened the gate and walked out into the street. All she carried was a small handbag. Minutes later, her small figure stopped at the corner. She turned and waved.

"Auf Wiedersehn, Ruth," I said softly and turned so Wolfgang wouldn't see me cry. Mutti put her arm around me, but I shrugged it off and walked a few steps ahead.

"Come, boys," she said. "We have to find something to eat. Why don't you go over there to the gardens and see if you can find some carrots in the ground or potatoes."

I turned around and went over to the gardens, walking ahead of Wolfgang. We looked but couldn't find anything. On the way back we passed what looked like a small store in a house spared by bombs and fire. "Maybe here there is something, Dicker." But the door was locked.

"Hello!" a voice called from across the street.

A boy about my age stood on the opposite sidewalk. *What does he want?* I waited for him to cross the street.

He held his hand out. "Guten Morgen. Mein Name ist Rudolf. Wer bist Du?"

"I'm Dieter. This is my brother, Wolfgang. What do you want?"

He shrugged. "A friend? Around here there are not many boys. Do you have lights again?"

"In our house there are lights, but the Russians threw us out. Where we are living there are none."

"My mother heard this morning that they have repaired many lines and that we'll have lights, maybe by tonight already. You want to go swimming later?"

"Swimming?" *He must be crazy.* "Where? The canal? It's full of rubble."

"No, in the Stölpchen See."

"I might. I'll ask my mother. If I can, I'll be right back."

"Go ahead," Mutti said. "But get back early. Wolfgang and I will go across the tracks and maybe find something for the stove."

Rudolf and I crossed the Teltow Canal on a makeshift foot bridge, two wooden boards laid side by side between metal beams. When we reached the middle of the canal, the boards, held together by upright pieces of lumber, sank into the water a little bit. I carefully slid my feet over the boards. My foot hit something, and I looked down.

The bent arm of a dead soldier had hooked itself over the boards, holding him against the current. His fingers looked like a cluster of fat, blue sausages. I stepped over the arm, and saw the upper body of the soldier bobbing in the water. His face was swollen like a blue balloon. *Jesus! How many dead people have to stare at me?* Behind me Rudolf chuckled.

"He is only a Russian. Serves him right, das Schwein."

For another kilometer, along the cobblestone road to the lake, we stepped over and around more dead soldiers and a few dead horses. All of the soldiers were missing boots. "People always take the boots," said Rudolf. "They are better than the shoes you get with stamps."

"Ja, if you want to wear them." *Like the helmet I had to wear.*

"There is another one, Dieter." He pointed to a bloated body to his left.

I swatted at the flies. "Don't walk so near. I hate these flies." I covered my face and ran a little ways.

"Watch it. There is another one, right there." He pointed. I ducked the flies and zig-zagged around the body. Rudolf covered his nose and mouth and followed me. "Let's get to the lake," he said.

Vati had taken us to this sandy stretch along the Stölpchen See many times on weekends. Then it was filled with bathers from the city, children giggling and laughing as they fed the swans and ducks. Now it was deserted. But the awful smell of decaying flesh followed us even to this open stretch of lakeshore.

"It still smells, Rudolf. Even out here."

"We will have to get used to this smell, I guess. No one buries the bodies."

We stood, silent, and stared at the water.

"Dieter! Look there!"

I looked in the direction he pointed. Perhaps a hundred meters from the edge of the lake, the tail of a plane stuck upright. I could see the small black Swastika on its rear rudder. "Ja. One of ours. See the bodies? To your right. In the cattails."

Rudolf nodded. "Three I see."

"Ja. I don't know if we should go in this water . . . "

"But it's so hot . . . " He wiped his forehead.

"Well, I don't want to swim in this stuff. Let's go home."

"Wait. I'll just swim to the plane and back. You can wait that long for me."

I stood and watched as he reached the plane and disappeared under the tail. Seconds later, his head bobbed up again, and he swam back. Soaking wet, he sank down on the shore beside me. "You should have been there. That pilot. He is still in the plane. He looks like this." Rudolf stared at me with his mouth and eyes opened as wide as he could make them. "He looks just like he's alive."

"They always do. I'm used to it."

On the way back, every time I looked at Rudolf, he opened his eyes wide again and stared at me. "Oo-o-o-o-h," he said. "I'm dead."

357

I pushed him and tried to make a more horrible face, leaning my head to the side, opening my eyes and sticking out my tongue. "I've been dead for three months," I said. "Now I'm coming to get you. Arg-g-gh."

We wound our way around trenches and foxholes in the woods along the side of the street.

"They really camouflaged these foxholes good," I shouted at Rudolf, several meters behind me. "You'll step in them if you're not careful." I moved to the right to dodge a suspected hole. "Here's one, I think." I looked back at Rudolf. "Right there," I said, pointing a few feet away.

A terrible, gagging smell engulfed me, and I fell in a hole and landed on something soft and spongy. I stood in the stomach of a soldier crunched in the bottom of the hole. His head was twisted and ants and flies crawled on his face. His arm had curled around my knee.

"Hilfe! Hilfe!" I clawed wildly at the sides of the foxhole.

"Was ist los?" Rudolf cried as he looked down. He jumped back.

"Schnell," I yelled. "Hilfe!"

Rudolf came back to the edge and held out his hands.

I tried to jump but couldn't reach him. In one quick movement, I stepped on the soldier's head, grabbed Rudolf's hands, and pulled myself out of the hole.

Mutti held her nose. "Outside. You should know better than to come in here in those clothes. You have been rolling in manure?"

"Nein. Bring me something to wear, and I'll take these off outside."

"Ja. And you will burn them, too. How stupid to ruin your clothes, Dieter. You do not have many, and you crawl around and ruin what you have? Idiot!"

I went outside, and when she brought me clean ones, I

went around in back and took the smelly pants off. I rubbed dirt all over my shoes, and it helped a little bit. *At least no one is on the ground to smell them.*

"You look awful, Dieter. But you smell better. Didn't you get to swim?"

"Nein. Too many bodies in the water."

She held up her hand. "Genug. I will tell you what we did. Some wood we found, but we saw something interesting you should know about. Along the tracks toward the S-Bahn station we walked. There are several freight cars standing on the old tracks. You know, along the Red Cross warehouses?"

"Ja? Freight cars?"

"Two or three open cars are at this end. Coal is in them." She looked at me expectantly. "Coal, Dieter."

"That's for the Russians, Mutti. I'm sure there are guards."

"I guess you are right. But we didn't see any." She moved to the window. "Too bad they are not closer . . . " She turned around. "Don't you want to take a look?"

I laughed. "Ja. Tonight. I'll take Wolfgang, and we'll find out."

We left just before it was completely dark, both of us carrying small burlap sacks. In little more than five minutes, I saw the outline of the freight cars.

"Crouch down—low," I whispered. "Don't make any noise. We'll just sit here and listen and watch the cars. If we don't see any movement, we'll sneak up there."

"This is exciting," he whispered back.

"How long are we going to wait, Dieter?"

"It's been about half an hour. I haven't seen anyone, have you?"

"Nein. Can we go over now?"

"All right, but we have to be very quiet." Crouched low, we moved to within ten or twenty meters of the nearest car. We lay flat on the ground, barely breathing, and waited again. Nothing moved. There was no noise. We crawled to the darkest side of the last car, which faced thick bushes along the warehouse. We waited underneath it for a few more minutes, listening and watching.

"I'll count to three," I whispered. "Then I'll lift you up into this car. You tell me what's in it. Don't make any noise."

I counted. In a split-second, he was inside.

"Only a small stack of briquets, Dieter."

"Go ahead, fill your sack and throw it down. Schnell!"

I scooted back under the car, anxiously watching in both directions. I could barely hear Wolfgang above me. *He's good. I'll have to take him again.*

I caught the first sack with my arms, but the second landed with a low thud in the grass behind me.

"Climb over the top. I'll help you down. Schnell!"

A few seconds passed, but he didn't appear.

"Dicker," I called in a loud whisper. "Schnell!"

"The pile of briquets is too small now. There aren't enough to stand on. I can't reach the top."

Verdammt! Why's he have to be so short? Why didn't we get into a full car? I picked up one of the sacks he'd thrown over.

"I'll throw some of them back to you. You can stack them until you're high enough. Ready?

"Ja."

"Here it comes. Catch."

I threw. He caught. One after the other.

"Keep going, Dieter. It's not enough yet".

I threw more briquets. "What about now?"

"Nein, not yet."

He dropped three in a row, and each one clunked when

it hit. "They'll hear us, Dicker. You've got to catch better."

"You can say that. You're standing out there. I can't see in the dark. You think you could throw better maybe?"

I threw more, and he caught more. At last, he came over the top, and both of us rolled into the ditch. Wolfgang giggled. We looked around us once more, then, crouched low, we ran from the tracks, carrying home just a small supply of briquets.

"Das ist Gold! Now we can cook. All we need is some food." Mutti rubbed her hands together. "Did you see any guards?"

Still out of breath, I shook my head. Wolfgang told her what we had to do. She sat in a chair and laughed.

"It wasn't very funny, Mutti. We were scared."

"But Dieter, it is so good to laugh again."

"Mutti! I was at our house. The Russians are gone. All of them. The house is empty."

"Ja, Dieter? Oh, my. Are you sure? Did you go to the door?"

"Ja. There is no one there. The door is open. Some of our stuff is still there. Can we go back?"

Mutti sat down. "I will think for a moment." She closed her eyes and sat with her hands folded in her lap. After a moment, she opened her eyes and smiled. "Ja. We will go back. But we must be sure it is safe. Go back there now and walk around in the yard. If there are Russians in Ludwigs' or at the apartment house, see how they act. If they chase you or holler for you to leave, do not argue. See if we will be safe there."

I left immediately, and after I did just what she said to, I rushed back to Kohlhasenbrück.

We moved back the next day.

361

Wolfgang shook his head. "I don't know what they're doing with the S-Bahn tracks, Dieter. They're taking them away on long trucks. No more S-Bahn?"

"Who's taking them away?"

"The prisoners, but the guards are Russians with guns."

"I don't know, Wolfgang. Let's go to the bridges and look around for some wood."

Two sets of tracks were still untouched. *Why the S-Bahn tracks, but not these?* When we got to the canal, we sat down to watch. One of two giant cranes lifted a large section of the bridge out of the water.

"Look at all the men, Dieter. What are they doing?"

"Re-building it, I guess."

We sat awhile, watching men with drills and hammers work on the piece pulled out of the water. Other men carried long wooden beams and put them in place.

"Let's go back and tell Mutti." I pulled Wolfgang to his feet. "If they see us, those Russians will put us to work."

"They're putting a bridge back up, Mutti," Wolfgang yelled, running up the stairs ahead of me. "Why only one bridge?"

She stood at the window, with her back toward us, not answering. I leaned against the wall next to her.

"Why are you crying? What's wrong, Mutti?"

"Nothing there is to eat. I worry that you boys will get sick, and then what? There are no doctors anywhere. I should have sent all three of you to Würzburg. You would be living on a farm now . . . "

I stared out into the yard, desperately trying to think of something to say to make my mother feel better.

"I could walk through Steinstücken and Drewitz, Mutti, then come the first farms and maybe I can—"

"You are not strong enough to walk that far. None of us are strong anymore." Suddenly, she grinned. "Look at that

362

green grass out there and all those dandelions between the trees. I read somewhere that you can eat dandelions if you boil them long enough."

"Eat grass? And dandelions? Like our rabbits did? Are you really serious?"

"Ja, I am. You get Wolfgang and pick the freshest grass, and only the leaves of the dandelions. I will start a fire in the stove."

I shook my head, but we did what she asked. Crawling on hands and knees, I came across a section where someone must have had a garden a long time ago. Its long rows of dirt mounds were now covered with grass and weeds, but in a few spots I saw a weed with broad leaves of potatoes. I pulled hard on one.

"Dicker, come here. Look."

He ran over. "Potatoes!"

"Look for this kind of leaf," I said, "and pull it out." We found another half a dozen plants and brought home about three pounds of potatoes.

She smiled and whistled, too, while she kept the fire going for two small pots of water. The stifling heat didn't seem to bother her. She boiled the grass and dandelion leaves until it had turned into green mush.

That first night we savored each bite of potato, like it was a holiday feast. Then it was time for the green mush.

Mutti put a bowl of it in front of Wolfgang.

"I hate this. Do I have to eat it, Mutti?"

Mutti chuckled. "It is spinach, we pretend. It looks like it, ja? Almost tastes like it, too."

It tasted bitter, but we ate it all. The next day we ate the potato peels, and the following day Mutti added flour to the potato water and we had potato soup.

Mutti smiled when she took the bowls from the table. "For three days, we have had something to eat. See how lucky we are?"

A week later the bridge was repaired, and even the train tracks were back in place. We were told that water was available again on the other side of the Teltow Canal, but we had to use the makeshift board crossing. Because many Russian soldiers guarded the railroad bridge, no one could go near it.

I sat on the steep embankment sloping down toward our side of the canal, next to the foot bridge. Nearby, an old woman stared at her fishing line. I watched as a hand with part of the arm drifted past me and the woman, but she paid it no attention. I promised myself never to fish again. German prisoners criss-crossed the woods across the canal carrying bodies. They dumped them onto trucks, and a man sprinkled them with white powder before the trucks drove off.

Across from me, two men grabbed a floating body out of the murky water and, holding onto legs and arms, hurled it on top of the pile of bodies already on a truck. *Maybe the smell will go away soon.*

"Hey, Junge, wake up! You have a home?"

Startled, I jumped and squinted into a blinding sun. The face of the old woman I saw fishing nearby came into focus.

I almost stumbled downhill. "Ja, I have a home, over there. What time is it?"

"Junge, nobody has watches anymore." The woman shook her head and mumbled as she moved away.

I stared at the twisted hulks of the bridges before me. Across the canal, between shredded and blackened trees, a truck stood waiting to be loaded with more bodies.

"Back here, Dieter." I walked around the house to the backyard. Mutti was sitting and talking with a man when I walked up. "Dieter, where have you been for over two hours?"

I ducked when she raised her hand, but she only put it hard on her forehead. "Do not do that again without telling me where you go." She nodded toward the man. "This is Herr Braun. He lives around the corner. His family burned to death in the city."

"Your mother was worried about you." He put out his hand, and I shook it.

"I only went to the canal and watched them pick up dead soldiers."

"You entertain yourself strangely," Mutti said, turning around to Herr Braun. "And do not go into the woods across the street. Herr Braun here said there are some grenades and bombs buried that didn't explode."

"Ja. I know."

Quietly, we sat together on the overturned boxes in the shade behind the house. I listened to the high-pitched song of a million crickets.

"I heard," said Herr Braun, "there is a new policeman here, Dieter. A communist. Be careful what you say. I think his name is Heussler."

Loud knocks on the front door woke me up. Mutti was already there. I saw the dark uniform of a man.

"Frau, tomorrow you are ordered to stay inside. Russian sharpshooters will be posted along the railroad tracks behind your yard, and if you are seen outside, or you look out the window, they will shoot to kill you. Verstanden?"

Before Mutti could open her mouth, he disappeared noisily down the steps.

"That must have been Herr Heussler, Mutti. If he's the new Polizei—I don't know . . . he's not any better than—"

"Do not talk! You have to learn not to make trouble." Mutti combed her hair. "I am going for a walk. Maybe someone knows what this is all about." She turned and looked at us.

"You can go with me, but comb your hair first. You look like cavemen."

Wolfgang hopped into the bathroom, his shoulders bent forward. Snorting loudly, he pounded his chest with both hands. Then he combed his hair.

Herr Bauer stood in front of a house with another older man and two women. They stopped talking when we got close to them.

"Guten Morgen," Mutti said and nodded. "What do you think about this order for tomorrow? Does anyone know why?"

"Ja. Heussler said a big conference starts tomorrow in Potsdam, and Josef Stalin is coming from Russia by train. That Englishman Churchill is already there, and the American president."

I pulled Mutti's arm. "That's why they fixed that bridge so fast, and the tracks are still there."

That afternoon I helped Mutti put up a heavy blanket to cover the window. *I'll be able to look out at the edge of the blanket and still not be spotted.*

"Wolfgang, go back there, close to the tracks, and tell me if you can see anything."

Through the tiniest slit between blanket and wall, I watched him as he backed up all the way to the embankment. He stood there for a moment, then trotted back.

"Did you see me?" he asked. "Did you even look out?"

"Ja, of course I did. So, did you see anything? Could you see me looking?"

"Nein, nothing."

Mutti joined us. "You are not going to do anything foolish."

Wolfgang pulled on her arm. "Come with me, Mutti. See for yourself."

When they came back up, my mother was quiet, which I took as her approval. For a long time that night I thought about the morning. *Will I be able to see Stalin? Maybe he'll stand by a window. There's a sharp curve up there . . . The train will have to slow down . . .*

Barely awake, I went straight to the window. I carefully moved the edge of the blanket less than a centimeter away from the window frame.

In the early morning light, I could see maybe fifty meters of track. And two Russian soldiers. They stood motionless, but both of them seemed to look straight at me. *They're too far away to see me.* They held rifles across their chests. I stepped away from the window.

"Wolfgang, stand by the door. You listen for the train there, and I'll listen here at the window. But don't open the door."

An hour passed, then almost another. Mutti sat on the sofa across from me, both of us silent, listening. We jumped when Wolfgang came in.

"That floor is hard! Maybe the train won't come."

"Ja, it will come. Why did they repair the bridge? Go back."

I looked at the calendar on the wall above Mutti's head.

"Change the date, Mutti," I whispered. "It shows Monday."

With both hands, she carefully and quietly tore off the paper. Now it was correct. *Tuesday, July 17, 1945.*

Suddenly, I heard the familiar sound of a locomotive. Wolfgang came running. My cheeks turned hot, and my heart beat fast as I stood close to the window, waiting, my fingers ready. When the sounds of a train were directly behind the house, I moved the blanket.

As I expected, the train had to slow down. The locomotive and a long coal car passed, then I started counting . . . "one, two, three" . . . *All the windows are covered with steel plates.*

367

"Mutti, you should see this train," I whispered. "Come see. Some really old cars, three or four of them, and they have gold decorations on the side." I stepped away from the window and let Mutti take a look. She peered through the curtain, and I stood behind her. At last, the two red lights on the last car of the train disappeared around the curve toward Potsdam. Mutti let the blanket fall back in place.

"Gott Sei Dank, boys. We'll never forget this horrible time. After this, there will be no more wars."

After 1945

Even after his tour of duty, Colonel Wise visited us every year or so. He always asked if I was ready to visit him in America, reminding me of his first invitation in 1936. In 1953 I decided to fulfill my dream. I arrived in New York City in October as an immigrant. I was finally in the land of the free. Three months later, Selective Service ordered me to register at my local draft board.

The Army? Guns? War? Never again!

I emigrated to Canada.

But I still wanted to be an American. Could I carry a gun again and be ready to go to war? Would I be on the right side this time?

I kept in touch with Colonel Wise, who knew of my dilemma, but who wisely allowed me to find my own way. A year later I decided I was ready. I arranged with the American Embassy to re-enter and enlist for three years in the U.S. Army. On October 24, 1955 I walked across the Peace Bridge at Buffalo, New York. When I reached the American side, I entered a souvenir shop. I wanted to find a gift for the Colonel.

I spied one immediately.

It was the prettiest flag I had ever seen — red and white, and a blue box with lots of little white stars.

Dieter Steiner enlisted in the United States Army in January 1956. Three years later he received an honorable discharge. On July 2, 1959, he became a United States citizen. He retired in 1989 as Graphic Production Manager at Oscar Mayer Foods Corporation, Madison, Wisconsin, where he was employed for thirty years. He now lives in St. Petersburg, Florida.

Elizabeth (Mutti) lived in Berlin until February 14, 1993, when she died at the age of eighty-seven. She never remarried. Wolfgang and Peter still live in Berlin. Wolfgang is an accountant and the father of three children. Peter works as a systems analyst. He has two children.

Although Dieter never saw Ruth again, she did visit his mother once or twice after the war.

GLOSSARY

Ach Du Lieber	Oh my dear
Ausweis	Identification card
Auf Wiedersehn	Goodbye
Bitte	Please
Bist Du froh?	Are you happy?
Bist Du ein Soldat?	Are you a soldier?
Brötchen	Hard roll
Buddel Kiste	Sand box
Danke (sehr)	Thanks (much)
Das Schwein	The pig
Das ist Gold	That is gold
Die	The
Dicker	Fat One
Du bist verrückt	You are crazy
Dummkopf	Dumbhead
Engel	Angel
Für uns	For us
Genug	Enough
Gott Sei Dank	Thank God
Guten Morgen	Good morning
Tag	Good day
Abend	Good evening
Gute Nacht	Good night
Halt, wer ist da?	Stop, who's there?
Hausfrau	Homemaker
Helf mir	Help me
Hilfe	Help
(Die) Hitler Jugend (HJ)	(The) Hitler Youth
(Pronounced "Haa Yott")	
Hund (Hunde Tage)	Dog (Dog Days)
Ich bin gesund	I am healthy
spreche Deutsch	I speak German
bin kein Soldat	I'm not a soldier
verstehe Sie nicht	I don't understand you
Jungvolk (Pimpf)	Youngest branch of Hitler Youth

Junge (mein Junge) ....Boy (my boy)
Junger Herr .... Young man
Jüdisches Schwein .... Jewish swine
Kinderstuhl..................................... High chair
Krüppel .... Cripple
Koks ....Long burning coal
Komm' (schnell, hier) ....Come (quick, here)
Konzentrations-Lager .... Concentration Camp
Liebe Familie .... Dear family
Mit Liebe .... With love
Mein Gott...................................My God
Nein Danke .... No, thanks
Oma, Opa .... Grandma, Grandpa
Panzerfaust .... Bazooka
Polizei (Polizist)............................Police (Man)
Rohrstock..................................Bamboo stick
Schatz.............................. Sweetheart
Scheisse.............................. Shit
Scheisskopf........................... Shithead
Schnell!. .... Hurry!
Sei ruhig............................ Be quiet
Spass ....Joke
Sprechen Sie Deutsch .... You speak German?
Sturmtruppen ....Storm Troopers
Tante.. Aunt
Um Gottes Willen ....For God's sake
Unser ....Our
Verboten............................. Forbidden, prohibited
Verdammt........................... Damned
Verstanden....................................Understand?
Viel Glück.................................. Much luck
Was ist los?.......................What's the matter?
(mit dem Kleinen) .... (with the little one)
Weihnachtsmann.......................... Santa Claus
Wir danken unserem Führer .... We thank our leader
Wohnungsamt............................City Housing Department
Wunderbar ....Wonderful
Zwerg................................. Dwarf